MW01092040

Strength-Based Clinical Supervision

John C. Wade, PhD, is an associate professor of psychology and the director of the clinical psychology program at Emporia State University. He earned his doctorate in counseling psychology at Pennsylvania State University and completed an internship and post-doc at the University of Missouri, specializing in supervision. He has published articles and book chapters on various topics, including positive psychology, supervision and training, career counseling, multiculturalism, and group therapy. He is currently also coediting the book *Positive Psychology on the College Campus*, scheduled for release in late 2014.

Janice E. Jones, PhD, is an associate professor in the doctoral leadership studies department at Cardinal Stritch University and serves as chair of the department. She earned her doctorate in counseling psychology from the University of Wisconsin–Milwaukee and completed pre-doc and an internship at the Medical College of Wisconsin. She has published chapters and articles on various topics, including vocational psychology, working with people with disabilities, and diversity and multiculturalism.

Strength-Based Clinical Supervision

A Positive Psychology Approach to Clinical Training

John C. Wade, PhD
Janice E. Jones, PhD

SPRINGER PUBLISHING COMPANY
NEW YORK

Copyright © 2015 Springer Publishing Company, LLC

All rights reserved.

No part of this publication may be reproduced, stored in a retrieval system, or transmitted in any form or by any means, electronic, mechanical, photocopying, recording, or otherwise, without the prior permission of Springer Publishing Company, LLC, or authorization through payment of the appropriate fees to the Copyright Clearance Center, Inc., 222 Rosewood Drive, Danvers, MA 01923, 978 750-8400, fax 978-646-8600, info@copyright.com or on the Web at www.copyright.com.

Springer Publishing Company, LLC
11 West 42nd Street
New York, NY 10036
www.springerpub.com

Acquisitions Editor: Nancy S. Hale
Production Editor: Brian Black
Composition: Graphic World Inc.

ISBN: 978-0-8261-0736-7
e-book ISBN: 978-0-8261-0737-4

14 15 16 17 / 5 4 3 2 1

The author and the publisher of this Work have made every effort to use sources believed to be reliable to provide information that is accurate and compatible with the standards generally accepted at the time of publication. The author and publisher shall not be liable for any special, consequential, or exemplary damages resulting, in whole or in part, from the readers' use of, or reliance on, the information contained in this book. The publisher has no responsibility for the persistence or accuracy of URLs for external or third-party Internet websites referred to in this publication and does not guarantee that any content on such websites is, or will remain, accurate or appropriate.

Library of Congress Cataloging-in-Publication Data

Wade, John C., author.
  Strength-based clinical supervision : a positive psychology approach to clinical training / John C. Wade, Janice E. Jones.
    p. ; cm.
  Includes bibliographical references.
  ISBN 978-0-8261-0736-7 -- ISBN 978-0-8261-0737-4 (e-book)
  I. Jones, Janice E., author. II. Title.
  [DNLM: 1. Mental Health Services--organization & administration. 2. Personnel Management--methods. WM 30.2]
  RA790.75
  616.890068'3--dc23
                          2014019332

Special discounts on bulk quantities of our books are available to corporations, professional associations, pharmaceutical companies, health care organizations, and other qualifying groups. If you are interested in a custom book, including chapters from more than one of our titles, we can provide that service as well.

For details, please contact:
Special Sales Department, Springer Publishing Company, LLC
11 West 42nd Street, 15th Floor, New York, NY 10036-8002
Phone: 877-687-7476 or 212-431-4370; Fax: 212-941-7842
E-mail: sales@springerpub.com

Printed in the United States of America by Courier

*To my parents, who instilled in me a love of learning,
and my wife Susan and daughters Angelica and Andrea
for their unending love and support.*

JW

*To V. Scott H. Solberg, PhD, Amy Ridley Meyers, PhD,
and my children, Christian and Evan Diehnelt
and Jillian and Lauren Jones.*

JJ

Contents

Preface

I, John Wade, must confess that I usually don't read prefaces; therefore, I will certainly not hold it against you if you don't, and chances are I will never know. But consequently, I will try to keep this short and useful.

This book intentionally approaches positive psychology from two perspectives: One is the application of specific positive psychology constructs, such as strengths or the broaden-and-build model, to supervision and training. The second perspective, which is probably more pervasive throughout the book and provides the underlying conceptual framework, is to operate from the definition of positive psychology as simply "the study and science of what works." Based on this conceptualization, we have tried to infuse the book with research findings on optimal functioning and success or "best practices" in the various domains we cover related to supervision and training.

Although both Janice and I are psychologists, we firmly believe that all mental health disciplines have much to offer and that the similarities among the different specialties far outnumber the differences. Therefore, we have intentionally researched and drawn from all mental health disciplines, including social work, counseling, psychiatry, alcohol and substance abuse, and marriage and family therapy. In some instances, such as for Chapter 5, "Evaluation and Feedback," we have even researched some non–mental-health-related fields that also involve clinical training, such as speech-language pathology and law, to provide a more comprehensive understanding of the topic.

The first chapter, "Perspectives on Supervision," provides a broad overview of some of the most influential supervision theories and perspectives, and the second chapter, "Foundations of Positive Psychology," introduces the key research findings and constructs from positive psychology. The rest of the chapters focus on the factors and practical applications that will have the most impact on providing supervision from a positive psychology framework, ranging from ways supervisors can help ensure that the supervisory relationship begins well to identifying and developing our supervisees' strengths and fostering the development of expertise and lifelong learning. One of our favorite chapters is Chapter 7, "Addressing Problems and Framing Solutions," which acknowledges that even the best-laid plan can go awry (and often does in clinical work) and provides pragmatic suggestions for dealing with the inevitable setbacks and difficulties that can occur.

Questions for reflection and discussion are provided for Chapters 1 through 9. Reflection leads to increased awareness and broadened perspective and is the cornerstone of almost all therapeutic approaches. It is the foundation for intentional and thoughtful supervision and training. The questions are intended to serve as useful prompts for discussion in either classroom settings or supervision sessions.

We hope this book will help you provide supervision and training with increased flexibility, creativity, and effectiveness. We especially hope that it will help bring out the best in you as a supervisor and give you tools to more effectively bring out the best in the people you supervise.

John C. Wade
Janice E. Jones

Acknowledgments

We are very grateful to many people who provided insight and guidance for our book. Our agent, Neil Salkind, had passion and enthusiasm for the book from the start and was very instrumental in bringing the potential ideas to actual fruition. We also appreciate his willingness and confidence to take a chance on first-time book authors. Steve Ilardi, psychology professor at the University of Kansas, provided helpful perspective and suggestions regarding the organization and flow of the book. We are grateful to Tom Baker, director and founder of Heartscope Learning, for his reading and astute feedback on several chapters. Thanks go to Jim Kreider, professor of social work at the University of Kansas, for providing feedback and insight on refining the strength-based framework. We are also thankful for the countless conversations we have had with students, supervisees, and colleagues over the years that have helped to broaden our understanding and appreciation of training and supervision.

We are very grateful for having the kind and generous support and insightful feedback of our editor, Nancy S. Hale of Springer Publishing Company. She has been a wonderful source of support throughout the process of writing the book. We are also grateful and deeply appreciative of the sacrifices our families have made and their unending support as we devoted time to the writing of this book.

John Wade would like to acknowledge the profound impact that his internship training director, Dr. Helen Roehlke at the University of Missouri, had on his development, both as a psychologist and a supervisor. She embodied the strength-based perspective long before "positive psychology" was a recognized term, and has helped countless trainees recognize and more fully realize their potential.

Finally, Janice Jones would like to thank A. J. Metz, PhD, at the University of Utah, for her continued collegiality and support for over 17 years.

Perspectives on Supervision

"There is divine beauty in learning. . . . To learn means to accept the postulate that life did not begin at my birth. Others have been here before me, and I walk in their footsteps."

—Eli Wiesel

"The mind is not a vessel to be filled, but a fire to be kindled."

—Plutarch

"The mediocre teacher tells. The good teacher explains. The superior teacher demonstrates. The great teacher inspires."

—William Arthur Ward

Historical Overview of Supervision

For as long as work has existed, there has been supervision, whether in the form of a father passing down his craft to his son, a more formalized apprenticeship program to become certified to perform a trade, or the highly structured training programs that many professional disciplines and businesses have today. In the apprenticeship model, the goal is for the novice to learn from a more experienced or expert clinician by observing, assisting, and receiving feedback. Milne (2009) ironically notes that the Zen Buddhist training of monks, in which trainees are routinely rejected as they try to gain access to training and are subjected to hardships and humiliation, is unfortunately not unlike the experience some graduate students in mental health professions face, given the highly competitive nature of many programs and the arduous journey toward licensure. However, although observing experienced clinicians can be a very useful component of training (and probably should be used more than is customary today), becoming proficient in delivering mental health services requires much more than simply observing the practice of more senior clinicians (Falender & Shafranske, 2004).

The importance of supervision in developing clinical proficiency seems to have been recognized from the dawn of psychotherapy. Freud routinely held Wednesday evening meetings in his house with other therapists, consisting of both theoretical and case discussions, in effect conducting group supervision (Hess, Hess, & Hess, 2008). This de facto supervision appears to be predated by social workers, who in the 19th century offered guidance to volunteers who provided assistance and comfort to the poor (Harkness & Poertner, 1989). Milne (2009) notes that the apprenticeship system of supervision in the helping professions has been relied upon heavily since ancient Greek times.

This chapter presents an overview of supervision and a brief introduction to several models of clinical supervision. The essential tasks and functions of supervision and the roles of the supervisor are also discussed.

Definitions and Importance of Supervision

Even if you have had no formal training at all in supervising people (which is frequently the case among practicing supervisors), you probably still have a working understanding of supervision from your own experience of being supervised in various activities, likely ranging from part-time jobs held as a teenager to more formal and focused clinical supervision. A broad definition of supervision usually roughly equates with "overseeing" and assuming responsibility for both the development of the trainee and the quality of the work done. Bernard and Goodyear (2004) note that clinical supervision has similarities to and overlaps with teaching, counseling, and consultation but is also unique from each of these functions. They define supervision as "an intervention provided by a senior member of a profession to a more junior member or members. This relationship is evaluative, extends over time, and has the simultaneous purposes of enhancing the professional functioning of the more junior person or persons, monitoring the quality of professional services offered to clients, and serving as a gatekeeper to those attempting to enter the profession" (p. 8).

Falender and Shafranske (2004) offer a slightly different definition of clinical supervision: a "distinct professional activity in which education and training aimed at developing science-informed practice are facilitated through a collaborative interpersonal process. It involves observation, evaluation, feedback, and facilitation of supervisee self-assessment, and the acquisition of knowledge and skills by instruction, modeling, and mutual problem solving" (p. 3). Although their model emphasizes a competency-based orientation, they acknowledge the benefits of a strength-based approach, noting that "by building on the recognition of the strengths and talents of the supervisee, supervision encourages self-efficacy" (p. 3). It is generally acknowledged that effective supervisors tend to adopt a number of roles, such as observing, mentoring, coaching, and inspiring, and create an atmosphere that promotes self-motivation, learning, and professional development (Center for Substance Abuse Treatment, 2007, p. 7).

Functions and Responsibilities of Supervision

Although supervisors have many responsibilities, supervision can be conceptualized as encompassing two broad functions: fostering the supervisee's professional development and ensuring client welfare (monitoring client care and serving as a gatekeeper for the profession). Regarding supervisee development, Bernard and Goodyear (2004) note that supervisors have the advantage of being able to view the clinical process with a clarity of perspective, because unlike the individual therapist, they are not involved in the clinical process. However, they caution that this "rarified air" can be seductive, and that insight naturally is much easier to come by as a "Monday morning quarterback" (p. 7).

Supervision has much in common with other professional roles but is also different in some important ways, and like most responsibilities in the provision of mental health services, it is important to be clear on the distinctions. The following are helpful guidelines regarding the similarities and differences between supervision and teaching, counseling, and consultation (Bernard & Goodyear, 2004, pp. 8–9):

Supervision vs. Teaching

Similarities:

Both impart new skills and knowledge and have an evaluative function.

Differences:

Teaching is driven by the need to meet the learning objectives of the curriculum for the entire class, whereas supervision is highly individualized and guided by the needs of the supervisee and the supervisee's clients.

Supervision vs. Counseling or Therapy

Similarities:

Both can address the recipient's problematic behaviors, thoughts, or feelings.

Differences:

Supervision is evaluative, counseling is not. Clients typically have more choice of therapists than supervisees have of their supervisors. Any therapeutic work done with a supervisee must only be to increase his or her effectiveness with clients, and only with careful attention to the potential for boundary concerns.

Supervsion vs. Consultation

Similarities:

Both are concerned with helping the recipient work more effectively as a professional. For more advanced trainees, the overlap between supervision and consultation becomes greater.

Differences:

> Consultation is a relationship between equals (and, in fact, the recipient usually can fire the consultant), whereas the supervisory relationship is hierarchical, and as with teaching, supervision is evaluative, whereas consultation is not.

Although supervision has important commonalities with these other professional roles, problems can easily occur if supervision becomes too focused on teaching (overly didactic), too focused on therapeutic endeavors (potential ethical concerns), or too focused on consultation (as there is always an inherent power and responsibility differential).

The commonalities between therapy and supervision probably warrant a little additional discussion. There are certainly many areas of overlap. Both supervision and therapy should ideally involve increasing perspective, developing heightened awareness of the self, increasing the range of options and possibilities, and exploring specific behavioral alternatives. However, the therapeutic realm must be approached with great intentionality and clear respect for appropriate boundaries. Although good supervision will at times involve making the supervisee aware of aspects of the self that may hinder effective therapy and exploring ways to use more effective behavior, supervision and therapy must not be confused. (If you are asking your supervisee about his mother, you are on the wrong track.) Again, the power differential is crucial here; whereas clients can stop the therapy process at any time (at least voluntary clients), supervisees cannot.

Flexibility is central. Effective supervision depends upon the ability of the supervisor to accurately assess the various developmental and immediate needs of the supervisee, combined with the client needs and situational factors, and adjust accordingly.

Approaches to Supervision

The next section will provide a brief overview of some of the more influential clinical supervision models. This is not meant to be an exhaustive list or a full explanation of each model, but rather merely to quickly acquaint the reader with some of the more noteworthy, different approaches to supervision.

Therapy-Based Models

Morgan and Sprenkle (2007) noted that early clinical supervisors often had little or no formal training in supervision and tended to merely apply clinical theories to the supervision process. It is generally accepted that the assumptions therapists have of human nature will also impact how they construe all interpersonal behavior, including supervision. Moreover, although there are important differences between therapy and supervision, many of the techniques used in therapy are used in supervision as well (Bernard and Goodyear, 2004, p. 76).

Psychotherapy-based supervision models can feel like a natural extension of the therapy model, often heavily sharing the same concepts, areas of focus, and terminology. Even today, it is still very common practice to apply theories of therapy to supervision. This has to be done thoughtfully and intentionally, however, given that the supervisory relationship is not equivalent to the client–therapist relationship, and the skills and areas of emphasis differ.

Psychodynamic Therapy

Given the prevailing influence of Freudian concepts during the formative years of psychology as a profession, the psychodynamic model heavily influenced the early years of supervision. This approach required the supervisee to undergo psychoanalysis so that the therapist would not be reactive to the client and hinder the therapeutic process. (Although most training programs today do not formally require students to have personal experience with psychotherapy, we highly encourage it. As we frequently tell our students and supervisees, it feels very different in the client chair than in the therapist chair, and often what feels comfortable from the perspective of the therapist is not necessarily what feels comfortable or helpful from the client's perspective. Although it is possible to become a good therapist without having personal therapy experience, it is akin to expecting someone to become an exceptional basketball coach without ever having played the game—certainly possible, but likely the exception.)

Psychodynamic supervision focuses on client processes from the psychodynamic orientation, viewing the supervisee through the lens of Freudian psychological processes, such as transference and countertransference, defense mechanisms, conflict, and so on. Commenting on the parallels between psychodynamic therapy and supervision, Dewald (1997) noted that both processes need a solid alliance and the feeling of safety, as well as empathic understanding and attunement to the processes of transference and countertransference. Given the similarities, Dewald stated that "if one were a skilled analyst, one would be able to do skilled supervision" (p. 41). However, it is likely that just as good therapists do not necessarily make good clinical faculty members, their ability to make good supervisors is also probably subject to individual differences.

Psychodynamic supervision is broadly classified into three categories depending upon the area of focus: patient-centered, supervisee-centered, and supervisory-matrix-centered (Frawley-O'Dea & Sarnat, 2001):

- Patient-centered psychodynamic supervision focuses on the patient's presentations and concerns. Reflecting the expert role of the therapist in psychodynamic therapy, psychodynamic supervision is primarily didactic, focusing on helping the supervisee understand the patient's dynamics and content.

- Supervisee-centered psychodynamic supervision focuses on the content and process of the supervisee's experience, examining the supervisee's resistances and anxieties (Falender and Shafranske, 2004). Because the focus of supervision is more on the supervisee and gaining understanding of his or her psychological processes, the process is more experiential than patient-centered supervision.

- The supervisory-matrix-centered approach incorporates examining the supervisor–supervisee relationship. This shifts the role of the supervisor away from that of a detached expert (in the patient-centered approach), and moves the focus to examining the supervision process and relationship and its parallel process, meaning the supervisee's interaction with the supervisor that parallels the client's behavior with the supervisee as the therapist (Haynes, Corey, & Moulton, 2003).

Person-Centered Supervision

Person-centered supervision is based on the application of Carl Rogers's (1957) facilitative conditions of psychotherapy to the practice of supervision. Rogers regarded his counseling theory as influencing his supervisory approach and believed that the facilitative conditions of genuineness, warmth, and empathy are essential for effective supervision, just as they are central to psychotherapy. Regardless of theoretical orientation, the underpinnings of most counseling skills training programs in most countries today (e.g., microskills training) rests upon Rogerian foundations and acknowledges the importance of creating an atmosphere of safety, understanding, and authenticity.

Person-centered supervision assumes that the supervisee has the innate ability and resources to develop as a therapist, and the task of the supervisor is to create a collaborative partnership with the supervisee to provide the conditions in which the supervisee can be present to the client's experience and be fully engaged with the client (Lambers, 2000). The "attitudes and personal characteristics of the therapist and the quality of the client–therapist relationship" are regarded as the prime determinants of the therapeutic outcome in psychotherapy (Haynes, Corey, and Moulton, 2003, p. 118), and in supervision, the working alliance is regarded as the primary vehicle to facilitate the trainee's learning and growth.

Rogers's conceptualization of supervision leans more toward the therapy end of the continuum than many other supervision approaches. In an interview with Goodyear, Rogers stated "I think my major goal is to help the therapist grow in self-confidence and to grow in understanding the therapeutic process. And to that end, I find it very fruitful to explore any difficulties the therapist may feel he or she is having working with the client. Supervision for me is a modified form of the therapeutic interview" (Hackney and Goodyear, 1984, p. 283).

Cognitive Behavioral Supervision

As with psychodynamic and person-centered supervision, cognitive behavioral supervision infuses the supervision process with many of the techniques and theoretical concepts of the underlying theoretical orientation. Padesky (1996) asserted that the same processes and methods that characterize the cognitive behavioral therapy (CBT) process can be used to teach and supervise therapists (p. 289), and noted that both therapy and supervision incorporate many similar activities, such as goal setting, checking-in, and eliciting feedback.

CBT-oriented supervisors typically negotiate an agenda with the supervisee at the beginning of each session and continuously assess and monitor the supervisee's progress. Behavioral practice may be stressed during both counseling and supervision sessions, including through such means as behavioral rehearsals and role playing. CBT-focused supervisors rely heavily on Socratic questioning and challenging the supervisees' misconceptions. Other areas of focus include establishing a strong working relationship, skill analysis, and assessment; setting supervision goals and strategizing and implementing methods to achieve the goals; follow-up evaluation and generalization of learning; and, at times, assigning homework to the supervisee (e.g., Liese & Beck, 1997; Rosenbaum and Ronen, 1998). Cognitive behavioral supervision also emphasizes the use of the trainee's observable cognitions and behaviors, especially regarding reactions to the client (Hayes et al., 2003).

Systemic Supervision

Systemic supervision, based upon the theoretical perspective of systemic family systems therapy (e.g., Haley, 1987; Watzlawick, Weakland, and Fisch, 1974), is characterized by focusing importance and attention on the similarities between family systems and supervisory systems. Consequently, issues such as structure and boundaries take on special importance in supervision.

Within the systemic model, which is widely used by marriage and family therapists and supervisors, among others, it is believed that there should be a close correspondence and theoretical consistency between therapy and supervision (e.g., McDaniel, Weber, & McKeever, 1983). This close correspondence between therapy and supervision is referred to as *isomorphic translation* (Rigazio-DiGilio Daniels, & Ivey, 1997, p. 224) or *parallel processes*. One implication, grounded in structural family therapy, is that supervision should maintain clear boundaries between the supervisor and supervisee, similar to the clear boundaries a marriage and family therapist would want to maintain with families in therapy.

The systemic supervision process, as with systemic therapy, is also premised upon collaboratively establishing clear, meaningful, and effective goals (e.g., Haley, 1987; Watzlawick, Weakland, & Fish, 1974). This "coconstructive process" is based upon the emerging and evolving relationship between supervisor and supervisee

(Milne, 2009, p. 30). Haley (1987) and Liddle, Breunlin, and Schwartz (1988) stress the importance of a successful first session to serve as the foundation for both successful therapy and clinical supervision.

A key principle is that as the structure of the supervision process is constructed and solidifies, this emerging structure becomes the vehicle through which the supervisee will learn and develop. Mirroring typical family therapy, the supervisor takes on an active, directive, and collaborative role (Liddle et al., 1997, p. 413). Papadopoulos (2001) notes, similar to Yalom and Leszcz's (2005) seminal distinction between a process and content orientation, that systemic supervision distinguishes between *information* and *data*. One of the primary tasks of supervision is to help the supervisee realize that not everything heard in session is helpful to the therapeutic process and to learn to "discriminate between information and data and to increase their effectiveness in eliciting appropriate information" (pp. 406–407).

Developmental Supervision

Developmental models of supervision are based on the assumption that clinicians in training pass through predictable stages of development as they gain increased knowledge and skill. The task of the supervisor is to identify the stage of the supervisee and to tailor the focus and approach of supervision in accordance, with the general assumption that a beginning therapist needs more structure and guidance, whereas a more advanced clinician benefits from a more collaborative and conceptual focus. The stages of growth and learning are qualitatively different from each other, and each stage of development requires different approaches and emphases in supervision. Developmental supervision models became particularly prominent in the 1980s, prompted especially by the work of Cal Stoltenberg (1981) and Ursula Delworth (Stoltenberg & Delworth, 1987).

Influential developmental psychologist Lev Vygotsky (e.g., Vygotsky, 1978) regarded it as important for supervisors to provide tools and models designed through carefully "scaffolding" their supervisees' training experiences to meet their developmental needs. He coined the term "zone of proximal development" (ZPD) to describe the difference between what learners can do on their own and what they can do with assistance. Development occurs though the use of scaffolding offered by someone with more knowledge and experience who provides increasingly challenging experiences as the learner acquires greater mastery. The supervisor helps to elicit and clarify what the supervisee already knows, building upon these strengths and drawing out the supervisee's understanding. Milne (2009) likens the scaffolding process to the metaphor of taking a journey with a guide. The supervisee must exert effort and take some chances, thereby contributing to what is undertaken and achieved, but the process works best with a supervisor who behaves like an experienced guide who can draw on the experience of already having traveled the path (p. 131).

Developmental models such as Stoltenberg and Delworth's (1987) focus on tailoring the supervision process to meet the supervisees' current level of development, based on the premise that supervisees go through predictable stages of development. As the supervisee develops competence or mastery, the supervisor gradually moves the scaffolding to encourage the supervisee to apply the learning to the next and more difficult stage.

Developmental models of supervision typically define progressive stages of supervisee development (e.g., from novice to expert), and describe specific characteristics, tasks, and skills expected for each stage. Developmental supervision depends upon the supervisor accurately identifying the supervisee's current stage of development and adapting the supervision focus and approach to appropriately meet both the competencies and the interpersonal needs of the supervisee. The supervisee is ideally both supported (which provides a sense of security) and challenged to stimulate growth and learning.

Heppner and Roehlke (1984) studied supervisees over a 2-year period to examine the implications of supervisee development on the supervision process. Beginning-level practicum students reported valuing support combined with skills training, essentially wanting to know the "right way" to conduct therapy. As supervisees gained more experience, they gained more of an appreciation for conceptualizations and a deeper understanding of the therapy process. Beginning practicum students identified issues of support and self-awareness as "critical incidents," whereas the most advanced trainees (doctoral interns) tended to report more critical issues around personal issues and defensiveness affecting therapy.

Although developmental models are intuitively appealing to both supervisors and supervisees, in actual practice, supervisors appear to provide the same sort of supervision to all supervisees regardless of their level of experience (Sumerall et al., 1998). Fortunately, supervisees seem not to mind. In a study of 100 supervisees, Ladany, Marotta, and Muse-Burke (2001) found no differences in supervisee preferences based on level of clinical experience and asserted that the concept of developmentally different levels of supervision may be "based more on clinical lore than on research" (p. 215).

Developmental Supervision Models

The next section will detail two of the more influential and complete developmental supervision models. Although most models present their unique stages, Hess (1987) defined a four-stage sequence that seems to provide a helpful understanding of the common developmental sequence:

1. Inception Stage—supervisees tend to feel insecure and value basic skill building, role definitions, and boundary setting. The demystification of therapy is important at this stage.

2. Skill Development Stage—supervisees become more adept at identifying clients' particular needs and selecting appropriate strategies. Supervisees begin to identify with a system of therapy and a philosophy of human nature. This stage involves a shift to the apprenticeship model, with supervisees developing greater autonomy.

3. Consolidation Stage—supervisees (and others) begin to recognize individual skills and talents. The previously acquired building blocks are integrated. The role of the therapist's personality emerges, and skill refinement and competence more fully emerge.

4. Mutuality Stage—the supervisee role in supervision becomes more of an autonomous professional seeking consultation, similar to peer consultation. The supervisee becomes more comfortable and proficient problem solving and creating solutions. (pp. 251–252)

One of the most influential and researched developmental models of supervision is the integrated developmental model (IDM). First developed by Stoltenberg (1981), it has been updated by Stoltenberg and Delworth (1987) and then by Stoltenberg and McNeill (1997). The IDM categorizes three levels of counselor development:

- Level 1—beginning supervisees with little or no experience; generally eager and motivated but anxious and fearful of evaluation

- Level 2—mid-level regarding experience; fluctuating confidence and motivation

- Level 3—more advanced experience; feeling more secure in their abilities; are able to use self in the therapy process

Across each stage of development, three main factors or structures are progressing and growing:

- Self–other awareness (both cognitive and affective)

- Motivation

- Autonomy

As with other developmental theories, the basic premise is to match learning characteristics with the optimal learning environment. In other words, supervision should be designed to optimize the supervisee's learning at each stage of development. The Stoltenberg IDM model emphasizes the importance of professional development in various domains, such as intervention skills, assessment techniques, interpersonal assessments, client conceptualization, theoretical understanding, professional ethics, diversity awareness, and treatment planning and goal setting.

The emphasis is on the supervisor using skills and approaches that correspond with the supervisee's level of development. For example, beginning-level supervisees need more support and guidance, whereas experienced supervisees would more likely benefit from supervision that is more collegial and challenging. Mismatches can be problematic; for example, a supervisor who expects autonomy from a beginning-level supervisee will very likely intensify the supervisee's anxiety, and a supervisor who is too prescriptive with an experienced trainee will likely hinder the development of autonomy, as well as likely create a frustrating supervision environment.

Unlike other models that are linear, the Loganbill, Hardy, and Delworth (1982) model assumes that therapists will re-cycle through the stages, increasing their level of integration each time. The three repeating stages of development they identify are:

- Stagnation—"stuckness" or blind spots for experienced clinicians; unawareness of difficulties for beginning supervisees. This stage is characterized by simple black-and-white thinking and lack of insight.

- Confusion—this stage is characterized by instability, disorganization, confusion, and conflict. During this stage, the supervisee realizes that the answers will not come from the supervisor, which can be disconcerting.

- Integration—this stage is characterized by calmness, new understanding, and flexibility, and the supervisee takes more responsibility for the supervision process and meaningful use of the supervision time.

Rønnenstad and Skovholt (2003) developed a model of supervision based on interviews with 100 therapists ranging in experience from novice to senior clinicians with decades of experience. Their model is unique in that it focuses on therapist development throughout the life span of one's career. They proposed the following six stages of development:

- Phase 1: The Lay-Helper Phase—although individuals in this stage have had some experience helping others (e.g., friends and family), they are prone to boundary problems and becoming overly involved.

- Phase 2: The Beginning-Student Phase—supervisees feel anxious and dependent and value their supervisors' support and encouragement. They typically are looking for models and role models to emulate.

- Phase 3: The Advanced-Student Phase—supervisees at the advanced-practicum or internship stage feel pressure to operate at a level of professional competence. Supervision helps supervisees feel confirmed in their skill-attainment level and helps to consolidate learning.

- Phase 4: The Novice-Professional Phase—new therapists typically begin integrating their personalities more into treatment and feel more comfortable in their professional roles.

- Phase 5: The Experienced-Professional Phase—the challenge is to find a style that feels authentic and congruent with their values and identity.

- Phase 6: The Senior-Professional Phase—they have more than 20 years of experience. Therapists at this stage of practice often become more modest about their impact on clients. Loss can become a theme at this stage (looking ahead to their own retirements, loss of their professional elders, etc.).

The first three stages roughly correspond with the levels of the IDM; however, the later three stages expand development into the professional realm postgraduation.

Based on the results of their cross-sectional and longitudinal quality study, Rønnestand and Skovholt (2003) formulated the main findings into 14 themes of counselor development, as follows:

1. Professional development involves an increasing higher-order integration of the professional self and the personal self.

2. The focus of functioning shifts dramatically over time from internal to external and back to internal.

3. Continuous reflection is a prerequisite for optimal learning and professional development at all levels of experience.

4. An intense commitment to learn propels the developmental process.

5. The cognitive map changes: Beginning practitioners rely on external expertise; seasoned practitioners rely on internal expertise.

6. Professional development is a long, slow, continuous process that can also be erratic.

7. Professional development is a lifelong process.

8. Many beginning practitioners experience much anxiety in their professional work. Over time, most master this anxiety.

9. Clients serve as a major source of influence and serve as primary teachers.

10. Personal life influences professional functioning and development throughout the professional life span.

11. Interpersonal sources of influence propel professional development more than impersonal sources of influence.

12. New members of the field view professional elders and graduate training with strong affective reactions.

13. Extensive experience with suffering contributes to heightened recognition, acceptance, and appreciation of human variability.

14. For the practitioner, there is a realignment from self as hero to client as hero. (pp. 27–38)

Throughout the stages of development, Rønnestad and Skovholt emphasize the importance of continuous reflection on the part of the supervisee for growth to occur.

Other Models of Supervision

Several other approaches have had an influence on the field of supervision as well. Social role models provide a framework for organizing the different functions and roles of supervision. Bernard's (1979) discrimination model is a 3 × 3 conceptualization that matches functions of supervision (helping supervisees learn the skills of process, conceptualization, and personalization) with the supervisor role (teacher, counselor, and consultant). Each cell suggests different ways a supervisor might help supervisees master specific skills. For example, the supervisor might take on the role of consultant with an experienced supervisee to consider different ways to conceptualize a challenging client.

Holloway (1995) proposed a more complex and comprehensive model of supervision, creating a 5 × 5 grid of supervision, again combining supervision functions with tasks or areas of focus of supervision. Her five functions are: (a) monitor and evaluate, (b) instruct and advise, (c) model, (d) consult, and (e) support and share. The five tasks or areas of focus of supervision are: (a) counseling skills, (b) case conceptualization, (c) professional role, (d) emotional awareness, and (e) self-evaluation. She terms her functions and tasks grid the "process matrix." In addition, she encourages supervisions to also consider the impact of the following contextual factors: (a) the supervisor, (b) the supervisee, (c) the client, and (d) the setting where the supervision takes place. Holloway also emphasizes the centrality of the working relationship in the supervision process, framing it as the core around which the functions and tasks of supervision and contextual factors all connect.

Outcome-oriented supervision, advocated by Worthen and Lambert (2007), aims to pragmatically focus on feedback data, relying upon tracking clinical outcomes, namely the progress or lack of progress experienced by clients, to guide the supervision process. Consistently collected data, such as the use of short feedback measures each session, serve to provide feedback to both the supervisee and supervisor, highlighting both successes and failures. Competency-based models such as Falender and Shafranske's competency-based approach (2004), the discrimination model (Bernard, 1997), and the task-oriented model (Mead, 1990), also focus on measurable outcomes, with strategies to operationalize, assess, and reach these goals.

Common Factors Approach

Despite the many different supervision models that exist, there is no evidence to suggest that any one model of supervision is in any way superior to any other (Morgan and Sprenkle, 2007). Goodyear and Bradley (1983) examined the similarities and differences between the five most dominant clinical supervision theories at the time (rational emotive, behavioral, client-centered, developmental, and psychoanalytic), and stated they were "struck with the extent to which supervision techniques must be similar across supervisors, regardless of theory" (Goodyear & Bradley, 1983, p. 63). Noting the absence of superiority of any one model, Sprenkle (1999) argued for the need to examine the aspects of supervision that transcend the various different approaches. With increased experience, clinical supervisors seem to focus less on the differences between theoretical approaches and to gravitate toward the common factors in their practice. Less experienced supervisors tend to differ in ways based on their theoretical orientation, whereas more experienced supervisors share much more of their emphases in common (Goodyear and Robyak, 1982).

Morgan and Sprenkle (2007) note that whereas the common-factors approach in psychotherapy emerged from empirical studies on clinical outcomes, there is not yet a comparable body of research in supervision from which the common factors of supervision can be drawn. However, they suggest that this does not negate the potential benefits of identifying important elements shared by supervision models (p. 6). And, as there is a lack of empirical support for adopting one theoretical model to the exclusion of others (Storm, Todd, Sprenkle, and Morgan, 2001), it seems only reasonable to focus on the common factors. "We believe that it is unlikely that any one model, common factors or otherwise, will ever emerge as the best way to supervise everyone under every situation. Human beings and the process of supervision are too complex to brook such hubris. But there are likely a set of elements that most good supervision will have in common" (Morgan & Sprenkle, 2007, p. 7).

The results of the review by Morgan and Sprenkle (2007) identified a number of general supervision domains:

- Develop clinical skills

- Acquire knowledge about client dynamics, clinical theories, intervention strategies, and other issues

- Learn to function as professionals and comply with professional practice and ethical standards

- Personal growth, awareness, and emotional management

- Supervisee autonomy and confidence

- Monitoring and evaluating the supervisee

The literature also finds commonalities regarding a variety of areas to which supervisors must attend during supervision. These include the following responsibilities:

- Needs of the individual supervisee
- Needs of the specific client
- Profession or field as a whole—maintaining standards and protecting the public

A third element widely regarded as important to supervision is the quality of the supervisory relationship, which was almost universally described as a critical element. This seems to apply whether the relationship is collaborative or more hierarchical and directive. However, the research from a variety of studies seems to suggest that supervisees prefer to have a high degree of support from their supervisors, regardless of how directive or collaborative the relationship is (p. 10).

The review of literature on common factors suggests four frequently identified supervision roles, as follows:

- Coach—involves an emphasis on clinical competence at the idiosyncratic level, with the supervisor assisting the supervisee's direct work with the supervisee's clients, helping the supervisee apply and refine clinical skills. This includes activities such as helping supervisees attend to the therapeutic relationship, applying assessment skills, developing case conceptualizations, and offering feedback on the supervisee's clinical work.

- Teacher—emphasizes clinical competence as well, but at a more general level. The supervisor encourages the acquisition of broadly applicable knowledge and information about clinical work, such as general skills and theories.

- Mentor—focuses on the personal development of the supervisee as a growing professional, including helping the supervisee identify and address his or her own contribution to the therapeutic alliance, recognizing personal strengths and limitations, and helping the supervisee to develop a role as a practicing member of the professional community.

- Administrator—focuses on the broad professional, ethical, legal, and other standards that guide clinical practice. The supervisor ensures that the supervisee meets minimum standards, thus protecting clients. This role involves evaluation and feedback. (Morgan & Sprenkle, 2007, pp. 11–12).

Good supervision involves flexibility and the ability to work from within multiple supervisory roles (Morgan & Sprenkle, 2007, p. 12). It should also be noted that although many theoretical models exist, as with the application of psychotherapy, practice is often very eclectic. Probably resulting from the fact that formal training in supervision is often the exception and not the rule, surveys indicate that the most popular supervision model actually used is simply to draw upon one's own supervision experiences (Falender and Shafranske, 2004).

Although drawing from one's own experience can be a valuable and important component of the practice of supervision, it is doubtful that anyone would argue that is the method of choice for any professional activity, ranging from flying a plane to performing medicine to offering supervision. Given the importance and influence of supervision, hopefully formal training in supervision will soon become the norm and the expectation.

Conclusion

We believe that all respected supervision models and approaches have valuable contributions to offer, and that likely no single model, even ours, will meet the needs of all supervisors and all supervisees in every situation. The story of the three blind men asked to describe an elephant seems appropriate. The first blind man walked up to the head, and feeling the head, ears, and trunk described these features to the other two men. The second blind man walked up to the midsection, and feeling this region of the elephant, dutifully reported this to the others. The last blind man (sometimes it pays not to be last) walked up and felt the backside of the elephant and reported his findings. Needless to say, each description of the elephant, based on reporting the empirical findings and grounded in truth, was radically different, depending upon the point of reference of the teller. Hopefully, our model of strength-based supervision, grounded in the constructs and research findings of positive psychology, will add useful information and perspective to the understanding of the supervision process. However, it is also offered with a spirit of deep gratitude to the volumes of research and clinically based knowledge that already exists.

Questions to Consider

- Reflect on some of your best experiences being supervised. Describe your supervisor.

- What did your supervisor do to make the supervision experience work so well?

- Reflect on some of the times that you were at your best as a supervisee. What helped to make this happen? What specifically were *you* doing to make it such a good experience?

- If you imagine yourself supervising exactly as you would want to, what is happening? How are you interacting with your supervisee? What are you emphasizing?

- What values do you want to make sure that you exemplify and pass on to your supervisees?

- How do you anticipate that your theoretical orientation as a clinician will influence your approach as a supervisor?

- What do you regard as the similarities between supervision and therapy? What are the key differences?

Recommended Readings

Books

Bernard, J. M., & Goodyear, R. K. (2013). *Fundamentals of clinical supervision* (5th ed.). Boston, MA: Allyn and Bacon.

Everett, C. A., & Lee, R. E. (2005). *The integrative family therapy supervisor: A primer.* New York: Routledge.

Falender, C.A., & Shafranske, E.P. (2004). *Clinical supervision: A competency-based approach.* Washington, DC: American Psychological Association.

Holloway, E. (1995). *Clinical supervision: A systems approach.* Thousand Oaks, CA: Sage Publications.

Lee, R. E., & Nelson, T. S. (2013). *The contemporary relational supervisor.* New York: Routledge.

Milne, D. (2009). *Evidence-based clinical supervision: Principles and practice.* New York: Wiley-Blackwell.

Stoltenberg, C. D., & Delworth, U. (1998). *Supervising counselors and therapists: A developmental approach.* San Francisco, CA: Jossey-Bass.

Articles and Book Chapters

Harkness, D., & Poertner, J. (1989). Research on social work supervision: A conceptual review. *Social Work, 34,* 115–199.

Morgan, M. M., & Sprenkle, D. H. (2007). Toward a common-factors approach to supervision. *Journal of Marital and Family Therapy, 33*(1), 1–17.

Rønnestad, M. H., & Skovholt, T. M. (2003). The journey of the counselor and therapist: Research findings and perspectives on professional development. *Journal of Career Development, 30,* 5–44.

Stoltenberg, C. D., & McNeill, B. W. (1997). Clinical supervision from a developmental perspective: Research and practice. In C. E. Watkins (Ed.), *Handbook of psychotherapy supervision* (pp. 184–202). New York: John Wiley & Sons.

References

Bernard, J. M. (1979). Supervisor training: A discrimination model. *Counselor education and supervision, 19*(1), 60–68.

Bernard, J. M. (1997). The Discrimination Model. In C. E. Watkins, *Handbook of psychotherapy supervision* (pp. 310–327). New York: Wiley.

Bernard, J. M., & Goodyear, R. K. (2004). *Fundamentals of clinical supervision* (3rd ed.). Boston, MA: Allyn and Bacon.

Bernard, J. M., & Goodyear, R. K. (2013). *Fundamentals of clinical supervision* (5th ed.). Boston, MA: Allyn and Bacon.

Center for Substance Abuse Treatment. (2007). *Competencies for substance abuse treatment clinical supervisors.* Technical Assistance Publication (TAP) Series 21-A (Rep. No HHS Publication No. (SMA) 07-4243). Rockville, MD: Substance Abuse and Mental Health Services Adminstration.

Dewald, P. A. (1997). The process of supervision in psychoanalysis. In C. E. Watkins (Ed.), *Handbook of psychotherapy supervision* (pp. 31–43). New York: John Wiley & Sons.

Falender, C. A., & Shafranske, E. P. (2004). *Clinical supervision: A competency-based approach.* Washington, DC: American Psychological Association.

Frawley-O'Dea, M. G., & Sarnat, J. E. (2001). *The supervisory relationship: A contemporary psychodynamic approach.* New York: Guilford Press.

Goodyear, R. K., & Bradley, F. O. (1983). Supervision in counseling: II. Integration and evaluation: Theories of counselor supervision: Points of convergence and divergence. *The Counseling Psychologist, 11,* 1983, 59–67.

Goodyear, R. K., & Robyak, J. E. (1982). Supervisors' theory and experience in supervisory focus. *Psychological Reports, 51*(3), 978.

Hackney, H. L., & Goodyear, R. K. (1984). Carl Rogers' client-centered supervision. In R. F. Levant & J. M. Schlien (Eds.), *Client-centered therapy and the person-centered approach* (pp. 278–296). New York: Praeger.

Haley, J. (1987). *Problem-solving therapy.* San Francisco, CA: Jossey-Bass.

Harkness, D., & Poertner, J. (1989). Research on social work supervision: A conceptual review. *Social Work, 34,* 115–199.

Haynes, R., Corey, G., & Moulton, P. (2003). *Clinical supervision in the helping professions: A practical guide.* Pacific Grove, CA: Brooks/Cole.

Heppner, P. P., & Roehlke, H. J. (1984). Differences among supervisees at different levels of training: Implications for a developmental model of supervision. *Journal of Counseling Psychology, 31,* 76.

Hess, A. K. (1987). Psychotherapy supervision: Stages, Buber, and a theory of relationship. *Professional Psychology: Research and Practice, 18,* 251–259.

Hess, A. K., Hess, K. D., & Hess, T. H. (2008). *Psychotherapy supervision: Theory, research, and practice.* New York: John Wiley & Sons.

Holloway, E. (1995). *Clinical supervision: A systems approach.* Thousand Oaks, CA: Sage Publications.

Ladany, N., Marotta, S., & Muse-Burke, J. L. (2001). Counselor experience related to complexity of case conceptualization and supervision preference. *Counselor Education and Supervision, 40*(3), 203–219.

Lambers, E. (2000). Supervision in person-centered therapy: Facilitating congruence: In E. Mearns & B. Thorne (Eds.), *Person-centered therapy today: New frontiers in theory and practice* (pp. 196–211). London: Sage Publications.

Liddle, H. A., Becker, D., & Diamond, G. M. (1997). Family therapy supervision. In C. E. Watkins, Jr. (Ed.), *Handbook of psychotherapy supervision* (pp. 400–418). New York, NY: John Wiley & Sons.

Liddle, H. A., Beunlin, D. C., & Schwartz, R. C. (Eds.). (1988). *Handbook of family therapy training and supervision.* New York: Guilford Press.

Liese, B. S., & Beck, J. S. (1997). Cognitive therapy supervision. In C. E. Watkins, Jr. (Ed.), *Handbook of psychotherapy supervision* (pp. 114–133). New York: John Wiley & Sons.

Loganbill, C., Hardy, E., & Delworth, U. (1982). Supervision: A conceptual model. *Counseling Psychologist, 10,* 3–42.

McDaniel, S., Weber, T., & McKeever, J. (1983). Multiple theoretical approaches to supervision: Choices in family therapy training. *Family Process, 22,* 491–500.

Mead, D. E. (1990). *Effective supervision: A task-oriented model for the mental health professions.* New York: Brunner/Mazel.

Milne, D. (2009). *Evidence-based clinical supervision: Principles and practice.* Chichester, UK: Wiley-Blackwell.

Morgan, M. M., & Sprenkle, D. H. (2007). Toward a common-factors approach to supervision. *Journal of Marital and Family Therapy, 33*(1), 1–17.

Padesky, C. A. (1996). Developing cognitive therapist competency: Teaching and supervision models. In P.M. Salkovskis (Ed.), *Frontiers of cognitive therapy* (pp. 266–292). London, UK: Guilford Press.

Papadopoulos, R. K. (2001). Refugee families: Issues of systemic supervision. *Journal of Family Therapy, 23,* 405–422.

Rigazio-DiGilio, S. A., Daniels, T. G., & Ivey, A. E. (1997). Systemic cognitive-developmental supervision: A developmental-integrative approach to psychotherapy supervision. In C. E. Watkins (Ed.), *Handbook of psychotherapy supervision* (pp. 223–245). New York: John Wiley & Sons.

Rogers, C. R. (1957). The necessary and sufficient conditions of therapeutic personality change. *Journal of Consulting Psychology, 21,* 95.

Rønnestad, M. H., & Skovholt, T. M. (2003). The journey of the counselor and therapist: Research findings and perspectives on professional development. *Journal of Career Development, 30,* 5–44.

Rosenbaum, M., & Ronen, T. (1998). Clinical supervision from the standpoint of cognitive-behavior therapy. *Psychotherapy: Theory, Research, Practice, Training, 35,* 220.

Sprenkle, D. H. (1999). Toward a general model of family therapy supervision: Comment on Roberts, Winek, and Mulgrew. *Contemporary Family Therapy, 21*(3), 309–315.

Stoltenberg, C. (1981). Approaching supervision from a developmental perspective: The counselor complexity model. *Journal of Counseling Psychology, 28,* 59.

Stoltenberg, C. D., & Delworth, U. (1987). *Supervising counselors and therapists: A developmental approach.* San Francisco, CA: Jossey-Bass.

Stoltenberg, C. D., & McNeill, B. W. (2009). *IDM supervision: An integrative developmental model for supervising counselors and therapists.* New York: Taylor & Francis.

Storm, C. L., Todd, T. C., Sprenkle, D. H., & Morgan, M. M. (2001). Gaps between MFT supervision assumptions and common practice: Suggested best practices. *Journal of Marital and Family Therapy, 27*(2), 227–239.

Sumerall, S. W., Barke, C. R., Timmons, P. L., Oehlert, M. E., Lopez, S. J., & Trent, D. D. (1998). The adaptive counseling and therapy model and supervision of mental health care. *The Clinical Supervisor, 17*(2), 171–176.

Vygotsky, L. S. (1978). *Mind in society: The development of higher psychological processes.* Cambridge, MA: Harvard University Press.

Watzlawick, P., Weakland, J. H., & Fisch, R. (1974). *Change: Principles of problem formation and problem resolution.* New York: WW Norton.

Worthen, V. E., & Lambert, M. J. (2007). Outcome oriented supervision: Advantages of adding systematic client tracking to supportive consultations. *Counselling and Psychotherapy Research, 7,* 48–53.

Yalom, I., & Leszcz, M. (2005). *The theory and practice of group psychotherapy* (5th ed.). New York: Basic Books.

2

Foundations of Positive Psychology

"Success is achieved by developing our strengths, not by eliminating our weaknesses."

—Marilyn vos Savant

"Happiness is mostly a by-product of doing what makes us feel fulfilled."

—Benjamin Spock

Positive psychology has received a lot of popular press and media attention in the past several years. Positive psychology has also created quite a splash in the scholarly community as well. Martin Seligman's 1998 presidential address to the American Psychological Association, imploring the field to study success and well-being, not just pathology and "disease," launched it to the forefront of the academic spotlight. Although this increased attention has helped to raise awareness of positive psychology, much confusion still exists as to what it really is. Put very simply, *positive psychology* is the scientific study of ordinary human strengths and virtues: "Positive psychology revisits 'the average person,' with an interest in finding out what works, what is right, and what is improving" (Sheldon and King, 2001, p. 216). Positive psychology has also been defined as "the study of the conditions and processes that contribute to the flourishing or optimal functioning of people, groups, and institutions" (Gable & Haidt, 2005, p. 104). Linley, Joseph, Harrington, and Wood (2006) define positive psychology as the "scientific study of optimal human functioning" (p. 8), and Peterson (2006) states that it is "the scientific study of what goes right in life, from birth to death, and all stops in between" (p. 4). Although much has been written in the popular self-help press recently using the term "positive," true positive psychology is distinguished by the primacy placed on sound, empirical research.

A core assumption of positive psychology is that people want to live lives of meaning and purpose, beyond simply avoiding hassles or correcting problems. Although it is of much value for someone who is miserable to move from a 1 or 2 to a 5 or 6 on the 10-point scale of well-being, people who are at a 4, 5, or 6 on the scale generally want to move to an 8, 9, or 10. We want to feel like we are making the most of our abilities and have rich lives full of meaning, purpose, and good relationships. Positive psychology attempts to more accurately understand the factors that facilitate or impede the pursuit of the good life, such as personal and social relationships, working environments, organizations, institutions, communities, and the broader social, cultural, political, and economic systems (Linley et al., 2006, p. 7).

A common misperception of positive psychology is that it is simply "looking at the bright side" and minimizes or ignores real distress. Of course, this can be the end result of any poorly executed therapeutic approach. However, the real aim of positive psychology is to elucidate an amplify strengths and successes and thus add balance to the conceptual picture, simultaneously rejecting the assumption that understanding problems and symptoms alone yields a complete understanding of a person. Gable and Haidt (2005) explain that the goal of positive psychology is not the denial of distress or suffering, but rather it is the attempt to look at the other side of the coin, at positive experiences, healthy families, and nurturing institutions as well, to address the "full spectrum of human experience" (p. 105). Gelso and Woodhouse (2003) further emphasize that positive psychotherapy is not simply "covering up problems and deficits," admonishing that doing so would be "naïve psychotherapy at best and a duplicitous therapy at worst" (p. 179). They note that strengths can sometimes be embedded in vulnerabilities.

Positive psychology arose from within the context of the mental health profession, having been heavily influenced by the medical model and the corresponding emphases on pathology, illnesses, and weaknesses, with "scant knowledge of what makes life worth living" (Seligman and Csikszentmihalyi, 2000, p. 5). One of the goals of positive psychology was "to begin to catalyze a change in the focus of psychology from preoccupation only with repairing the worst things in life to also building positive qualities" (Seligman and Csikszentmihalyi, 2000, p. 5). Researching concepts such as resilience, strength, growth, and excellence helps us to more fully understand psychological functioning and the human experience. Moreover, positive psychology can serve a motivating function by shifting attention from only those things that cause and drive pain to the factors and experiences that energize and pull people forward (Kauffman, 2006, p. 220).

Seligman (2002) initially posited that positive psychology is founded upon three "pillars": (1) positive subjective experience or emotion; (2) positive traits such as strengths, virtues, and abilities; and (3) positive institutions (p. xiii). He more recently reformulated this conceptualization to focus away from the temporal state of happiness and emphasizes the more stable and enduring construct of well-being (2011), consisting of the following elements:

- Positive emotion

- Engagement

- Relationships

- Meaning

- Achievement

The aim of this book is to apply the core principles of positive psychology to training and supervision. As will be detailed later, experiencing positive emotions is not simply enjoyable; it also helps promote both learning and good work. Subsequent chapters elucidate the characteristics associated with learning and growth and steps to help foster these attributes. In addition, we discuss the characteristics of "enabling" institutions to provide a model for not merely promoting individual supervisee growth but also for creating a scientifically grounded nurturing and supportive setting that can serve as rich soil for supervisee potential to flourish.

Historical Overview

Although positive psychology is often perceived as a "new" science (a claim reinforced by the assertions of "newness" on many positive psychology book covers), the field has very deep roots. Many of the fundamental questions addressed by contemporary positive psychologists such as "What is the good life?" "What does it mean to be happy?" and "Can happiness be pursued directly or only as a by-product of other pursuits?" have been contemplated for millennia by philosophers such as Plato and Aristotle in the West and Confucius and Lao-Tzu in the East (Peterson, 2006). Religious figures and theologians (e.g., Jesus, Buddha, Mohammed, Thomas Aquinas, and many others) have also posed countless questions about the good life and its attainment (Peterson, 2006, p. 6). Although characterized and expressed differently in different cultures, the pursuit of well-being has played a central role in cultural identity and values. This is certainly apparent in the collective consciousness of the United States, so much so that the "pursuit of life, liberty, and happiness" is the cornerstone of the Declaration of Independence (and is probably one of the few lines from the Declaration that most people know).

An emphasis on strengths and potential has been present since the early days of psychology as a discipline. Even though various deterministic perspectives have seemed to carry the day at times (e.g., human beings were believed to be determined by their past experiences [Freudian]; determined by their environment [behaviorism]; or constrained by their genetic make-up [biological model]), a focus on strengths and identifying the best in people have also been espoused by many of the early and influential psychological theorists. Shortly after the turn of the century, William James (1902) wrote about "healthy mindedness," and Beers (1908) published *A Mind That Found Itself,* focusing on resilience and strengths and promoting the new idea that these attributes could help individuals recover from mental problems.

Applied psychology's interest in improving human productivity served to launch the birth of industrial/organizational (I/O) psychology in the early 20th century. Jung (1933) posited the idea of individuation, which some regard as a precursor to the human potential movement that came several decades later. Well-known and influential psychiatrist Karl Menninger championed remediation, prevention, and the revolutionary perspective that mental illness is amenable to change and improvement (e.g., Menninger, Mayman, and Pruyser, 1963). Marie Jahoda (1958), in her seminal work *Current Concepts of Positive Mental Health,* clearly advocated for the conceptualization of mental health not as the absence of illness, but rather as characterized by self-acceptance, growth, personal integration, realism, autonomy, and mastery.

During the mid-20th century, humanistic psychology arose in contrast to the arguably bleak view of human existence posited by psychoanalysis and behaviorism, the dominant perspectives within psychology at the time. Erik Erikson (1959) focused on healthy development, and Gordon Allport (1961) emphasized the growth-oriented personality. Don Blocher (1966) theorized about five qualities that characterize effective personalities: consistency, commitment, control, competence, and creativity (it's interesting how success lends itself to alliteration). And humanistic psychologists such as Carl Rogers (1961) and Abraham Maslow (1968, 1970) emphasized the "fully functioning person" and the importance of creating the right conditions to enable potential to flourish and human beings' innate potential and propensity toward self-actualization. Humanistic psychology stressed many of the concepts that positive psychology is studying today, such as goals and striving, choice and responsibility, striving to achieve full potential, and meaning and purpose (Peterson, 2006, p. 8). Although often guided by humanistic principles and constructs, positive psychology has elaborated and expanded upon them through solid empirical research.

Before World War II, psychology had three distinct missions: curing mental illness, making the lives of all people more productive and fulfilling, and identifying and nurturing high talent (Seligman and Csikszentmihalyi, 2000, p. 6). However, shortly after World War II, the Veteran's Administration (now called the Department of Veteran's Affairs) and the National Institute of Mental Health (NIMH) were created, shifting the focus and economic incentives for psychologists to the treatment and research of mental illness, and the other missions of psychology—improving the human condition and nurturing achievement and talent—began to be neglected.

Although positive psychology is considered a new science, it can perhaps more accurately be thought of as returning psychology back to its roots and remembering the two neglected missions of making normal people stronger and more productive and making high human potential actual (Seligman & Csikszentmihalyi, 2000, p. 8). The emergence of positive psychology as a discipline has helped to bring the research on many disparate constructs focusing on strengths and human potential under a unifying umbrella and emphasize empirical support for the use of these constructs to improving human functioning (Lopez et al., 2006, pp. 209–210). Linley and Joseph (2004) suggest that although many of the constructs studied in positive psychology have long-standing historical traditions, its more recent emergence has provided a collective identity and common voice and language for researchers and practitioners interested in the fulfillment of potential, as well as the amelioration of pathology (p. 4).

Core Concepts

Positive psychology is more than just a simple construct or principle; it is a collection of constructs and research findings that support the fundamental premise of nurturing and developing potential. It is hard to think of anything more well suited for training and supervision! The Positive Psychology Section of the American Psychological Association recently identified more than 70 positive psychology constructs and applications to post to the group's website. The goal of this chapter is much less ambitious—that is, to simply introduce a few of the key concepts from the research that are relevant to supervision and clinical work. Most of these constructs will be explained in more detail in later chapters, and several other positive psychology applications will be introduced in later chapters as well.

Well-Being vs. Happiness

Fundamentally, positive psychology is the study of factors that contribute to well-being. Although the term *happiness* is often used interchangeably with *well-being*, emotional well-being differs from happiness in that happiness is an appraisal of pleasant or unpleasant feelings in one's immediate experience, whereas emotional well-being refers to a long-term assessment of life satisfaction (Keyes and Magyar-Moe, 2003). Happiness reflects one's current subjective mood, whereas well-being indicates one's global satisfaction with life. Our level of experienced happiness is determined by three factors: our genetic set-point for happiness, our circumstances, and our actions and experiences. Put into a formula: Happiness = Genetics + Circumstances + Actions (Lyubomirsky, Sheldon, & Schkade, 2005).

As for many things, biology plays a large role, and genetics accounts for approximately 50% of the happiness equation (Lyubomirsky et al. 2005). However, similar to many abilities such as intelligence and athletic ability, although we are born with a biological range and some of us tend to experience joy and contentment more easily than others, our life experiences and daily practices can cause us to operate at the high or low end of our range. It is tempting to place the greatest emphasis on circumstances when we think about increasing happiness (e.g., I'll be happier when I get a better job or nicer house), but circumstances generally account for only about 15% of our experience of happiness.

An important caveat, similar to Maslow's hierarchy of needs, is that if our basic life needs are not adequately met, happiness is harder to achieve. Homeless people in America were found to be less satisfied with their lives, but surprisingly, only slightly more dissatisfied (Diener and Biswas-Diener, 2008). However, there rapidly reaches a point of diminishing returns for having a bigger and fancier house once our basic needs are met (Diener and Biswas-Diener, 2008). Although actions—the things we do—only account for about 35% or roughly a third of our experience of happiness, this is the most important area to focus on because unlike biology where we have no control and circumstances where we often have only limited control, actions are the only realm where we have total control. (It has been said that the choice of our parents is the most important decision we make in life, but unfortunately, that choice does not translate into a proactive formula.)

The Role of Circumstances

When thinking about happiness and well-being, it is tempting to focus heavily on the role of circumstances. But we tend to be very poor predictors of what will make us happy (e.g., Gilbert, 2006). Given the choice between winning the lottery or suffering a debilitating accident and becoming paraplegic or quadriplegic, probably very few of us would willingly choose the second option (even those of us thinking that this is probably a leading question, which it is). However, research indicates that both groups returned to their average preexisting level of happiness within about a year (Brickman, Coates, & Janoff-Bulman, 1978).

This dramatically illustrates the process of adaptation. The good news is that *adaptation* helps us cope with adversity and tragedy, and we typically do recover from negative circumstances, although often not without significant pain and struggle. The downside of adaptation is that the newness tends to quickly wear off with those things that temporarily boost our mood, and the new sports car stops giving us chills after a few weeks or months; and our perspective on the house we bought can easily shift to wanting an even bigger house to keep up with the Jones's. This process of needing more and bigger to experience the same increase in satisfaction—which is a boon for a consumer-driven society such as ours—is known as the "hedonic treadmill."

However, unlike circumstances, our actions are not prone to adaptation (e.g., Lyubomirsky et al., 2005). If we help a little old lady across the street every single day for a year, we will still experience the same glow of altruism on day 365 as on the first day, and the boost in mood does not diminish because we've been exercising three times a week for the past 15 years. Moreover, doing good for others appears to have a greater and longer-lasting impact on our happiness than doing good for ourselves. Although life events and circumstances show only a small correlation with happiness, and the happiness after the change tends to be short-lived, our perspective makes a very significant difference.

Seligman (2003) initially conceptualized well-being as: Well-being = Pleasure + Meaning + Engagement, with pleasure being the "icing on the cake" if the two other factors are met. More recently (2011), he has updated this conceptualization to also include the additional factors of relationships and accomplishments. This conceptualization flows well with another key principle of positive psychology—the importance of strengths and virtues. Namely, if we are able to exercise our strengths and live according to our character virtues, we will likely experience well-being.

Strengths

Much of psychology has been built upon the premise that improving deficits will help us lead fuller and more productive lives. There is some truth to this, up to a point. Certainly, if someone is debilitated with overwhelming depression, helping to alleviate or reduce the symptoms will improve the quality of that person's life. However, much of the success and satisfaction we experience results not from improving weaknesses but rather from using and accentuating our strengths. Clifton and Nelson (1992) identified several misassumptions that lead us to overly focus on weaknesses, including the belief that fixing a weakness will make the person or organization stronger; that strengths will just naturally develop so they don't need attention; and the belief that weaknesses and strengths are opposites and that shoring up the weakness will make it become a strength. (My [John Wade] wife recently met with an instructor from one of the well-known standardized test preparation agencies as our older daughter approaches college. I was very pleased to learn that the agency's philosophy reflects the strength-based approach, as the instructor told my wife that it is much easier for students to gain additional points by further developing their areas of strength versus trying to gain points by focusing on weak areas.) A high school student making Cs and Ds in math is unlikely to make a very successful (or happy) accountant, no matter how much effort is spent trying to improve this area of weakness. However, if a student consistently receives positive feedback for the work done on the student newspaper, the student is much more likely to be better served pursuing those strengths in English and journalism, or targeting another career where the strengths of persistence and creativity will be rewarded.

Although this may seem intuitive, the perspective of emphasizing our strengths does not always come naturally. When I (John Wade) give workshops on strengths and ask participants how they would respond if they hypothetically had a school-aged child who brought home a report card with three As, two Bs, a C, and an F, the almost universal response is that the F would be the focus of attention and the topic of most discussion. This is not to say that the F is not important or should be ignored. However, from a strengths perspective, a more productive conservation would be to start with the As and ask the child what was done to earn those good grades. Once the strengths and study habits that led to the successes have been identified and discussed, then a frank conversation can be had about the need to improve the problem area from the perspective of applying the student's strengths and proven study strategies to the weaker areas.

Positive psychology can partially trace its roots back to the Aristotelian notion that strengths must be developed through education and practice, which enables us to more fully reach our potential (Jorgensen & Nafstad, 2004). Two classification systems of strengths are widely used: the Clifton Strengths Finder 2.0 (CSF 2.0; Asplund, Lopez, Hodges, & Harter, 2007) and the Values in Action Inventory of Character Strengths (VIA-IS; Peterson and Seligman, 2004). The Clifton Strengths Finder is supported by decades of research in business and education based on the simple premise, "What would happen if we studied what is right with people?" (e.g., Buckingham & Clifton, 2001; Clifton and Nelson, 1992). The Clifton Strengths Finder 2.0 is a 180-item instrument yielding information and ranking on 34 themes, the top five of which are revealed to the respondent, along with suggestions for putting these themes into action, and a "strength-based action plan" translating the talents into both short- and long-term goals.

The Values in Action Classification of Strengths (VIA-IS; Peterson & Seligman, 2004) was developed as a counterbalance to the Diagnostic and Statistical Manual of Mental Disorders (DSM), providing a common language to talk about strengths and encouraging a more strength-based approach to diagnosis and treatment. Unlike the Gallup measure of strengths (the Clifton Strengths Finder), the VIA-IS instrument identifies and focuses on "character strengths" as opposed to more skill- or talent- based strengths. The character strengths chosen for inclusion had to meet the criterion of being widely recognized across cultures and contribute to individual fulfillment, satisfaction, and happiness (Peterson, 2006, p. 141). Peterson notes that historically, psychologists have been interested in studying character, but concern about personal values contaminating the research, and theory and debate about whether constructs with a moral component are properly under the purview of psychology led to the banishment of academic discourse on character until recently. The Values in Action approach regards good character as a family of positive dispositions and characteristics, and termed the individual components "character strengths" (Peterson, 2006, p. 139). Both religious and philosophical traditions were surveyed during the development of the classification system, and 24 strengths were found to have near unanimous recognition and are believed to transcend culture and time. They were categorized under six overarching virtues: wisdom and knowledge, courage, humanity, justice, temperance, and transcendence (Peterson & Seligman, 2004). The Values in Action Inventory of Character Strengths is available for free online at www.viastrengths.org. It is a 240-item measure that taps the 24 different character strengths, and provides respondents information on their top five strengths and a ranking of the list of 24 strengths.

Broaden-and-Build Theory

The broaden-and-build theory of positive emotions illustrates the adaptive value of positive affect. It basically helps to answer the "bottom line" question, namely that it feels good to experience positive emotions, but so what? Positive emotions have traditionally been thought to be merely markers or indicators of flourishing or optimal well-being. However, Fredrickson's research underlying the broaden-and-build theory indicates that positive emotions are not simply an end in themselves but are a means of achieving psychological growth and improved well-being over time (Fredrickson, 2001, p. 218). Positive affect appears to facilitate approach behavior, whereas negative emotions narrow the focus to avoidance or attacking behavior (p. 219). The specific action tendencies of various negative emotions spark quick and decisive action (e.g., fear prompts avoidance, anger prompts defending or attacking), making them evolutionarily adaptive.

In contrast, the broaden-and-build theory of positive emotions posited by Fredrickson (1998) states that positive emotions such as joy, interest, contentment, pride, and love have the ability "to broaden people's momentary thought-action repertoires and build their enduring personal resources, ranging from physical and intellectual resources to social and psychological resources" (p. 219). This results in the widening of the array of thoughts and actions that come to mind (Fredrickson, 1998; Fredrickson & Branigan, 2001). The broaden-and-build theory posits that positive emotions broaden thought-action repertoires and build enduring personal resources, and consequently, positive emotions have adaptive significance. Whereas negative emotions have evolutionary value mainly from a survival perspective (e.g., taking quick and decisive action and fleeing when a lion or a mugger is approaching), positive emotions are adaptive over the long term because of the broadened thought-action repertoires associated with their experience that lead to the building of personal resources and strategies (Fredrickson & Branigan, 2005).

A clever experiment illuminates this principle. Research participants were shown short, emotionally evocative film clips to induce the specific emotions of amusement, contentment, anger, anxiety, or a neutral, emotionless control condition. Participants were asked to imagine being in a situation in which similar feelings would arise, and to list what they would like to do at that time given the feeling, recording their responses on up to 20 blank lines that began with the phrase, "I would like to." Participants in the two positive emotional conditions identified more things they would like to do than those in the negative emotional or control condition. This pattern of results suggests that feeling positive emotions widens the array of thoughts and actions that come to mind

(Fredrickson and Branigan, 2005). Another study using the film clips eliciting the two negative, two positive, or nonemotional state applied to a global-local visual processing task found that the experience of positive emotions was associated with a more global perspective, again lending support to the proposition that positive emotions broaden the scope of awareness and perception (Fredrickson & Branigan, 2005).

However, the significance of positive emotions is not limited to broadening the scope of attention and expanding the use of personal resources; positive emotions actually appear to partially "undo" the negative or damaging effects of negative emotions. Experiencing positive emotion can quell or "undo" the lingering cardiovascular effects of negative emotions (Fredrickson and Levenson,1998; Fredrickson, Mancuso, Branigan, & Tugade, 2000). Positive emotions may also help us gain better perspective and place the events of our lives in broader context, lessening the effects of particular negative events.

We are very familiar with the "downward spiral of negative emotions," leading to maladaptive behavior resulting in negative outcomes, further deepening the initial negative emotion and perspective. Cognitive literature of depression documents this downward spiral phenomenon in which depressed mood and the narrowed, pessimistic thinking it cultivates influence one another reciprocally, leading to ever-worsening moods (Peterson & Seligman, 1984). The broaden-and-build model suggests that the spiral can also operate in the other direction, and that positive emotions can be transformational and fuel upward spirals toward optimal individual and organizational functioning (Fredrickson, 2003, p. 163). Positive emotions are not just good for individuals within an organization, but produce optimal individual functioning that serve as a means to achieve organizational transformation. "Positive emotions trigger upward spirals by broadening individuals' habitual modes of thinking and action and building lasting resources that promote future experiences of positive emotions. As this cycle continues, positive emotions transform individuals into more resilient, socially integrated, and capable versions of themselves. So, positive emotions not only make people feel good in the present, they also increase the likelihood that people will function and feel good in the future" (Fredrickson, 2003; p. 169).

Eastern and Western Perspectives

Although many of the constructs associated with positive psychology, such as hope, optimism, and personal self-efficacy, are particularly valued in Western culture and have been prominent throughout Western history, Eastern constructs also have much to contribute to a full understanding and appreciation of positive psychology (Snyder, Lopez, & Pedrotti, 2011, p. 19).

There are significant differences in perspective between Eastern and Western thought. The Western perspective emphasizes a linear, generally deterministic view of the world, focusing more on understanding specific situations and events with less emphasis on the larger picture. Individuals from within a Western perspective tend to value individualism and control and believe that control can be had through understanding the parts of the whole.

On the other hand, the Eastern perspective values collectivism and emphasizes a circular perspective, as exemplified by the concept of the *yin* and *yang,* which are dependent upon each other and only exist because of the other. From the Eastern perspective, the world is constantly changing and the current situation is given less primacy than the holistic, "big-picture" viewpoint. Good fortune is expected to be followed by bad and vice versa, lessening the attachment placed upon any particular experience or moment in time. This belief is eexemplified by the Chinese proverb, "*A good fortune may forebode a bad luck, which may in turn disguise a good fortune"* (Snyder et al., 2011, p. 19).

Both Eastern and Western traditions have placed much value on seeking the "good life." Living according to virtues has been emphasized both in Western and Eastern philosophy. Both Plato and Aristotle heavily emphasized the importance of living a virtuous life as the path to well-being and excellence; the Ten Commandments and the Beatitudes are testaments to the value ascribed to virtue. Eastern traditions have similarly emphasized the guiding principles of virtue (e.g., the Buddhist's eight-fold path or the morality infused in Confucian teachings). Although positive psychology has primarily arisen from within a Western worldview, the integration of Eastern perspectives and traditions into the understanding and formulization of positive psychology is helping to broaden the conceptualization and understanding of human strengths and well-being (Snyder, et al., 2011).

Positive Organizational Scholarship

Enabling Institutions

Peterson (2006) coined the term "enabling institution" to suggest that, similar to characteristics that promote individual well-being, counterpart characteristics exist at the organizational level to produce organizational well-being. These organizational attributes contribute not only to the goals of the institution but also to the fulfillment of the individuals within it (p. 280). The term "enabling institutions" connotes the idea that specific institutional variables such as a shared sense of purpose, fairness, dignity, and helping people to operate from their strengths tends to enable some institutions to have more beneficial outcomes than other institutions (p. 277).

Institution-level virtues refer to the characteristics of the group as a whole, not simply composites of the individual member. For example, a school may employ many teachers dedicated to the growth of their students, but if the school does not have in place practices that allow this dedication to survive personnel turnover, it is not an institutionally held virtue (Peterson, 2006, p. 280).

Peterson states that "institutional-level virtues serve the goals of an organization and not simply its bottom line, whether this be profit, power, or persistence" (p. 281). These organization-level virtues are often celebrated and serve as a source of identity and pride for the organization's members (pp. 281–282). Peterson asserts that fulfillment results from actions that manifest virtue. This is similar to the Aristotelian notion of *eudaemonia,* which holds that well-being is not a consequence of a virtuous action but rather is an inherent aspect of it (p. 281). For example, when a supervisor fairly adjudicates a dispute between two workers, the act does not cause the supervisor (or the workers) to feel satisfied at some later point in time, but rather being satisfied is an inherent aspect of justice in action (pp. 281–282).

Psychological Capital

Luthans (2002a) reflected that positive psychology has direct relevance to the workplace, and implored that the organizational behavior field needs a proactive, research-driven positive approach emphasizing strengths rather than focusing on remediating weaknesses. The literature on "psychological capital" serves as a bridge between organizational behavior and positive psychology. It can be viewed as taking positive psychology to the workplace, and applies the theory and research of positive psychology to companies, managers, and workers. Luthans, Norman, Avolio, and Ivey (2008) investigated the role of positive psychological capital (consisting of hope, resilience, optimism, and efficacy), and found that psychological capital is positively correlated with increased performance, satisfaction, and commitment and that a supportive workplace climate is related to employees' satisfaction and commitment. These capabilities are open to learning, development, and change in the workplace through training programs and/or self-learning. These four constructs identified as critical to positive organizational behavior are briefly explained in the following sections.

Hope

Meaningful *hope* is defined as a positive motivational state that is based on an interactively derived sense of successful (1) agency (goal directed energy) and (2) pathways (planning to meet goals) (Snyder et al., 1996). Stated another way, hope consists of willpower and way power.

Resilience

Much of the research on resilience has been done in the context of positive coping or adaptation in the face of significant adversity and risk. Applied to the workplace, *resiliency* has been defined as the "positive psychological capacity to rebound, to 'bounce back' from adversity, uncertainty, conflict, failure, or even

2. FOUNDATIONS OF POSITIVE PSYCHOLOGY **33**

positive change, progress, and increased responsibility" (Luthans, 2002b, p. 702). Resiliency has been found to be correlated with work attitudes of satisfaction, happiness, and contentment (Youssef & Luthans, 2007).

Optimism

Realistic *optimism* is the objective assessment of what can be accomplished in a specific situation, given the available resources (Peterson, 2000).

Efficacy

This construct is based on Bandura's (1997) extensive research on *self-efficacy*, defined as the judgment or belief of how well one can execute courses of action required to deal with prospective situations (Bandura, 1982, p. 122). Increased confidence leads to the increased likelihood that we will immerse ourselves in the task and welcome the challenge, leading to increased effort and motivation and increased persistence in the face of obstacles (Bandura 1986, 1997). Confidence is very situation specific and can fluctuate widely between situations and contexts (Bandura, 1997, p. 42).

Bandura (1997) asserts that *efficacy* can be enhanced in four ways: (1) experiencing success (task mastery), (2) vicariously learning by observing others, (3) persuasion from respected others, and (4) through physiological and/or psychological arousal and wellness (managing or reframing distressing emotions). A meta-analysis conducted by Stajkovic and Luthans (1998) of 114 studies found a stronger relationship between self-efficacy and work-related performance than other popular organizational behavior concepts such as goal setting, feedback, and job satisfaction.

From the framework of psychological capital, a positive psychological state can be characterized by: (1) having the confidence (self-efficacy) to take on and put in the necessary effort to succeed at challenging tasks; (2) making a positive attribution (optimism) about succeeding; (3) persevering toward goals and, when necessary, redirecting paths to goals (hope) in order to succeed; and (4) when facing adversity, sustaining and bouncing back and even beyond (resiliency) to attain success (Luthans et al., 2008, p. 223).

Applied to the workplace, when employees feel supported, they are more likely to use the pathway generation characteristic of hope to try unproven or new methods to accomplish tasks within the organizational context. A supportive climate can serve as a "contextual resource" for individuals to quickly bounce back after setbacks. And if the climate is nurturing, employees are likely to feel supported in terms of their abilities even if they have made a mistake. A supportive atmosphere implicitly or explicitly sends the message of "let's try this again in a different way" when the expected result does not occur, enabling the employee to focus on the learning potential inherent in mistakes (Luthans et al., 2008, p. 226).

Psychological capital—the intrinsic characteristics the individual brings to the workplace situation—might play a role in not just enabling potential to emerge but also in leveraging the impact that a positive or supportive organizational climate can contribute to performance (p. 235).

Positive Psychology in the Workplace

The application of positive psychology constructs in the workplace can help both the individual employee and the organization as a whole to flourish and thrive in a reciprocal, reinforcing relationship. Positive psychology constructs such as emotional intelligence, flow, hope, and many others can provide a strong foundation for leaders to bring out the best in their employees (Froman, 2010). For example, hope provides emotional strength, and when we have a more hopeful perspective on life, we are more likely to notice and to respond to opportunities when they are present (p. 60). Pride and a sense of achievement, when shared with others, can create, inspire, and kindle dreams of even larger accomplishments (p. 61). Experiencing *flow*—a state in which time seems to stop and self-consciousness is blocked during engagement in intrinsically satisfying and motivating activities—can trigger self-determining attitudes and behaviors that can lead to positive work and organizational outcomes and also serve as a protective mechanism against external pressures and constraints (p. 61).

How employees perceive their organization and the psychological climate can influence their adjustment, job satisfaction, psychological well-being, and organizational commitment (Martin, Jones, & Callan, 2005). "When team members behave in ways that demonstrate support, encouragement, and appreciation, people feel safe and trusting enough to ask questions, learn from one another, and test out new and creative approaches beyond the confines of the group and organization" (Froman, 2010, p. 65).

Enabling leaders engage their employees through an ongoing process of listening and learning, build relationships based on mutual trust and respect, and help shape their organizational culture to become organizations of virtue (Froman, 2010, p. 67). Losado and Heaphy (2004) found that greater connectivity and being more attuned to and responsive to one another is correlated to higher performance in organizational teams. Effectiveness is also increased through being grounded in our core values and principles, which can foster a sense of inner strength and confidence (Froman, 2010, p. 61).

Harter, Schmidt, and Keyes (2002) assert that positive well-being transfers from the individual level to the workplace, stating that positive feelings in the worker should result in happier and more productive workplace (p. 205). Flourishing individuals (as distinguished from languishing or those in moderate mental health) feel good about life and are functioning well in life. However, only about 2 in 10 Americans rate themselves as flourishing. Studies of U.S. workers indicates that languishing or even moderate well-being is associated with increased impairment as measured by lost work productivity, increased disability, increased risk of cardiovascular disease, more chronic physical illnesses at all ages, worse psychosocial functioning, and increased health care utilization (Keyes and Annas, 2009, p. 200).

Positive Deviance

Systems are usually focused on preserving the status quo, either knowingly or unknowingly. *Positive deviance,* defined as intentional behaviors that deviate from the norm in positive ways, is an important mechanism to move beyond the ordinary toward excellence, focusing on the positive end of the bell curve (Spreitzer & Sonensheim, 2003). The authors referenced the often-cited case example of trying to improve nutrition among Vietnamese villagers (Pascale, Millemann, & Gioja, 2000) as a dramatic illustration of positive deviance. The common approach to trying to reduce hunger in third-world countries was typically to have outside experts come in and diagnose the nutritional deficiency and then provide nonnative foods to remedy the nutritional deficit. Not surprisingly, the problem of malnutrition usually returned in full force once the outside help was withdrawn.

Pascale et al. (2000) shifted the focus of their efforts away from identifying and studying the problem to that of finding the positive exceptions. Their team studied the small number of Vietnamese children who were found to be exceptions and were healthy and well fed in spite of having the same basic amount of food as the other village children who were malnourished. What the researchers learned was that the mothers of these healthier and better-nourished children supplemented the standard rice-based diet with freshwater shrimp and crabs and sweet potato leaves that were readily available in their surroundings. These mothers who exemplified *positive deviance* were then enlisted by the researchers to educate other local villagers.

Reflecting on the Vietnamese nutrition example, Heath and Heath (2010) noted that knowledge alone does not change behavior. Simply telling the mothers about nutrition would not have changed their behavior; they had to practice it themselves and to act their way into a new way of thinking. This example also illustrates that, at times, relatively small changes can help solve big problems.

The following are some of the conditions that must be present to facilitate positive deviance, or going beyond expectations:

- *Meaning*—A sense of personal meaning is important to prompt the desire to take action. With intrinsic motivation, we are more likely to extend and exercise our capacities and more likely to initiate new behavior (Spreitzer & Sonensheim, 2003, p. 212).

- *Other-focus*—Other-focused leadership emphasizes helping those being supervised to grow as persons and become wiser and more autonomous (p. 213).

- *Self-determination*—This is positively correlated with greater autonomy and perceived internal locus of control. Goals that are self-endorsed are typically regarded as worthy of more effort. Increased personal agency facilitates positive deviance, linking thought with action, whereas external loci of control and the belief that things are not under personal control are associated with more maladaptive behavior (p. 215).

- *Personal efficacy*—Bandura (1989) found that high levels of self-efficacy are related to setting higher goals and firmer commitments to reaching those goals. Efficacy beliefs influence motivation and persistence. When we feel high levels of personal efficacy, we have a hunger to grow and develop our full potential as human beings (Spreitzer & Sonensheim, 2003, p. 216).

Strength-Based Social Work Practice

Although the term *positive psychology* reflects the renewed focus on strengths and potential within the field of psychology, social work also has a rich tradition of embracing a strength-based orientation (e.g., Cowger, 1994; Greene, Lee, & Hoffpauir, 2005; Saleebey, 1992). In fact, from within the social work literature, Cohen (1999) has proposed a strength-based supervision model grounded in the premise of focusing on practitioners' achievements rather than problems, mirroring the strength-based intervention model of focusing on strengths rather than pathology (p. 460). He argues that although the helping professions have abandoned the idea that human failings are the result of a moral defect, some of the "baggage" of the pathology orientation has been retained, namely, that failure and problems should be the major focus of helping professionals' work. This idea is articulated through diagnostic and clinical taxonomy systems (e.g., the DSM and International Classification of Diseases (ICD)), and "weaknesses, limitations, problems, and failures remain the filters through which the majority of helping professionals see their clients" (p. 460). This can easily influence the nature and shape of the therapeutic relationship. Cohen asserts that "the centrality of problems and pathology is the reality against which the strengths perspective is rebelling" (p. 460).

The strengths perspective recognizes that although clients may have serious problems or significant mental disorders, they have also used their inner resources and have coped and survived, even if imperfectly, and it is therapeutically beneficial to identify these strengths and tap into them. "Professionals trained to view their clients as human beings using their strengths and resources to cope with adversity as best they can have a much better chance of helping those clients find the means to improve their situation" (Cohen, 1999, p. 461). This does not mean ignoring the impact of serious problems or distress; however, overlooking or minimizing the coping skills the person has developed to deal with problems would be failing to use a very valuable inner resource from which to build. Resilience often is born from trauma or hardship, and identifying and illuminating resilience and building a collaborative relationship with clients to elicit their knowledge and resources to tackle problems are the cornerstones of the strengths perspective.

The strengths perspective can also be usefully translated to supervision, framing supervision to focus on recent successes to create a more supportive and less threatening environment than targeting problems for correction (p. 462). Statements such as "Let's talk about your most successful recent clinical work" can serve as a springboard for supervision to elucidate learning opportunities, provide support, and enhance supervisee motivation. The supervisor can guide the discussion to analyzing the specifics involved in successful interactions and exploring possible ways to transfer the interventions to other situations and cases.

Positive Psychology's Contributions to Clinical Supervision

Howard (2008) posits that one of the key functions of clinical supervision is the restoration of well-being, where the supervisor attends to the emotional effects of the work and the well-being of the supervisee (p. 106). Research into concepts from positive psychology such as work engagement, sense of coherence, self-efficacy, flow, and resilience has begun to provide a detailed understanding of workers' happiness, health, and betterment. Supervision appears to have a restorative function and to decrease work stress and burnout. For example, Butterworth et al. (1997) found that rates of emotional exhaustion and depersonalization stabilized when nurses began receiving clinical supervision but increased again when there was no supervision. In a study of higher-education employees, Bakker, Demerouti, and Euwema (2005) found that work overload, emotional demands, physical demands, and home–work interferences did not result in high levels of burnout if employees experienced autonomy, received feedback, had social support, or had a high-quality relationships with their supervisors.

Howard (2008) identified several constructs that have positive impacts on well-being, including meaningfulness, work engagement, self-efficacy, flow, and resilience. Thoughtful supervisors can directly contribute to increasing these constructs through supervision, for example, appropriately matching goals to skills while maintaining some challenge could contribute to the experience of flow (p. 109).

Howard discussed narrative supervision as an example of a positive psychology–based supervision intervention. Narrative therapy emphasizes collaborative inquiry between therapist and client, with the therapist helping clients reauthor their stories in ways to allow for more distance from their problems, and reasserting their core intentions, hopes, and values. The following are some positive psychology constructs with supervisor tasks and dialogue examples from a narrative therapy approach (Howard, 2008, p. 110):

Self-efficacy:

The supervisor task is to build supervisee belief in the supervisee's ability to apply skills, succeed at tasks, and tackle new responsibilities, or in narrative language, "to construct and perform a preferred identity." Self-efficacy can be enhanced through the use of role play.

Narrative supervision questions:

What in your experience tells you that you will be able to achieve this?

How can you remind yourself of your competence when you are faced with a difficult situation?

Work engagement:

The supervisor's task is to strengthen the supervisee's professional identity and involvement in the work by developing a sense of history and giving to the events in the supervisee's professional life. This can be enhanced by celebrating success and achievement (mirroring the narrative therapy concept that creating an audience helps to support and reinforce positive change).

Narrative supervision questions:

What sense of purpose first brought you into this work?

When you look back at this year's work, what are you most satisfied with?

Sense of coherence (manageability):

The supervisor's task is to identify interests and areas for growth and assist the supervisee to have control over the supervisee's work tasks. This can be enhanced by recognition and articulation of skill growth and the anticipation of further development that can occur in supervision. Role playing anticipated situations can be helpful.

Narrative supervision questions:

Given this goal, what new skills or resources do you need?

What might others have noticed about your growing independence in your work?

Conclusion

In their account of the historical origins of positive psychology, Lopez et al. (2006) offered recommendations for becoming strength-focused practitioners and scholars. To date, very little has been written that applies the concepts of positive psychology to supervision and training. The goal of this book is to extend similar recommendations to supervisors and supervisees for becoming strength-based supervisors. The following chapters will provide a comprehensive framework and concrete, practical suggestions for providing strength-focused supervision and training.

Questions to Consider

- When have you experienced well-being? What seemed to contribute to your positive state?

- Think of a time when you experienced a "positive spiral." What were you doing to enable this to occur?

- Reflect on the most engaging, supportive work environment you have experienced. What factors contributed to the workplace being so positive?

- Reflect on a life experience or event that showed you at your best. Name as many strengths or virtues as you can that you displayed during this event.

- Are you currently using your strengths on a frequent basis? Are there ways you could incorporate some strengths more fully into your everyday life?

- Who are your role models? What characteristics do you try to emulate?

Recommended Readings

Books

Diener, E., & Biswas-Diener, R. (2008). *Happiness: Unlocking the mysteries of psychological wealth*. Malden, MA: Blackwell Publishing.

Peterson, C. (2006). *A primer in positive psychology*. New York: Oxford University Press.

Seligman, M. E. P. (2002). *Authentic happiness: Using the new positive psychology to realize your potential for lasting fulfillment*. New York: Free Press.

Seligman, M. E. P. (2011). *Flourish: A visionary new understanding of happiness and well-being*. New York, NY: Free Press.

Snyder, C. R., Lopez, S. J., & Pedrotti, J. T. (2011). *Positive psychology: The scientific and practical explorations of human strengths* (2nd ed.). Thousand Oaks, CA: Sage Publications.

Articles

Fredrickson, B. L. (1998). What good are positive emotions? *Review of General Psychology, 2,* 300–319.

Fredrickson, B.L. (2001). The role of positive emotions in positive psychology: The Broaden-and-Build theory of positive emotions. *American Psychologist, 56*, 218–226.

Froman, L. (2010). Positive psychology in the workplace. *Journal of Adult Development, 17*, 59–69. doi: 10.1007/s10804-009-9080-0

Gable, S. L., & Haidt, J. (2005). What (and why) is positive psychology? *Review of General Psychology, 9*, 103–110.

Linley, P. A., Joseph, S., Harrington, S., & Wood, A. M. (2006). Positive psychology: Past, present, and (possible) future. *The Journal of Positive Psychology, 1*, 3–16.

Luthans, F. (2002). Positive organizational behavior: Developing and managing psychological strengths. *Academy of Management Executive, 16*, 57–72.

Lyubomirksy, S., Sheldon, K. M., & Schkade, D. (2005). Pursuing happiness: The architecture of sustainable change. *Review of General Psychology, 9*, 111–131.

Seligman, M. E., & Csikszentmihalyi, M. (2000). Positive psychology. *American Psychologist, 55*, 5–14.

References

Allport, G. W. (1961). *Pattern and growth in personality*. New York: Holt, Rinehart, & Winston.

American Psychiatric Association. (2013). *Diagnostic and statistical manual of mental disorders* (5th ed.). Washington, DC: Author.

Asplund, J., Lopez, S. J., Hodges, T., & Harter, J. (2007). *Technical report: Development and validation of the Clifton Strengths Finder 2.0*. The Gallup Organization.

Bakker, A. B., Demerouti, E., & Euwema, M. C. (2005). Job resources buffer the impact of job demands on burnout. *Journal of Occupational Health Psychology, 10*, 170–180.

Bandura, A. (1982). Self-efficacy mechanism in human agency. *American Psychologist, 37*, 122–147.

Bandura, A. (1986). *Social foundations of thought and action*. Englewood Cliffs, NJ: Prentice-Hall.

Bandura, A. (1989). Regulation of cognitive processes through perceived self-efficacy. *Developmental Psychology, 25*, 729–735.

Bandura, A. (1997). *Self-efficacy: The exercise of control*. New York: Freeman.

Beers, C. W. (1908). *A mind that found itself*. New York: Longmans Green.

Blocher, D. H. (1966). *Developmental counseling*. Oxford, UK: Ronald Press.

Brickman, P., Coates., D., & Janoff-Bulman, R. (1978). Lottery winners and accident victims: Is happiness relative? *Journal of Personality and Social Psychology, 36*, 917–927.

Buckingham, M., & Clifton, D. O. (2001). *Now, discover your strengths*. New York: Free Press.

Butterworth, T., Carson, J., White, E., Jeacock, J., Clements, A., & Bishop, V. (1997). *It's good to talk: An evaluation study in England and Scotland*. UK: University of Manchester.

Clifton, D. O., & Nelson, P. (1992). *Soar with your strengths*. New York: Dell Publishing.

Cohen, B. (1999). Intervention and supervision in strengths-based social work practice. *Families in Society: The Journal of Contemporary Human Services, 80,* 460–466.

Cowger, G. (1994). Assessing client strengths: Clinical assessment for client empowerment. *Social Work, 39,* 262–268.

Diener, E. & Biswas-Diener, R. (2008). *Happiness: Unlocking the mysteries of psychological wealth*. Malden, MA: Blackwell Publishing.

Erikson, E. H. (1959). Identity and the life cycle. *Psychological Issues, 1,* (Monograph 1).

Fredrickson, B. L. (1998). What good are positive emotions? *Review of General Psychology, 2,* 300–319.

Fredrickson, B. L. (2001). The role of positive emotions in positive psychology: The broaden-and-build theory of positive emotions. *American Psychologist, 56,* 218–226.

Fredrickson, B. L. (2003). Positive emotions and upward spirals in organizations. In J. E. Dutton, R. E. Quinn, & K. S. Cameron (Eds.), *Positive organizational scholarship* (pp. 163–175). San Francisco, CA: Berrett-Koehler Publishers.

Fredrickson, B. L., & Branigan, C. A. (2001). Positive emotions. In T. J. Mayne & G. A. Bonnano (Eds.), *Emotion: Current issues and future developments* (pp. 123–151). New York: Guilford Press.

Fredrickson, B. L., & Branigan, C. A. (2005). Positive emotions broaden scope of attention and thought-action repertoires. *Cognition and Emotion, 19,* 313–332.

Fredrickson, B. L., & Levenson, R. W. (1998). Positive emotions speed recovery from the cardiovascular sequelae of negative emotions. *Cognition and Emotion, 12,* 191–220.

Fredrickson, B. L., Mancuso, R. A., Branigan, C., & Tugade, M. M. (2000). The undoing effect of positive emotions. *Motivation and Emotion, 24,* 237–258.

Froman, L. (2010). Positive psychology in the workplace. *Journal of Adult Development, 17,* 59–69. doi: 10.1007/s10804-009-9080-0

Gable, S. L., & Haidt, J. (2005). What (and why) is positive psychology? *Review of General Psychology, 9,* 103–110.

Gelso, C. J., & Woodhouse, S. (2003). Toward a positive psychotherapy: Focus on human strength. In B. Walsh (Ed.), *Counseling psychology and optimal human functioning* (pp. 171–197). Mahwah, NJ: Lawrence Erlbaum Associates, Inc.

Greene, G. J., Lee, M. Y., & Hoffpauir, S. (2005). The languages of empowerment and strengths in clinical social work: A constructivist perspective. *Families in Society, 86,* 267–277.

Harter, J. K., Schmidt, F. L., & Keyes, C. L. (2002). Well-being in the workplace and its relationship to business outcomes: A review of the Gallup studies. In C. L. Keyes & J. Haidt (Eds.), *Flourishing: The positive person and the good life* (pp. 205–224). Washington, DC: American Psychological Association.

Heath, C., & Heath, D. (2010). *Switch: How to change things when change is hard.* New York: Broadway Books.

Howard, F. (2008). Managing stress or enhancing well-being? Positive psychology's contributions to clinical supervision. *Australian Psychologist, 43,* 105–113.

Jahoda, M. (1958). *Current concepts of positive mental health.* New York: Basic Books.

James, W. (1902). *The varieties of religious experience: A study in human nature.* New York: Longman, Green.

Jorgensen, I., S., & Nafstad, H. (2004). Positive psychology: Historical, philosophical, and epistemological perspectives. In P. A. Linley & S. Joseph (Eds.), *Positive psychology in practice* (pp. 15–34). Hoboken, NJ: John Wiley & Sons, Inc.

Jung, C. G. (1933). *Modern man in search of a soul.* London: Kegan, Paul, Trench, Trubner.

Kauffman, C. (2006). Positive psychology: The science at the heart of coaching. In D. R. Stober & A. M. Grant (Eds.), *Evidence based coaching handbook: Putting best practices to work for your clients* (pp. 219–254). Hoboken, NJ: John Wiley & Sons, Inc.

Keyes, C. L., & Annas, J. (2009). Feeling good and functioning well: distinctive concepts in ancient philosophy and contemporary science. *The Journal of Positive Psychology, 4,* 197–201.

Keyes, C. L. M., & Magyar-Moe, J. L. (2003). The Measurement and utility of adult subjective well-being. In S. J. Lopez & C. R. Snyder (Eds.), *Positive psychological assessment: A handbook of models and measures* (pp. 411–425). Washington, DC: American Psychological Association.

Linley, P. A., & Joseph. S. (2004). Applied positive psychology: A new perspective for professional science. In P. A. Linley & S. Joseph (Eds.), *Positive psychology in practice*(pp. 3–14). Hoboken, NJ: John Wiley & Sons, Inc.

Linley, P. A., Joseph, S., Harrington, S., & Wood, A. M. (2006). Positive psychology: Past, present, and (possible) future. *The Journal of Positive Psychology, 1,* 3–16.

Lopez, S. J., Magyar-Moe, J. L., Petersen, S. E., Ryder, J. A., Krieshok, T. S., O'Byrne, K. K., et al. . (2006). Counseling psychology's focus on positive aspects of human functioning. *The Counseling Psychologist, 34,* 205–227. doi: 10.1177/001100000523393

Losado, M., & Heaphy, E. (2004). The role of positivity and connectivity with the performance of business teams. *American Behavioral Scientist, 47,* 740–765.

Luthans, F. (2001). The need for and meaning of positive organizational behavior. *Journal of Organizational Behavior, 23,* 695–706.

Luthans, F. (2002b). Positive organizational behavior: Developing and managing psychological strengths. *Academy of Management Executive, 16,* 57–72.

Luthans, F., Norman, S. M., Avolio, B. J., & Ivey, J. B. (2008). The mediating role of psychological capital in the supportive organizational climate–employee performance relationship. *Journal of Organizational Behavior, 29,* 219–238. DOI: 10.1002/job.507.

Lyubomirksy, S., Sheldon, K. M., & Schkade, D. (2005). Pursuing happiness: The architecture of sustainable change. *Review of General Psychology, 9,* 111–131.

Martin, A. J., Jones, E. S., & Callan, V. J. (2005). The role of psychological climate in facilitating employee adjustment during organizational change. *European Journal of Work and Organizational Psychology, 14,* 263–289.

Maslow, A. H. (1968). *Toward a psychology of being.* New York: Van Nostrand.

Maslow, A. H. (1970). *Motivation and personality* (2nd ed.). New York: Harper & Row.

Menninger, K., Mayman, M., & Pruyser, P. W. (1963). *The vital balance.* New York: Viking Press.

Pascale, R. T., Millemann, M., & Gioja, L. (2000). *Surfing the edge of chaos: The laws of nature and the new laws of business.* New York: Crown Business.

Peterson, C. (2000). The future of optimism. *American Psychologist, 55,* 44–55.

Peterson, C. (2006). *A primer in positive psychology.* New York: Oxford University Press.

Peterson, C., & Seligman, M. E. (1984). Causal explanations as a risk factor for depression: theory and evidence. *Psychological review, 91,* 347–374.

Peterson, C., & Seligman, M. E. P. (2004). *Character strengths and virtues: A handbook and classification.* Washington, DC: American Psychological Association..

Rogers, C. R. (1961). *On becoming a person: A therapist's view of psychotherapy.* Boston, MA: Houghton Mifflin.

Saleebey, D. (Ed.). (1992). *The strengths perspective in social work practice.* White Plains, NY: Longman.

Seligman, M. E., & Csikszentmihalyi, M. (2000). Positive psychology. *American Psychologist, 55,* 5–14.

Seligman, M.E.P., (1998). Building human strength: Psychology's forgotten mission. *APA Monitor, 29* (1).

Seligman, M. E. P. (2002). *Authentic happiness: Using the new positive psychology to realize your potential for lasting fulfillment.* New York: Free Press.

Seligman M. E. P. (2003). Foreword: The past and future of positive psychology. In C. L. M. Keyes & J. Haidt (Eds.), *Flourishing: Positive psychology and the life well-lived* (pp. 15–36). Washington, DC: American Psychological Association.

Seligman, M. E. P. (2011). *Flourish: A visionary new understanding of happiness and well-being.* New York: Free Press.

Sheldon, K. M., & King, L. (2001). Why positive psychology is necessary. *American Psychologist, 56,* 216–217.

Snyder, C. R., Lopez, S. J., & Pedrotti, J. T. (2011). *Positive psychology: The scientific and practical explorations of human strengths* (2nd ed.). Thousand Oaks, CA: Sage Publications.

Snyder, C. R., Simpson, S., Ybasco, F., Borders, T., Babyak, M., & Higgins, R. (1996). Development and validation of the state hope scale. *Journal of Personality and Social Psychology, 70,* 321–335.

Spreitzer, G. M., & Sonenshein, S. (2003). Positive deviance and extraordinary organizing. In K. S. Cameron, J. E. Dutton, & R. E. Quinn (Eds.), *Positive organizational scholarship: Foundations of a new discipline* (pp. 207–224). San Francisco, CA: Berrett-Koehler Publishers.

Stajkovic, A. D., & Luthans, F. (1998). Self-efficacy and work-related performance: A meta-analysis. *Psychological Bulletin, 124,* 240–261.

Youssef, C. M., & Luthans, F. (2007). Positive organizational behavior in the workplace: The impact of hope, optimism, and resiliency. *Journal of Management, 33,* 774–800.

Setting the Stage

"All systems are perfectly designed to achieve the results they are currently getting."
—Marv Weisbord

"First we shape our structures and then our structures shape us."
—Winston Churchill

Think back to the different experiences you have had being supervised. Many of these have likely involved formal, structured training. You have probably also had numerous other less structured training experiences. Reflect on your most positive supervision experiences. What stands out about these experiences? What made them so successful? How did your supervisor or trainer interact with you? How did your supervisor approach supervision? What personal characteristic did your supervisor possess that were conducive to your growth and development? What were the characteristics of the larger agency or department you worked for? Looking back at the contributions you made to the experience, how did you approach the training to make this a rewarding experience? If you have had some negative supervision or training experiences along the way, reflect on the same questions for these instances. Often, constructive factors become even more apparent when contrasted with the negative.

We have probably classified the negative experiences under the mental category of what not to do. Knowing what does not work is also valuable information. This chapter examines in detail the various components that are conducive to setting the stage for progressive, developing, and productive supervision to occur. Characteristics of "good" supervisees, supervisors, and training sites are explored that serve as templates for providing effective, research-based supervision. Other factors associated with setting the stage for the best practice of supervision are also discussed, including: exploring the learning process, creating positive expectations, getting the most from supervision, and creating a framework for reflective and intentional supervision.

Supervisee Characteristics

It might seem unusual to start with the qualities of effective supervisees instead of effective supervisors. However, similar to psychotherapy in which we know that client variables contribute significantly to the outcome of treatment (e.g., Bohart & Tallman (2010); Messer & Wampold, 2002; Wampold, 2001), the supervisee plays a pivotal role and bears much of the responsibility for the nature and the ultimate outcome of the supervision experience. Knowing the attributes of successful supervisees can serve as a guide for supervisees to aspire to and for supervisors to try to elicit and emphasize.

But similar to psychotherapy, in which much more research and investigation has been conducted on therapist than client variables, the same situation is true of supervision research, with more research attention focused on supervisor qualities than helpful or hindering supervisee attributes. Rodenhauser, Rudisell, and Painter (1989) are among a handful of researchers who have investigated supervisee attributes. They surveyed psychotherapy supervisors of psychiatric residents and asked them to list up to four supervisee characteristics that were deemed desirable for successful learning in psychotherapy supervision situations. Five categories emerged, and the top attributes within each category are listed (pp. 370–371):

- Basic personal qualities of supervisees

  o Psychological mindedness/openness
  o Reliability
  o Psychostructural soundness

- Facilitators of relationships with supervisors

  o Interest/desire
  o Motivation/initiative
  o Enthusiasm/eagerness

- Facilitators of relationships with patients

  o Interpersonal curiosity
  o Flexibility (personal, theoretical, clinical)
  o Empathy

- Facilitators of content/theory learning

  o Intellectual openness
  o A habit of reading/development of knowledge base

- Facilitators of process/skills learning

  o Minimal defensiveness
  o Introspection
  o Receptivity to feedback

Rodenhauser et al. (1989) assert that when used collaboratively, a list of generally agreed-upon qualities that constitute the hypothetical ideal supervisee can serve several constructive purposes in supervision, including: (1) a guide to assessment of the supervisee's attributes upon starting supervision; (2) an aid to facilitate supervisee role adoption; (3) a checklist for discussing mutual expectations; (4) a motivator for personal growth; (5) a predictor of problems; and, therefore, (6) an aid to problem prevention (p. 369). These characteristics can create or enhance a positive approach to training and supervision, helping to cultivate supervisee growth and development (p. 375).

A survey of both mental health supervisors and supervisees (Vespia, Heckman-Stone, & Delworth, 2002) found that both groups cited the following as most important supervisee behaviors/qualities:

- Demonstrates willingness to grow; takes responsibility for consequence of own behavior

- Actively participates in supervision sessions

- Respects and appreciates individual differences

- Understands own personal dynamics as they relate to therapy and supervision

Starting with a discussion of ideal supervisee characteristics early in the supervision process can facilitate setting high but realistic expectations, helping to mitigate against the tendency for both supervisees and supervisors to have lofty and unrealistic expectations of the supervision process that can lead to feelings of failure and disappointment (Rodenhuaser et al., 1989, p. 373).

Pearson (2004) encourages supervisors to (1) ask trainees to rate themselves on a list of positive supervisee characteristics, (2) choose two or three that provide the most challenge or difficulty, (3) form a goal related to each deficit, and (4) consider discussing these areas and related goals with their supervisors (p. 363). We would propose a similar exercise, however, from a strength-based perspective, asking the supervisee to first identify two or three areas of strength to serve as a springboard to tackle an area of weakness that the supervisee identifies. Supervisees could also be prompted to consider initiating a discussion of desired supervisee qualities with their supervisor, with questions such as: "What kinds of students have been the most successful and satisfied in supervision at this site?" "What kinds of students have been least successful?" or "What are some characteristics you value most in your work with supervisees?"

Pearson also offers the following suggestions to mental health students to get the most from the supervision experience (2004, pp. 371–372):

- Be proactive

- Remain flexible

- Ask for what you need; do not demand it

- Take responsibility for learning and growing in supervision
- Use self-assessment and reflection for improving and problem solving
- Avoid blaming and focus on planning and problem solving
- Instead of focusing on what your supervisor does not provide, ask what you can learn from your supervisor.

Supervisor Characteristics

Although the tasks of supervision and psychotherapy differ greatly, and problems occur when the two are confused, the fundamental importance of establishing a good working relationship is important for both. The ideal supervisor has been said to embody the same personal characteristics as the ideal psychotherapist (Pierce, Carkhuff, & Berenson, 1967). In psychotherapy, regardless of the orientation of the therapist, the facilitative conditions of empathy, genuineness, and warmth are considered necessary conditions for therapeutic effectiveness. Coche (1977) suggested that these factors are also necessary conditions for effective supervision, a sentiment echoed by Lambert (1980), who reflected that most researchers seem to agree that appropriate levels of empathy, respect, genuineness, and concreteness are required in supervisee–supervisor relationship. Supervisees whose supervisors provide high levels of empathy, regard, genuineness, and concreteness in their supervision sessions are able to increasingly model and transfer these facilitative factors as they provide therapy to their clients. Summarizing the importance of creating facilitative conditions to effective supervision, Carifio and Hess (1987) suggest that the ideal supervisor:

- Possesses appropriate levels of empathy, respect, genuineness, concreteness, and self-disclosure
- Is knowledgeable and experienced in both therapy and its supervision
- Sets clear and explicit goals and uses these goals as a guide in using various teaching techniques and modes of data collection
- Avoids combining supervision with psychotherapy
- Is generally supportive and noncritical
- Uses a variety of social influence processes, including direct and systemic feedback
- Is not overly direct, yet not particularly passive, either (p. 248)

A survey of supervisor preferences of psychology, psychiatry, and social work supervisees reveals that highly desired personality descriptors for supervisors include being flexible, self-revealing, permissive, and congenial or outgoing (Nelson, 1978). Supervisors who are practicing therapists and modeled therapeutic skill and theoretical knowledge are also highly valued by supervisees. Interestingly, general personality factors of supervisors, or the matching of personality factors between supervisors and supervisees, have been found to have negligible impact on the supervision outcome (Neufeldt Beutler, & Ranchero, 1997). However, the supervisor qualities of expertness, trust, and attractiveness were found to increase the supervisor's ability to influence supervisees (Dorn, 1985). Supervisor availability and approachability increase the likelihood of the supervisee seeking help and getting needs met (Berger & Graff, 1995).

The broaden-and-build model (Fredrickson, 1998; Fredrickson and Branigan, 2001) posits that positive emotions are contagious and create a more fertile ground for learning. Borders (1994) observed that good supervisors, not surprisingly, tend to enjoy supervision and transmit their comfort and enthusiasm to their supervisees throughout the process. Good supervisors share the following characteristics: (1) they are committed to helping the supervisee grow, (2) they are committed to the supervision process are prepared for and involved in supervision, (3) they are intentional about supervision and have a high level of conceptual functioning, (4) they have a clear sense of their own strengths and limitations as a supervisor, (5) they can identify how their personal traits and interpersonal style might affect the supervision process, and (6) very importantly, they have a sense of humor that helps both the supervisor and supervisee get through rough spots and achieve healthy perspectives (p. 1). Kauffman (2006) suggests that when possible, it is important for effective, strength-based supervisors to create conditions to support "flow" experiences (e.g., Csikszentmihalyi, 1991) for supervisees, which is characterized by the absence of self-consciousness and being fully engaged in the process. An affirming, supervisory perspective allows the supervisee to more fully devote cognitive resources to being fully present with the client rather than worried about potential supervisory disapproval. Helping the supervisee to identify and focus on areas of particular situations that are under the supervisee's control and "de-focus" from those that can't be controlled increases the odds for the supervisee to have a "flow" experience. The experience of positive emotions not only increases perception, thinking ability, problem solving, and general functioning, but can also spread through organizations by creating chains of events that carry positive meaning for others as well (Fredrickson, 2003, p. 172). The positive emotions of agency leaders might be especially contagious, impacting the performance of the entire group. The experience of positive emotions is even associated with improvements in performance evaluations and increases in pay, as well as improvements in social support from both coworkers and supervisors (Staw, Sutton, & Pellod, 1994).

Good Supervision Events

We have identified characteristics of good supervisees and supervisors, but what are the elements of good supervision itself? An investigation of "good" supervision events from the supervisee perspective (Worthen & McNeill, 1996) revealed that positive supervision experiences are characterized by a supervisory relationship experienced as empathic, nonjudgmental, and validating, with supervisor encouragement to explore and experiment. Struggle is normalized, resulting in nondefensive analysis, reexamination of assumptions, acquisition of a metaperspective, and a sense of "freeing" that consists of reduced self-protectiveness and receptivity to supervisory input. "Good" supervision resulted in (1) strengthened confidence, (2) refined professional identity, (3) increased therapeutic perception, (4) expanded ability to conceptualize and intervene, (5) positive anticipation to reengage in the struggle, and (6) a strengthened supervisory alliance (p. 28). The supervisee needs to be aware of inadequacies in order to be open to supervisory input and receptive to new learning (p. 29); however, a positive supervisory relationship enables the supervisee's concern about self and performance anxiety to be minimized and allows productive supervision..

The reduced need for self-protectiveness occurs as supervisees feel supported and sense the supervisor's benevolent interest in their learning and development (p. 30). Reducing the need for self-defensiveness creates the possibility for the supervisee to engage in nondefensive analysis, a reexamination of assumptions, and an honest introspection of therapeutic activities. One supervisee described this process as developing an "internal supervisor" (p. 31), reminiscent of the metagoal of psychotherapy, which is for clients to become their own therapists. The elements of good supervision yielded an increased ability for supervisees to see greater complexity, and a corresponding ability to make what was complex and confusing seem coherent (p. 31).

In contrast, supervisees identify the following supervisory styles as negative and constraining:

- Constrictive—the supervisee's use of certain techniques is dogmatically limited.

- Amorphous—the supervisee is given insufficient levels of guidance or direction.

- Unsupportive—the supervisor is seen as cold, aloof, uncaring, or hostile.

- Therapeutic—the focus is on the supervisee as the patient and on the supervisee's personality structure during supervision. (Rosenblatt & Mayer, 1975)

Just as a sense of inadequacy is necessary for supervisees to be open to improvement, the same is also necessary for supervisor growth. Unfortunately, part of the human condition is a difficulty with accurate self-appraisal, and supervisors are no different. Supervisors tend to rate their abilities highly, regardless of their training or experiences. In one study (Robiner, Saltzman, Hoberman, & Schirvar, 1997), 62 supervisors at clinical psychology internships had generally (1) received relatively little training in supervision, (2) read relatively little about supervision, and (3) had only limited supervisory experience. However, more than half of these supervisors indicated that they provided supervision "very well," and 15% indicated that they had "excellent" supervisory skills. Only 3% acknowledged an inadequacy in providing supervision. Interestingly, the amount of reading on supervision literature was positively correlated with self-appraisal of supervision proficiency; however, self-reported supervisory competence was not correlated (1) with years since earning a degree, (2) years of supervisory experience, (3) how many interns had been supervised, or (4) hours of group and peer supervision.

The Working Alliance

Much research and focus in psychology has been devoted to examining the efficacy of various psychotherapy treatment models; however, research indicates that focusing on specific treatment approaches is analogous to only looking at the tip of the iceberg above the water and ignoring the much larger and more potent role of the common factors in treatment that are responsible for the majority of the benefits of psychotherapy. The research on empirically supported treatments indicates that commonalities among treatment approaches, not "specific ingredients," are responsible for most of the benefits of psychotherapy (Wampold, 2001). The working alliance has been described as the "quintessential integrative variable" of psychotherapy (Wolfe & Goldfried, 1988, p. 449), and the alliance between client and therapist is the most frequently mentioned common factor in the psychotherapy literature (Grencavage & Norcross, 1990). Norcross and Halgin (1997) assert that because the therapeutic relationship has been shown to be the most potent of the common factors of therapy, "it does not involve a great leap of understanding to perceive the supervisory relationship as being comparably important in fostering growth in clinical trainees" (p. 212).

Supervision theorists have emphasized the importance of common factors across different models, with the supervisor–supervisee relationship playing a particularly important role (Ladany, Ellis, & Friedlander, 1999, p. 451). Bordin (1983) is credited with developing the working alliance model to explain the importance of the supervisor–supervisee bond to the effectiveness of the supervision process. A strong working alliance enables the four major sources of self-efficacy expectancies to be more fully experienced in supervision (performance accomplishments, vicarious experiences, verbal persuasion, and emotional arousal; Bandura, 1997). The supervisor's teaching and feedback, for example, can improve the supervisee's counseling skills, which will in turn strengthen the supervisee's subsequent performance with clients. In supervision, role playing might be a type of vicarious experience that can enhance self-efficacy expectations. Support and encouragement from the supervisor can be forms of verbal persuasion. And the emotional component of the supervisory relationship as a whole constitutes another source of self-efficacy expectations (Ladany et al., 1999, pp. 447-448). When the emotional bond in supervision becomes stronger over time, supervisees judge both their supervisor's and their own behavior more positively, leading to greater comfort with supervision. In addition, a greater emotional bond in supervision appears correlated with greater supervisee self-disclosure, which the supervisor can facilitate by modeling self-disclosure early in the relationship (p. 452).

Attention to the everyday experiences within supervision seems to be of particular importance. When supervisors pay attention to and respond uniquely to those they supervise, supervisees experience a higher frequency of joy, interest, and caring. Over time, this builds a stronger supervisory bond (Harter, Schmidt, & Keyes, 2002, p. 211), as well as creates positive emotions that correlate with improved learning and performance.

Institutional Variables

Just as certain individuals seem to bring out the best in us, so, too can organizations and institutions. Peterson (2006) uses the term "enabling institution" to refer to those institutions that possess traits that make them better able to engender positive outcomes, both for individual members as well as the organization as a whole. These characteristics are woven into the structural fabric of the institution, enabling institutions to create the context in which positive psychology constructs are encouraged and incorporated. Institutional-level virtues that are cultivated and celebrated serve as a source of identity and pride for the organization's members (p. 282), as well as providing fertile soil for the members' abilities and talents to be recognized and nourished into fuller fruition.

Leadership Characteristics

Transformational leaders can be thought of as those individuals who elevate followers to achieve greater levels of long-term well-being and effectiveness. Sivanthan, Arnold, Turner, and Barling (2004, p. 245) posit that transformational leaders incorporate Bandura's (1997) model of increasing self-efficacy by (1) inspiring their followers to greater heights (verbal persuasion), (2) manifesting positive behaviors that supervisees will want to emulate (vicarious experience), (3) exhorting their supervisees to think of challenges in ways that make it possible to confront them (verbal persuasion), and (4) providing a supportive climate in which this is all possible (successful accomplishments).

Although a supervisee might or might not have much direct interaction with the administration of the training site, the leadership sets the tone.

Influence is like water—it tends to flow down. Sivanathan et al. (2004) assert that transformational leadership is not dependent upon personal charisma (thank goodness!), but is a function of:

- Inspiring supervisees to be their very best and to aspire to and achieve greater levels than they thought possible by instilling realistic feelings of self-efficacy, "feelings of what can be accomplished rather than fears of what cannot be accomplished"

- Challenging supervisees to think more for themselves and to question assumptions

- Individualized consideration that demonstrates compassion and helps to cement a strong working alliance (pp. 243–244)

Lopez (2011) describes a strength-based approach to leadership grounded in positive psychology constructs. A clue to your current orientation is to ask yourself if, as a supervisor, do you spend more time talking about how to improve strengths or how to remedy weaknesses? Being successful as a supervisee (or as a professional) depends not only on personal effort and abilities but also on being in a setting conducive to growth and flourishing. Lopez asserts that the formula is success = determination + a great supervisor + good conditions. Operating from a strengths perspective tends to have a value additive function, in which adding strengths development to any training or learning endeavor makes it more effective and also helps to strengthen the working alliance. Through the use of "active constructive responding," the supervisor intentionally and actively tries to illuminate and maximize the supervisee's positive experience. One practical way to accomplish this is by "capitalizing," that is, enhancing the value and impact of any experience by following these simple guidelines:

- Ask about a positive experience

- Mirror the person's enthusiasm

- Ask meaningful question about the positive experience

- Ask a meaningful question that connects the experience to strengths

Although the actual impact of the trickle-down theory regarding economics is debatable, the principle seems to play a key role in human interactions. How we are treated by those with more power can inspire us to want to be the best we can be with those we supervise or to want to kick the dog when we get home. Supervisors' perceived organizational support has been found to be positively related to their subordinates' perceptions of supervisor support. In other words, supervisors who feel supported by the organization are more likely to reciprocate with more supportive treatment for their supervisees (Shanock and Eisenberger, 2006). Supervisors' supportive treatment of supervisees might originate, at least in part, from the supportive treatment that supervisors receive from the organization. Organizations that treat supervisors in ways that give them voice and autonomy might contribute substantially to their perceptions of organizational support" (p. 694). Thus, the organization's supportive treatment of supervisors tends to trickle down and positively increase the support experienced by all, often resulting in better performance. Good supervisors are ultimately effective because they meet their supervisees' needs. Research indicates that hope, stability, trust, and compassion are consistent supervisee needs, and that these factors should help define the goals of leadership and supervision (Lopez, 2011).

Although effective leaders or supervisors are able to identify and nurture the strengths of those they supervise, they often do not have a firm sense of their own strengths, and this compromises their effectiveness (Kaplan & Kaiser, 2009). For an organization to be well functioning, the system needs a mechanism in place for supervisors to regularly receive feedback regarding their strengths and accomplishments. Drawing upon the theoretical construct of "mirroring" formulated by influential psychoanalyst Heinz Kohut (1977)—in which children hunger for the mirroring provided by their mothers, which fosters self-acceptance—leaders and supervisors have a similar need for mirroring to develop an accurate sense of what they do well. Supervisors can't be expected to play to their strengths if they don't know what they are (p. 108). Moreover, to grow and improve, supervisors and supervisees not only need the information provided by accurate and corrective mirroring, they also need the affirmation provided by a reparative relationship (p. 109).

When we reflect on the supervisors who have made a difference in our lives, their impact undoubtedly extended well beyond techniques and conceptualization. Most of us who supervise want our influence to extend beyond simply helping our supervisees develop competencies to that of influencing and mentoring their professional and personal development. Ragins (2011) coins the term "relational mentoring" to describe mentoring as the capacity for mutual influence, growth, and learning, in which both partners feel a responsibility for learning and both are changed by the process. Influence is shared, and the power dynamic is experienced as "power with" versus "power over." This perspective is more likely to flourish in an organization if a relational mentoring culture is driven from the top (Ragins, 2011, p. 524). High-quality mentoring relationships can provide feedback that illuminates blind spots and provides insight into personal strengths and weaknesses. Mentoring relationships can also be inspirational, enabling the seeing of different and better possibilities and helping to energize and direct effort and behavior.

The relational mentoring model draws upon the idea of the *Michelangelo phenomenon* (Drigotas, Rusbult, Wieselquist, & Whitton, 1999). This concept is grounded primarily in research conducted on couples in which a close partner, affirming the other's pursuit of the ideal self, helps to shape the other's perceptions and behaviors. Ragins (2011) states that the Michelangelo phenomenon helps to explain the processes involved in high-quality mentoring. The mentor's affirmations take the form of behavioral affirmations and perceptual affirmation (viewing the supervisee in terms of the supervisee's best self). Through this process, the mentor helps supervisees engage in behaviors that are "aligned with their ideal selves by directly eliciting or creating opportunities to engage in desired behaviors, or by decreasing the opportunity to engage in behaviors that conflict with ideal selves" (p. 530). Grasping and affirming the "best self" of the supervisee within the mentoring relationship can help the supervisee start living into this "reflected best self" (p. 530).

Role Modeling

In the book *Discover Your Genius: How to Think Like History's Ten Most Revolutionary Minds*, historian Michael Gelb (2002) draws upon the lives and perspective of 10 history-changing individuals to illustrate exceptional examples of successful thinking and visioning. Part of the purpose of the book is to look to notable figures such as Plato, Columbus, Darwin, and Jefferson as models of uncommon and extraordinary thinking and perspective to help us expand our own perspectives and modes of thinking. Gelb notes that we are influenced by and model ourselves on others already, so why not model ourselves on those who achieved excellence? He asks readers to reflect on who they have chosen to inspire and guide them in life thus far, and what the essential lessons are that we can learn from these people (p. 5). Although we may never be able to compare to revolutionary, world-changing figures, we can try to emulate certain components of their mastery.

Contemplate who would be included on your list of 10 inspiring people. What characteristics do you admire about each person? What factors helped them achieve their success? It can also be helpful to identify different people as role models for different arenas of life. Einstein achieved great professional success but is probably not the person to emulate for a balanced, rich family life. Who are your role models for supervision? For life in general?

Gelb encourages us to "discover our genius" by mentally "dialoguing" with the historical geniuses or the figures we choose to serve as role models. Most of us are probably familiar with the acronym WWJD (What Would Jesus Do?) that serves as a guiding question for many religiously grounded individuals as they face daily decisions. Experiment with applying the concept of a guiding question or principle to the daily decision making you encounter as a supervisor. Consider the supervisors you have had who had a lasting impact on you, whose voice or voices you still hear in your head from time to time. Although you probably do not want to try to make yourself into a clone of your most impactful supervisor, it can help to broaden your perspective by frequently reflecting on what your influential supervisor would likely do in the various supervisory situations that you encounter.

The ancient philosopher Socrates, known for developing the Socratic method of teaching through questioning, is often considered synonymous with learning, so much so that his student Plato has been credited with formulating the basis of the modern university. Plato believed that the essence of learning is for the teacher to draw out the inner wisdom of the student. The role of the teacher is to facilitate the student's realization of this inner knowing through artful questioning leading to independent thought (Gelb, 2003, pp. 33–34). Given the innumerable, unique clinical situations that will be faced by the supervisee, it seems essential for good supervision to go beyond developing a competence with clinical knowledge and technique to also include the developing of "psychological mindedness" and metathinking skills. It is important for both supervisor and supervisee to contemplate and discuss the right conditions necessary to bring this inner potential to fruition.

Gelb noted that when Olympic medals are awarded and winners are invariably asked about the secrets of their success, almost without exception they answer that they owe their success to a parent, coach, teacher, or friend who believed in them. Good supervisors seem to have the guiding vision and skill to help their supervisees discover the potential they might have never known without external support and guidance. For Plato and his teacher and mentor Socrates, the process of questioning is the key to deepening wisdom. Effective leaders and clinicians are skilled at asking carefully worded questions, guiding people to greater understanding of the issues and problems, until appropriate solutions become obvious (Gelb, 2002). Well-known management consultant Peter Drucker states, "The leader of the past was a person who knew how to tell. The leader of the future will be a person who knows how to ask" (as cited in Goldsmith, 2003, p. 200). The future appears to be making its way back to the ancient Greeks.

Impactful supervisors have a strong guiding vision of both their role and the purpose of supervision. Skillfully asking questions is a key component of almost all supervision models. However, it seems important to take the next step and reflect on your guiding principles as a supervisor and continually examine and reflect whether your questions and approach are really supporting your values, visions, and those guiding principles. (For instance, I [John Wade] know that if I am not careful, I can find myself acting more like a case manager, getting much more caught up in the week-to-week details with my supervisees than reflects my principles, and a moment of reflection now and then helps me get back on track.)

It is vital for both supervisors and administrators to remain cognizant of their most important teaching tool—their own actions as role models. In 1993, NBA superstar Charles Barkley—also known as "Sir Charles" and "The Round Mound of Rebound"—famously asserted that he was not a role model, as he defended his "bad-boy" behavior off the court that had included such behavior as spitting on a fan and throwing a bar patron out a window. Nothing could be further from the truth. Although we probably do not have the public spotlight on us in the same way as "Sir Charles," as supervisors and/or administrators we are also role models, and we are constantly sending messages to our supervisees through our actions and decisions.

As social beings, we are all very sensitive to the environment and the culture and norms and expectations of the communities where we practice. Behavior is contagious, and especially in novel or ambiguous situations, supervisees are likely to look to others, especially senior staff, for indications about how to behave (Heath and Heath, 2010, p. 225). For example, if we want our supervisees to consult when diagnostic considerations are complicated and not easily discerned or when clients are at high risk, the best way to ensure this practice is for senior staff to do so themselves and publically receive positive reinforcement by administrators for doing so.

Getting the Most from Supervision

Knowing the variables associated with effective supervision is important, but it is only part of the equation. It is also important to understand how to make the best use of all of the components. The next section offers information regarding how to make the most of the supervision process.

The Pygmalion Effect

Getting the most from supervision depends upon both the supervisor and supervisee having the right expectations. The "Pygmalion effect" refers to the finding that leader expectations for subordinate performance can subconsciously affect leader behavior and consequently impact the performance of subordinates. The effect is named after Pygmalion, a sculptor in Greek mythology who fell in love with a female statue he had carved after his wish is granted that it become human.

The original Pygmalion research (e.g., Rosenthal and Jacobson, 1968) has been replicated with several other populations in different settings. For example, studies investigating the impact of leader expectations have been conducted with therapists and clients (Jenner, 1990) and managers and employees (Eden, 1990). The Pygmalion effect was also dramatically studied using instructors and trainees of the Israeli Defense Force (Eden & Shani, 1982). If ever there were a group that one might expect to be impervious to the effects of emotion and perception, it would be the military, but the Pygmalion effect held true even among highly disciplined military personnel. A random sample of trainees was identified to the instructors as having exceptionally high command potential, and by the end of the training, this group in fact outperformed the control group of trainees on objective exams.

The self-fulfilling prophecy of the Pygmalion effect has been largely explained in terms of the mediating variables of leadership behavior and self-expectations (White and Locke, 2000). Leadership has been identified as the mechanism through which teachers' expectations for different students were subconsciously translated into differential behavior, such as teachers smiling more and creating a warmer and friendlier environment for students they thought had greater ability or potential. Teachers have also been found to give high-expectancy students more challenging assignments, as well as more positive, constructive feedback (White & Locke, 2000).

Discussing the findings of the Israeli Defense Force training, Eden (1990) found that instructors displayed more of the following variables to trainees they thought had high-command potential:

- Coaching on effective work habits

- Stimulating enthusiasm for meeting a goal or achieving excellent performance

- Enhancing others' feelings of importance and self-worth

- Encouraging members to form relationships and work together as a team

These leadership traits were dubbed the "Pygmalion Leadership Style," which appears to include both deliberate and unconscious elements. Interestingly, even when the manipulation of the study was revealed to them, the leaders were still unaware of having treated trainees any differently based on their expectations. Eden (1990) described that the Pygmalion Leadership Style involves:

> . . . consistent encouraging, supporting, and reinforcing of high expectations resulting in the adoption, acceptance, or internalization of high expectations on the part of the subordinates. In the simplest and most straightforward instance, it is a manager reassuringly telling a subordinate "I know you can do this well." This message can be transmitted in an endless variety of ways. The hallmark of an effective leader is his ability to get this message across convincingly and to inspire high self-confidence among the other persons around him. (1990, p. 125)

The second mediator of the Pygmalion effect is that the self-expectations of the leaders are transmitted to their subordinates, leading them to raise their own expectations for how well they can perform (White & Locke, 2000). In the Israeli Defense Force training, raising instructors' expectations for trainees resulted not only in higher performance but also trainees having higher expectations for themselves. Research indicates that trainees' expectations were also increased by simply directly telling them they had high potential, which also resulted in increased performance (Eden & Ravid, 1982).

Although much of the research on the Pygmalion effect had the unsavory consequence of raising the expectancies of the experimental group while neglecting to do so—or perhaps even by default lowering the expectations—for control group members, White and Locke (2000) offer suggestions for intentionally creating positive expectancies for all students or supervisees using the information gained from research on the Pygmalion effect. Noting that increased performance occurred as a result of increased external expectations being internalized as an increased sense of internal self-efficacy, they recommend focusing on increasing self-efficacy using the four techniques identified by Bandura (1986, 1997):

1. Enacting mastery or building skills through practice. Supervisors can focus on guided mastery, achieved through breaking down complex tasks into simpler components, practicing the elements one at a time with instruction, and gradually reintegrating them into a whole. The goal is to set the stage for success by building the supervisee's sense of self-efficacy through a series of "small wins."

2. Role modeling or observing the performance of competent others with whom one can identify. Supervisors can emphasize to supervisees how to derive maximum benefit from observing models, such as mentally organizing what they observe (i.e., identifying principles) and planning opportunities to incorporate components of what they have observed.

3. Verbal persuasion or expressions of encouragement. Persuasive communication becomes more powerful when supervisors can share why and how they believe supervisees can succeed.

4. Interpreting ambiguous states of arousal in positive terms (e.g., encouraging someone to interpret butterflies in the stomach as excitement rather than fear). (pp. 405–408)

White and Locke also encourage supervisors to adopt a "learning orientation" versus a "performance orientation" with supervisees to enhance the benefits of Pygmalion training. They explain that,

> A learning orientation reflects the attitude that the pursuit of a goal is a learning process. As efforts are made to achieve a goal, people with learning orientations may devote time to trying to uncover what skills are necessary for performing a task, or what task strategies are most beneficial for reaching a goal. In addition, they are likely to view mistakes or setbacks on the road to reaching a goal as opportunities for learning and development. People with a performance orientation typically stress working on easy tasks to ensure success and getting recognition and praise rather than working on challenging tasks for the pleasure of learning and mastery. Mistakes are viewed in terms of slowing down progress toward a goal rather than as mechanisms for learning. (pp. 408–409)

In essence, the Pygmalion effect applies expectancy theory to learning and performance. When expectations are raised, positive links are created between expectations, effort, and performance, and higher performance tends to occur. The Pygmalion effect depends in part on trainers or supervisors creating positive expectancies during the brief, initial period when impressions are still being formed. It becomes very difficult to try to create a positive Pygmalion effect once negative appraisals have been made (White & Locke, 2000).

This is where a little intentional effort prior to the arrival of new trainees or supervisees can be very beneficial. Taking such steps as having the training director share the accomplishments and reasons why each trainee was chosen with all of the staff before new trainees arrive can help create a favorable lens through which early impressions and expectancies are created. The best supervisors seem to fully incorporate this principle into their being. (My [John Wade] internship training director had the gift of making everyone feel special and identifying each person's unique strengths. On the first day I arrived, she told me that she was so glad I chose their site and constantly seemed to see strengths in me I wasn't always sure that I had. In fact, I occasionally wondered if she had looked at the wrong vita, but she always backed her praise with specifics and helped to steer me in directions best suited to my strengths. Her positive impressions and expectations gave me the confidence to feel that with effort, I could grow to actually meet her impressions and expectations.)

Learning to Learn

Setting the stage for good supervision is, in part, setting the stage for learning to occur. Carol Dweck has investigated learning orientations for more than two decades, popularizing these findings in her book *Mindset: The New Psychology of Success* (2006). Both supervisors and supervisees know the fundamental tension of supervision—the defensive, protective stance focused on "saving face" versus the open stance of accepting the vulnerability of making mistakes during the learning process. Dweck's research has carefully examined this duality. Children with a "performance" orientation believe that intelligence and other abilities are fixed traits, and consequently focus their energy on trying to prove their ability. These children tend to do more poorly than those who have learning goals and view intelligence and other abilities as malleable and capable of growing through effort. Those who believe that intelligence is a fixed trait tend to focus on gaining favorable judgments of that trait (performance goals), whereas those who believe that intelligence is malleable tend to focus on learning and growth (learning goals; Dweck, 1986, p. 1041). In his classic book *Emotional Intelligence,* Daniel Goleman (2006) notes that renowned industry consultant William Deming admonished supervisors and managers to banish fear from the workplace because it undermines the ability to do good work.

Learning goals emphasize progress and mastery through effort. This creates the tendency to be energized by the challenge, whereas a focus on ability judgments can result in a tendency to avoid and withdraw from challenge

(Dweck, 1986, p. 1041). Children with learning goals are willing to risk displays of ignorance in order to acquire skills and knowledge and focus on the value of the skill to be developed or their interest in the task to be undertaken. In contrast, children with performance goals are more likely to interpret negative outcomes in terms of their abilities and become discouraged (p. 1042). Children with learning goals use obstacles as a cue to increase their efforts or to analyze and vary their strategies, which increases their likelihood of maintaining or improving their strategies under difficulty or failure. Effort is regarded as a means of using or activating their ability, surmounting obstacles, and of increasing their ability. "Not only is effort perceived as the means to accomplishment, it is also the factor that engenders pride and satisfaction with performance. The adoption of learning goals thus encourages children to explore, initiate, and pursue tasks that promote intellectual growth" (p. 1043).

Retraining children's attributions for failure (teaching them to attribute their failures to effort or strategy instead of ability) has been shown to produce sizeable changes in persistence over time and is generalizable across tasks (Dweck, 1986, p. 1046). Although Dweck's research focuses on K–12 education, it seems likely that these concepts apply to learning in general, regardless of age.

The tension between wanting to be open to learning versus wanting to look competent and save face is intrinsic to the supervision process. In fact, I can think of few other professions where the vulnerability level is as high as for mental health clinicians. An accountant and chemist may feel some discomfort if they make mistakes, but they don't have a videotape recording them during the process. It seems incumbent upon supervisors to set the stage for effective learning and growth by creating the conditions to foster a learning versus a performance orientation.

At the core, training and supervision are about learning. Individual supervisors and training agencies strive to create opportunities and support for supervisees to learn clinical skills and judgment. To experience the love of learning, people must feel or expect to acquire some competence and efficacy in the learning process; that is, they must feel that they are mastering a skill or filling in the gaps of knowledge. However, the paradox is that learning, by definition, also includes failure and times of realizing that the current path is not working (Peterson & Seligman, 2004, p. 166). Peterson and Seligman describe the differences between a mastery versus performance orientation toward learning. Students with a mastery (or task or learning) orientation strive for achievement defined in terms of individual mastery, with progress measured in terms of effort and against one's own performance standards. In contrast, students with a performance orientation strive for achievement with progress self-measured in terms of performance relative to others or some externally defined standard (e.g., grades, ranking, and so on; p. 166). The pursuit of mastery goals appears more likely associated with a love of learning, because it allows the person to maintain a sense of efficacy while learning.

The love of learning, which is the foundation of true growth and lifelong betterment, appears to be associated with:

- A sense of possibility

- Resourcefulness

- Positive feelings about learning new information

- The ability to self-regulate efforts to persevere, despite challenge and frustration

- Feeling supported by others in the efforts to learn

- Self-efficacy (p. 169)

Mastery-oriented supervision should strive for these to occur during the training process.

University administrator Laurie Schreiner (2010) has applied the growth mind-set concept to the college setting, asserting that higher education should build upon what students do well, not what they lack, and emphasized the goal of *thriving*, which is linked to both psychological and academic well-being. Schreiner defines thriving as reflecting: (1) engaged learning, (2) academic determination, (3) positive perspective, (4) diverse citizenship, and (5) social connectedness (p. 4). Drawing upon Dweck's research, Schreiner asserts that students who thrive know that it is the investment of effort on a regular basis that will help them succeed. They are motivated to do well and have educational goals that are important to them and strategies for reaching those goals. Most importantly, when things get tough or confusing, they don't give up but rather try new strategies or ask for assistance (pp. 4–5).

Optimism and social support are cornerstones of a thriving orientation. Students (1) who are engaged and investing effort in the learning experience, (2) who are connected in meaningful ways to others, (3) who believe they are making a difference, and (4) who have a positive outlook on life are significantly more likely to do better and have greater learning gains from their college experience (Schreiner, 2010, p. 5). Optimism and persistence are essential and fortunately can be learned and practiced. Three specific empirically supported practices that educators can incorporate that have a lasting effect on college students are: (1) equipping students with an optimistic, explanatory style, (2) helping students envision future success, and (3) teaching students to develop and apply their strengths (p. 7).

Providing peer mentors as role models who specifically address these issues in orientation and the first-year seminar can teach students specific, more helpful ways to interpret setbacks, and specifically incorporating a brief lesson on attributions early in the school year can be useful (Schreiner, 2010, p. 8). Schreiner also advocates helping students to envision future success. Drawing from the Markus and Nurius (1986) concept of "best possible self," Schreiner advises that visualizing one's "best possible self" leads to more positive emotions and taking actions to reach one's goals (p. 8).

Priming the Pump for Success

Investment and commitment to the learning process are usually not concerns for graduate students or clinical trainees; however, the will to work does not always mean working in the most effective way possible. Although orientation sessions for first-year college students are routine, many graduate-level clinical programs seem to miss the opportunity to use more advanced trainees as role models and mentors, which would not only help incoming students to know what it will take to be successful but also creating cognitive schema for success and practically focused goals. Berger and Buchholz (1993) echo this sentiment, and propose presupervisory preparation for supervisees in a more structured form than is usually given. Although it probably feels very obvious to supervisors, basic information such as how learning will take place and the roles and responsibilities of each party are usually unclear to new supervisees. In addition, supervisees "often feel that they are expected to demonstrate the expertise that they are there to learn" (p. 86), prompting a defensive mind-set that can be antithetical to learning.

The first step of presupervisory preparation is to provide an opportunity for supervisees to express their expectations, including wishes and fears. Openness and clear discussion can help ease supervisee anxiety, assist in identifying the most salient areas of focus, and provide a framework for future evaluative and/or problem-solving conversations. Discussing the supervisee attributes that supervisors commonly consider to be conducive to learning can help provide a useful framework for the goals and roles of supervision and help guide personal growth (Berger and Buchholz, 1993, p. 87).

At my (John Wade) previous job at Counseling and Psychological Services at the University of Kansas, the clinical training and supervision of graduate students was an integral part of our mission and daily work life. Each year, we would get a new cohort of graduate students, and during the several day orientation period, the policies and rules were explained in exacting and sometimes eye-glazing detail. Long sessions were held on workplace violence, rules against sexual harassment, what to do if sexually harassed, and so on. All of this is important and necessary information; however, during the crucial "setting the tone" period, the balance of attention was very heavily weighted on what not to do versus how to be successful. It was as though our graduate students were expected to somehow deduce how to be successful merely by knowing the policies and procedures.

This runs counter to the appreciative inquiry approach, which emphasizes focusing on what you want to create more of versus want you don't want. I raised these concerns to the administration who agreed to allow me to add a training workshop very early in the orientation process to provide research-based information and practical suggestions to the incoming supervisees on how to have a rewarding and growth-filled training experience. The supervisees' initial anxiety was normalized during the "Priming the Pump for Success"

workshop, and various topics were covered. The empirically supported characteristics of successful clinical supervisees were shared and discussed to help
create a clear image to aspire to. I introduced Carol Dweck's learning mind-set
model, which stresses the importance of viewing learning as a process with
mistakes to be expected. We discussed the deliberate practice model (see
Chapter 8) of setting a target, continually observing the results, making adjustments, and maintaining high levels of self-awareness and reflection. Finally,
I introduced Barbara Fredrickson's broaden-and-build model, demonstrating the link between positive emotions and increased learning and improved
problem solving. Whereas just focusing on acquiring procedural and policy
information and getting to know various offices on campus has value, it also
often feels like information overload and neglects to use the brief window
for shaping impressions about the culture and values of the training setting.
Feedback regarding the "Priming the Pump for Success" training suggests that
it was effective at generating positive energy and enthusiasm and creating a
practical template for approaching the training experience from a solution-
based, opportunity-focused mind-set.

Reflective Supervision

Regardless of the therapeutic approach, one of the implicit skills we teach our
clients in psychotherapy is the value of reflection. As Socrates famously said,
"the unexamined life is not worth living." Asking simple questions frequently
helps clients view their problems from a different perspective and consequently
get "unstuck." Engaging in reflection and questioning ourselves also helps us
identify our values and self-monitor whether our actions are in line with our
values and goals. Our unexamined, default habits are not always in line with our
values and intentions, and quick, simple reflection can help us identify these
discrepancies. Kreider (2011) advises us as supervisors to take time to examine
the assumptions of supervision we hold, especially regarding the supervisor–
supervisee alliance, supervision roles, and therapeutic techniques.

Clients frequently (and understandably) approach psychotherapy simply
wanting to reduce their distress and just "get the answer" from the expert clinician.
However, most therapists also know that although a certain amount of psycho-
education can be extremely valuable, simply giving clients "the answer" often is
met with ambivalence even when requested, and more importantly, it metaphorically simply gives the client a fish for the day but does not teach the client how to
fish. Supervision involves a similar tension between imparting information versus allowing the supervisee to grapple with dilemmas and using them as teaching moments to critically reflect on the decision-making process. Supervision
at times involves providing a holding environment and message of acceptance
for the inherent discomfort of the process. Problems during supervision are to

be authentically acknowledged, without amplifying them by the deficit perspective which dwells on problems and weaknesses. Ultimately, supervision is about developing psychological mindedness, developing a way of being for the clinician, not merely just developing a set of skills and a body of knowledge.

"Reflective supervision" is one method for achieving these goals. Reflective supervision is a model designed for the supervisor and supervisee to develop a partnership focused on intentionally illuminating and examining the supervisee's therapeutic process. In keeping with a strength-based approach to supervision, it builds the capacity of supervisees by cherishing their strengths and partnering around their vulnerabilities (Shahmoon-Shanok, 1991, p. 18). Reflective supervision provides the opportunity to "step back" from the clinical process and to contemplate and reflect on what occurred in the session and what still needs to be done, enabling the supervisee to plan and become ready for the next steps. Most importantly, reflection involves gaining perspective to consider the work from multiple perspectives.

The supervisory relationship is regarded as paramount. The reflective supervisor provides a reliable, respectful relationship over time, in which the reflective supervisor listens deeply, and both supervisor and supervisee share attention to the same phenomena. This supervisory space is characterized by authenticity and genuine interest that supports a nondefensive willingness on the part of the supervisee to share strengths and allow vulnerabilities to be seen. This shared thought, care, awareness, and planning between supervisee and supervisor helps to widen the supervisee's perspective (Shahmoon-Shanok, 1991, pp. 8–9).

One of the key goals of clinical supervision is for supervisees to learn to think psychologically and to begin to develop awareness of what to pay attention to and work with from among the thousands of data points of information contained in each therapy session. The reflective supervision perspective, in which both supervisor and supervisee are focused on the same phenomenon over time, discussing and exchanging viewpoints, seems well suited to foster both the enlargement of perspective and also the keen focus needed for good clinical judgment.

Supervision is regarded as a "holding environment" in which the supervisor and supervisee consider next steps, and the supervisory dyad looks "both at what is illuminated and toward the shadows, hunting for clues to clients' unfolding narratives" (Shamoon-Shanok, 2009, p. 18). Experiencing a holding environment in which "trial actions" are considered from multiple perspectives before being initiated helps to create a safe space that encourages growth and development. In addition, when a supervisee is experiencing emotional agitation, effective reflection involves emotional regulation and helps move a supervisee to a calmer state that enables access to the supervisee's full range of experience, insight, and ideas that are necessary to becoming a more resourceful clinician (p. 18).

Conclusion

Mental health clinicians have many tools in their toolbox, but probably none as powerful or as underestimated as simply asking questions and raising awareness within the context of a strong working alliance. Several years ago, my wife and I (John Wade) volunteered to have our house feng shui analyzed by a friend of ours who was going through the formal training to become certified. Although we learned some interesting information—for example, we had the trash can located in the relationship quadrant of the house (which we quickly moved)—I was not convinced enough of the ultimate value of feng shui to make the more difficult recommended changes to our living space. However, what did have a powerful impact on me was the detailed interview our friend conducted with my wife and me before ever looking at our house. She asked us each individually about our short- and long-term goals and dreams. It dawned on me that although I ask people questions on a daily basis for a living, it had been years since I had been asked meaningful and important questions that forced me to stop and think. As I answered the questions about my goals and priorities, I felt the energizing emotions of hope and motivation. The commitment to write this book in part arose from hearing myself articulate my loosely formed idea of wanting to write a book as an explicit goal during the interview.

Being forced to think about these questions helped raise awareness of "big" items such as life dreams, but the importance of reflection and raising awareness applies equally to small, everyday decisions—perhaps more so. Although it sounds easy in principle to approach our clinical work and supervision with reflection and awareness, making sure that our actions are in fact consistent with our personal priorities and the values of the profession, well, we all know the challenges of incorporating a few moments of reflection into our daily lives. Although we may value intentional awareness and self-regulation, the actual daily life of a clinician or supervisor often does not mirror that value, with the 10-minute breaks between clients becoming a mad scramble to visit the rest room, return a phone call, and get started on a client note.

David Blaine is famous for such feats as being suspended in a plastic box for 34 days without food and for holding his breath under water for more than 17 minutes. He also spent 63 hours encased in ice; however, this amazing and agonizing accomplishment isn't listed in the Guinness Book of World Records because he could never find the time to submit the paperwork to have this record documented and the deadline expired (Baumeister & Tierney, 2011). Even the master of willpower struggles with discipline for the routine!

At Johns Hopkins Hospital, as at many other hospitals, central line infections following surgery were a problem, resulting in many preventable deaths. When nurses in the ICU were asked to observe doctors for a month as they put lines into patients, in more than a third of the cases the doctor skipped at least one of the five critical steps for keeping the line sterile and free from infection.

It obviously was not a question of intelligence or commitment to patient care that resulted in these careless mistakes—these were world-class surgeons after all—but simply a reflection of the human condition that it is difficult to continually sustain attention on what is most important. When surgeon Atul Gawande (2009) introduced the "checklist system" to Johns Hopkins Hospital, doctors were given a checklist of the five critical steps to preventing line infection that were to be checked off after completing the task, and the 10-day line infection rate dropped from 11% to zero. It is estimated that these simple checklists have reduced deaths and complications by more than one-third in the hospitals that have adopted the system. The checklist has also been applied to other professions such as piloting jetliners, and seems particularly well suited to clinical supervision, which also is complicated but depends upon the presence of a few critical factors.

Unlike keeping an intravenous line site sterile or flying a jetliner, in which the correct steps are almost universally agreed upon, the critical steps or components of supervision are less universally agreed upon. It is hoped that this book will suggest some of the essential components for a strength-based approach to supervision, but the content of a checklist for supervision is probably much less important than the process of using a checklist. We will offer questions for consideration at the end of most chapters but encourage you to develop your own questions for reflection and supervision checklist items. We anticipate that these items will be fluid and flexible and will change over time, perhaps as frequently as session to session. Developing and using a checklist is a very quick and practical way to make sure that reflection, planning, and intentionality are integrated into your supervision every session. As with most things, simple is usually better. Our observation is that complicated, elaborate plans might sound wonderful but are seldom implemented, whereas something that is short and sweet is much more likely to be implemented. Intentionality and awareness almost always result in better outcomes, whereas activity that not intentional nor reflective often results in doing things because they "feel right," which typically, simply reflects our comfort level with what is most familiar.

Questions to Consider

For the supervisee

- How do my attributes compare to the preferred attributes of the "ideal" supervisee?

- Do I tend to approach supervision from a learning or a performance orientation?

- What would it take for me to operate from more of a learning orientation?

- How do I save a few moments of my time to regularly reflect on my clinical work?

- What five items would be most useful to me at this time to put on my checklist for conducting therapy?
- What five items would be most useful to me at this time to put on my checklist for getting the most out of supervision?

For the supervisor

- Based on what we do in supervision, what would my supervisees say that I value the most in supervision?
- If this does not reflect my priorities, what do I need to change?
- How do my attributes compare to the preferred supervisor attributes of the "ideal" supervisor?
- Do I regularly get feedback from my supervisees on the current status of the supervisory working alliance?
- What five items would be most useful to me at this time to put on my checklist for best meeting the needs of my supervisees?

For the leader/administrator

- As a leader, what are some ways I am meeting my followers' needs?
- How would supervisors and supervisees describe the culture of the organization?
- What are some ways I demonstrate positive Pygmalion leadership? If I am deficient in this area, what is a small change I can make to improve?
- How does my leadership contribute to the flourishing of the members of the organization?
- How would the members of the organization know that I value learning and growing?
- What five items would be most useful to me at this time to put on my checklist for best meeting the needs of my followers?

Recommended Readings

Books

Bandura, A. (1997). *Self-efficacy: The exercise of control*. New York: W.H. Freeman.

Dweck, C. (2006). *Mindset: The new psychology of success*. New York: Ballantine Books.

Gawande, A. (2009). *The checklist manifesto: How to get things right*. New York: Metropolitan Books.

Gelb, M. J. (2002). *Discover your genius: How to think like history's ten most revolutionary minds.* New York: HarperCollins Publishers, Inc.

Keyes, L. M., & Haidt, J. (2002). (Eds.). *Flourishing: Positive psychology and the life well-lived.* Washington, DC: American Psychological Association.

Articles and Book Chapters

Berger, S. S., & Buchholz, E. S. (1993). On becoming a supervisee: Preparation for learning in a supervisory relationship. *Psychotherapy, 30,* 86–92.

Carifio, M. S., & Hess, A. K. (1987). Who is the ideal supervisor? *Professional Psychology: Research and Practice, 18,* 244–250.

Dweck, C. (1986). Motivational processes affecting learning. *American Psychologist, 41,* 1040–1048.

Fredrickson, B. L. (2003). Positive emotions and upward spirals in organizations. In K. S. Cameron, J. E. Dutton, & R. E. Quinn (Eds.), *Positive organizational scholarship* (pp. 163–175). San Francisco, CA: Berrett-Koehler Publisher.

Pearson Q. M. (2004). Getting most out of clinical supervision: Strategies for mental health. *Journal of Mental Health, 26,* 361–373.

Ragins, B. R. (2011). Relational mentoring: A positive approach to mentoring at work. In K. S. Cameron & G. M. Spreitzer, (Eds.) *The Oxford handbook of positive organizational scholarship* (pp. 519–536), San Francisco, CA: Berrett-Koehler Publisher.

Rodenhauser P., Rudisell, J. R., & Painter, A. F. (1989). Attributes conducive to learning in psychotherapy. *American Journal of Psychotherapy, 3,* 368–377.

Shamoon-Shanrock, R. (2009). What is reflective supervision? In S. Scott Heller & L. Gilkerson (Eds.), *A practical guide to reflective supervision* (pp. 7–22).
Washington, DC: ZERO TO THREE.

References

Bandura, A. (1986). *Social foundations of thought and action: A social-cognitive view.* Englewood Cliffs, NJ: Prentice-Hall.

Bandura, A. (1997). *Self-efficacy: The exercise of control.* New York: W.H. Freeman.

Baumeister, R. F., & Tierney, J. (2011). *Willpower: Rediscovering the greatest human strength.* New York: Penguin Press.

Berger, N., & Graff, L. (1995). Making good use of supervision. In D. G. Martin & A. D. Moore (Eds.), *Basics of clinical practice: A guidebook for trainees in the helping profession* (pp. 408–432). Prospect Heights, IL: Waveland Press.

Berger, S. S., & Buchholz, E. S. (1993). On becoming a supervisee: Preparation for learning in a supervisory relationship. *Psychotherapy, 30,* 86–92.

Bohart, A. C., & Tallhman, K. (2010). Clients: The neglected common factor. In B. L. Duncan, S. D. Miller, B. E. Wampold, & M. A. Hubble (Eds.), *The heart and soul of change* (2nd ed., pp. 000–000). Washington, DC: American Psychological Association.

Borders, L. D. (1994). The good supervisor. *Eric Digest, 1–2,* EDO-CG-94-18.

Bordin, E. S. (1983). A working alliance based model of supervision. *The Counseling Psychologist, 11,* 35–41.

Carifio, M. S., & Hess, A. K. (1987). Who is the ideal supervisor? *Professional Psychology: Research and Practice, 18,* 244–250.

Coche, E. (1977). Training of group therapists. In F. W. Kaslow (Ed.), *Supervision consultation, and staff training in the helping professions* (pp. 235–263). San Francisco, CA: Jossey-Bass.

Csikszentmihalyi, M. (1991). *Flow.* New York: Harper.

Dorn, F. (1985). Utilizing the social influence model in clinical supervision. *The Clinical Supervisor, 3,* 77–84.

Drigotas, S. M., Rusbult, C. E., Wieselquist, J., & Whitton, S. W. (1999). Close partner as sculptor of the ideal self: Behavioral affirmation and the Michelangelo phenomenon. *Journal of Personality and Social Psychology, 77,* 293–323.

Dweck, C. (1986). Motivational processes affecting learning. *American Psychologist, 41,* 1040–1048.

Dweck, C. (2006). *Mindset: The new psychology of success.* New York: Ballantine Books.

Eden, D. (1990). *Pygmalion in management: Productivity as a self-fulfilling prophecy.* Lexington: D.C. Heath.

Eden, D., & Ravid, G. (1982). Pygmalion versus self-expectancy: Effects of instructor- and self-expectancy on trainee performance. *Organizational Behavior and Human Performance, 30,* 351–364.

Eden, D., & Shani, A.B. (1982). Pygmalion goes to boot camp: Expectancies, leadership, and trainee performance. *Journal of Applied Psychology, 67,* 194–199.

Fredrickson, B. L. (1998). What good are positive emotions? *Review of General Psychology, 2,* 300–319.

Fredrickson, B. L. (2003). Positive emotions and upward spirals in organizations. In K. S. Cameron, J. E. Dutton, & R. E. Quinn (Eds.), *Positive organizational scholarship* (pp. 163–175). San Francisco, CA: Berrett-Koehler Publishers.

Fredrickson, B. L., & Branigan, C. A. (2001). Positive emotions. In T. J. Mayne & G. A. Bonnano (Eds.), *Emotion: Current issues and future developments* (pp. 123–151). New York: Guilford Press.

Gawande, A. (2009). *The checklist manifesto: How to get things right.* New York: Metropolitan Books.

Gelb, M. J. (2003). *Discover your genius: How to think like history's ten most revolutionary minds.* New York: HarperCollins Publishers Inc.

Goldsmith, M. (2003). *Global leadership: The next generation.* Upper Saddle River, NJ: Pearson Education, Inc.

Goleman, D. (2006). *Emotional intelligence: Why it can matter more than IQ.* New York: Random House Digital, Inc.

Grant, A. M., & Spence, G. B. (2009). Using coaching and positive psychology to promote a flourishing workforce: A model of goal-striving and mental health. In P. A. Linley & S. Harrington (Eds.), *Oxford handbook of positive psychology and work* (pp. 175–188). New York: Oxford University Press.

Grencavage, L. M., & Norcross, J. C. (1990). Where are the commonalities among the therapeutic common factors? *Professional Psychology: Research and Practice 1990, 21,* 372–378.

Harter, J. K., Schmidt, F. L., & Keyes, C. L. M. (2002). Well-being in the workplace and its relationship to business outcomes: A review of the Gallup studies. In C. L. M. Keyes & J. Haidt (Eds.), *Flourishing: Positive psychology and the life well-lived* (pp. 205–224). Washington, DC: American Psychological Association.

Heath, C., & Heath, D. (2010). *Switch: How to change things when change is hard.* New York: Broadway Books..

Jenner, H. (1990). The Pygmalion effect: The importance of expectancies. *Alcoholism Treatment Quarterly, 7,* 127–133.

Kaplan, R. E., & Kaiser, R. B. (2009). Toward a positive psychology for leaders. In P. A. Linley & S. Harrington (Eds.), *Oxford handbook of positive psychology and work* (pp. 107–119). New York: Oxford University Press.

Kauffman, C. (2006). Positive psychology: The science at the heart of coaching. In D. R. Stober & A. M. Grant (Eds.), *Evidence based coaching handbook: Putting best practices to work for your clients* (pp. 219-254). Hoboken, NJ: John Wiley & Sons, Inc.

Keyes, C. L. M. (2003). Complete mental health: An agenda for the 21st century. In C. L. M. Keyes & J. Haidt (Eds.), *Flourishing: Positive psychology and the life ell-lived.* Washington, DC: American Psychological Association.

Kohut, H. (1977). *The restoration of the self.* New York: International Universities Press.

Kreider, J. (2011, March 9). Personal interview.

Ladany, N., Ellis, M. V., & Friedlander, M. L. (1999). The supervisory working alliance, trainee self-efficacy, and satisfaction. *Journal of Counseling and Development, 77,* 447–455.

Lambert, M. J. (1980). Research and the supervisory process. In A. K. Hess (Ed.), *Psychotherapy supervision: Theory, research, and practice* (pp. 423–452). New York: Wiley.

Lopez, S. J. (2011). Focusing on what's right: A strengths-based workplace. Workshop at University of Kansas Medical School, Wichita, KS.

Markus, H., & Nurius, P. (1986). Possible selves. *American Psychologist, 41,* 954–969.

Messer, S. B., & Wampold, B. E. (2002). Let's face facts: Common factors are more potent than specific ingredients. *Clinical Psychology: Science and Practice, 9,* 21–25.

Nelson, G. L. (1978). Psychotherapy from a trainee's perspective: A survey of preferences. *Professional Psychology, 9,* 539–550.

Neufeldt, S. A., Beutler, L. E., & Ranchero, R. (1997). Research on supervisor variables in psychotherapy supervision. In C. E. Watkins, Jr. (Ed.), *Handbook of psychotherapy supervision* (pp. 508–525). New York: John Wiley & Sons.

Norcross, J. C., & Halgin, R. P. (1997). Integrative approaches to psychotherapy supervision. In C. E. Watkins (Ed.), *Handbook of psychotherapy supervision* (pp. 203–222). New York: Wiley.

Pearson, Q. M. (2004). Getting most out of clinical supervision: Strategies for mental health. *Journal of Mental Health, 26,* 361–373.

Peterson, C. (2006). *A primer in positive psychology.* New York: Oxford University Press.

Peterson, C., & Seligman, M. E. P. (2004). *Character strength and virtue: A handbook and classification.* New York: Oxford University Press.

Pierce, R., Carkhuff, R., & Berenson, B. (1967). The effects of high- and low-functioning supervisors upon counselors in training. *Journal of Clinical Psychology, 223,* 212–215.

Ragins, B. R. (2011). Relational mentoring: A positive approach to mentoring at work. In K. S. Cameron and G. M. Spreitzer (Eds.), *The Oxford handbook of positive organizational scholarship* (pp. 519–536). San Francisco, CA: Berrett-Koehler Publisher.

Robiner, W. N., Saltzman, S. R., Hoberman, H. M., & Schirvar, J. A. (1997). Psychology supervisors' training, experiences, supervisory evaluation, and self-rated competence. *The Clinical Supervisor, 16*(1), 117–144.

Rodenhauser, P., Rudisell, J. R., & Painter, A. F. (1989). Attributes conducive to learning in psychotherapy. *American Journal of Psychotherapy, 3,* 368–377.

Rosenblatt, A., & Mayer, J. (1975). Objectionable supervising styles: Students' views. *Social Work, 18,* 184–189.

Rosenthal, R., & Jacobson, L. (1968). *Pygmalion in the classroom: Teacher expectation and pupils' intellectual development.* New York: Holt, Rinehart, & Winston.

Schreiner, L. A. (2010, May/June). The "thriving quotient." *About Campus,* 2–10. doi:10.1002/abc.20016.

Shamoon-Shanok, R. (1991). The supervisory relationship: Integrator, resource, and guide. *Zero to Three, 12,* 16–19.

Shamoon-Shanrock, R. (2009). What is reflective supervision? In S. Scott Heller & L. Gilkerson (Eds.), *A practical guide to reflective supervision* (pp. 7–22). Washington, DC: ZERO TO THREE

Shanock, L. R., & Eisenberger, R. (2006). When supervisors feel supported: Relationships with subordinates' perceived supervisor support, perceived organizational support, and performance. *Journal of Applied Psychology, 91,* 689–695. doi: 10.1037/0021-9010.91.3.689.

Sivanathan, N., Arnold, K. A., Turner, N., & Barling, J. (2004). Leading well: Transformational leadership and well-being. In P. A. Linley & S. Joseph (Eds.), *Positive psychology in practice* (pp. 241–255). New York: John Wiley & Sons.

Staw, B. M., Sutton, R. I., and Pellod, L. H. (1994). Employee positive emotion and favorable outcomes at the workplace. *Organizational Science, 5,* 51–71.

Vespia, K. M., Heckman-Stone, C., & Delworth, U. (2002). Describing and facilitating supervision behavior in counseling trainees. *Psychotherapy: Theory, Research, Practice, Training, 39,* 56–65.

Wampold, B. E. (2001). *The great psychotherapy debate: Models, methods, and findings.* Mahwah, NJ: Lawrence Erlbaum Associates, Publishers.

White, S. S., & Locke, E. A. (2000). Problems with the Pygmalion effect and some proposed solutions. *Leadership Quarterly, 11,* 389–415.

Wolfe, B. E., & Goldfried, M. R. (1988). Research on psychotherapy integration: recommendations and conclusions from an NIMH workshop. *Journal of consulting and clinical psychology, 56,* 448–451.

Worthen, V., & McNeill, B. W. (1996). A phenomenological investigation of "good" supervision events. *Journal of Counseling Psychology, 43,* 25–34.

Uncovering Potential: Identifying and Developing Strengths

"Moral excellence comes about as a result of habit. We become just by doing just acts, temperate by doing temperate acts, brave by doing brave acts.

—Aristotle

"We are what we repeatedly do. Excellence, then, is not an act but a habit."

—Aristotle

Typically, when I (John Wade) give workshops on strengths, I'll weave in an Aristotle quote or two early on, joking that at the very least quoting Aristotle makes you sound smart. But this also illustrates that the importance of developing strengths and character has been recognized for millennia. In addition to the writings of prominent philosophers, stories of strengths have often served as models and a source of inspiration throughout history. Stories and tales exemplifying strength and virtue, often tested under stress and hardship, predate even the ancient Greek scholars (Biswas-Deiner & Dean, 2007) and seem timeless in their appeal and their message.

Although the early years of psychology as a discipline certainly had a focus on pathology (e.g., think Freud), attention and research during this time was also given to studying success and exemplary behavior. Lopez et al. (2006) note that during much of the early 20th century, psychology was devoted to identifying the best in people, such as Terman's studies on giftedness and marital satisfaction (e.g., Terman and Oden, 1947; Terman, Buttenweiser, Ferguson, Johnson, and Wilson, 1938). Alfred Adler (1927), who foreshadowed much of what has more recently become known as "positive psychology," emphasized the development of meaningful life goals and the therapeutic value of identifying strengths in the therapy process and using them to work with problem areas.

However, during much of the mid- to late 20th century, the focus on success, strengths, and virtues began to take a secondary place relative to the emphasis placed on understanding and treating mental disorders. Linley and Harrington (2006a) suggested that since Allport claimed in 1937 that character was an unnecessary concept for psychology, that issues of character and strengths became generally ignored by the field until the recent interest in positive psychology during the past 15 years.

Recently, social work, counseling, and psychology have applied a renewed focus on the importance of studying successes and exemplary behavior and incorporating a strengths perspective into clinical work. Jones-Smith (2014) asserts that the social work field has been a chief proponent of the strengths perspective, noting that in 1989, Weick, Rapp, Sullivan, and Kisthardt introduced the term *strengths perspective,* and in 1992, Saleebey published a seminal work outlining the core constructs of this "new" perspective in *The Strengths Perspective in Social Work Practice.* Focusing on people's assets and strengths is also one of the core values of counseling psychology (e.g., Gelso and Fretz, 1992). For example, Jordaan, Myers, Layton, and Morgan (1968) articulated a strength-based approach to working with clients in the book *The Counseling Psychologist,* focusing on appraising and using client assets to help to plan, obtain, and derive maximum benefit from the kind of experiences that enable clients to discover and develop their potential (Jordaan et al. 1968, p. 1).

Lopez and Edwards (2008) reflect that counseling psychology has a rich tradition of studying and promoting the best in people, noting that in the *Second National Conference on Counseling Psychology in 1964,* Thompson and Super reported that the conference committed to a special emphasis on "the appraisal and use of assets for furthering individual development" (pp. 3–4). Lopez et al. (2006) stated that counseling psychology historically has been grounded in a strengths perspective, describing that ". . . counseling psychology has held to a philosophical focus and professional emphasis on identifying and developing personal and social resources and on helping individuals more effectively use these resources" (p. 206).

Within a strength-based supervision model, identifying and nurturing strengths is a crucial element. This chapter will present some of the theoretical- and research-based underpinnings of the strengths perspective, provide suggestions for identifying supervisee strengths, and offer tips for helping supervisees to further develop and capitalize on their potential. Often, it is assumed that a strength-based perspective means ignoring weaknesses. If this were the case, that would be a travesty, because all of us have weaknesses. However, from a strength-based perspective, a person's strengths can often be used in the service of managing their weaknesses. More on this later. The following section explores why—even though the benefits of focusing on strengths and successes might be intuitively apparent—it is often difficult for us to do so without conscious effort.

Bad Is Stronger Than Good

So, why do we need to focus intentionally on strengths? One of the key reasons, explained in copious detail by Baumeister, Bratslavsky, Finkenauer, and Vohs (2001), is that *bad is stronger than good*. (This probably is not what you were expecting to see in a book grounded in positive psychology!) It appears that from an evolutionary perspective, it is adaptive to give more weight and urgency to the negative than to the positive. In many respects, negative experiences and the fear of bad outcomes have a far greater impact than do neutral or positive experiences. Negative events are much more likely to be recalled, and we tend to be more influenced by negative experiences in the past in numerous ways. Painful emotions and negative feedback have more impact than good emotions or feedback, and bad information is processed more thoroughly than good (p. 323). As Brene Brown observantly noted in her TED talk on the power of vulnerability (2010), when we receive feedback, almost all of us focus on the one item of "constructive criticism" even if this is far outweighed by voluminous praise. John Gottman's (1994) research on romantic relationships found that positive and neutral interactions need to outnumber bad interactions at a ratio of approximately five to one for the relationship to succeed, suggesting that bad events seem to be significantly more powerful and impactful than positive ones (at least within the context of romantic relationships). Negative experiences can also quickly leave a lasting impact on our perception and expectations. Seligman (2002) observed that learned helplessness can develop just from a few failures, and it is hard to undo this perception even with numerous positive successes.

Baumeister et al. (2001) further explain that from an evolutionary perspective, organisms that were better attuned to bad things would have been more likely to survive threats, and consequently, would have increased the probability of carrying on their genes. "A person who ignores the possibility of a positive outcome may later experience significant regret at having missed an opportunity for pleasure or advancement, but nothing directly terrible is likely to result. In contrast, a person who ignores danger (the possibility of a bad outcome) even once may end up maimed or dead. Survival requires urgent attention to possible bad outcomes, but it is less urgent with regard to good ones. Hence, it would be adaptive to be psychologically designed to respond to bad more strongly than good" (p. 325).

For example, if a medium-sized fish is not paying attention and does not notice the smaller fish swimming near him that he could eat for breakfast, the smaller fish will live to see another day. However, if the medium-sized fish does not see the larger fish about to eat him, he becomes breakfast. From a survival perspective, keen attention to threats and danger is critical.

The greater power of bad events over good ones has also been found in many life domains, including social network patterns, interpersonal interactions, and learning processes. Bad emotions, bad parents, and bad feedback all have more impact than good ones, and bad information tends to be processed more quickly and less reflectively than good information. This seems especially note-worthy in the initial impression-forming stage of the supervisory relationship, when bad impressions and bad stereotypes can form quickly and are more resis-tant to disconfirmation than good ones.

Jones-Smith (2014) succinctly summarized that the mind predominantly has a negativity bias that causes most people not to recognize their strengths (p. 34). We tend to focus most on what captures our attention, which, given our evolutionary tendencies, means that we will often be drawn to the negative. This works well for survival, but is not very helpful for learning and growth. We'll detail later in the chapter why identifying and working from strengths can be very useful to the supervision process, but it is important to first recognize that although a strengths perspective may have intuitive appeal, that given our human tendencies, it will likely require conscious and intentional attention from both supervisors and supervisees.

Strengths Theories

Recognizing the importance of a strengths orientation is not new. Mid-20th-century humanistic psychologists such as Maslow (1954) and Rogers (1961) believed that human beings have a natural drive for positive growth and to actu-alize and express their strengths. If conditions are supportive and basic needs are met, human beings' natural inclination toward self-actualization and growth will cause them to flourish, just as plants thrive as long as they have enough sun-light, the right amount of water, and good soil. Graybeal (2001) succinctly artic-ulated the developmental and therapeutic value of building on strengths, stating that the fundamental premise of the strengths perspective is that individuals will do better in the long run when they are helped to identify, recognize, and use the strengths and resources available (p. 234). Seligman (2002) noted that strengths and virtues buffer against misfortune and build resilience, and that "the best therapists not merely heal damage; they help people identify and build their strengths and their values" (p. xiv). Moreover, the emergence of strengths is often the end product of a dialectical process involving a person's struggle with adversity (Jones-Smith, 2014, p. 66), and the goal of both therapy and supervi-sion during a time of difficulty is to help the client or supervisee understand the paradox of adversity.

This section provides a brief overview of two strength models.

Strength-Based Therapy (Jones-Smith)

Jones-Smith (2014) outlined a detailed strength-based theory designed for the process of psychotherapy. Her model assumes that we all have strength zones—areas in which we have some natural talent to perform well and potentially develop excellence (p. 17). Strengths may be conceptualized as part of the human adaptation system, dependent upon our ability to apply resources and skills in a flexible manner as required to solve problems or work toward goals (p. 15). By learning to identify these strengths and apply them to new situations or challenges, we broaden our skills and abilities and are better equipped to constructively and effectively face new challenges. Focusing on strengths in supervision can help our supervisees excel and provide new pathways for using the energy of hope and achieving positive goals.

However, it is often difficult for us to recognize and be aware of the strengths we have. Jones-Smith (2014) described this as "strength estrangement," namely, the lack of awareness of our talents and strengths, or, if we are aware of our strengths, we lack direction or flounder in using these strengths to achieve desired goals (p. 18). Adapting from the Jones-Smith theory, key tasks of strength-based supervision are to help supervisees identify and recognize their strengths and to coconstruct paths to effectively incorporate their strengths into their clinical work.

Jones-Smith (2014) posits that strength development is essentially relational and is best developed within the context of a trusted and supportive relationship (pp. 34–35). This certainly fits with the consensus understanding of developmental psychology (e.g., Davies, 2004), in which primary relationships must be consistently safe and secure for full cognitive and emotional development to occur. Almost invariably in everyday life experiences, other people are involved in our strength development and serve as part of the audience that either directly or indirectly provides feedback and helps us judge our abilities as strengths (pp. 13–14). This process is amplified within the supervision framework.

The following is an outline of Jones-Smith's (2014) stage model of how strengths develop:

1. *Brain development stage of strengths*—synaptic connections are formed in the brain, influenced by one's genetics, but strengthened or weakened by use or disuse of certain strengths and neural pathways.

2. *Strength awareness and identification*—almost always a reflective process (e.g., noticing that you do something well).

3. *Strength engagement*—naming and claiming of one's talents as points of strengths. Through engaging a strength in different settings, a person typically receives recognition or confirmation that the person has a particular strength.

4. *Strength refinement and practice*—practice and repetition leading to better performance

5. *Strength integration*—incorporation of strengths and talents into one's self-concept. People often identify themselves by what they are good at.

6. *Application of strengths in several different settings*—this can enhance the transferability and generalization of strengths.

7. *Use of strengths to manage one's weaknesses.* (pp. 62–63)

It is important to be mindful that strengths are inevitably culturally expressed, recognizing that characteristics that are regarded in some cultures as strengths can be perceived as weaknesses in others (e.g., the traditional Japanese value placed on respect and indirect communication can be misperceived in more direct cultures as lack of assertiveness).

Our mind-set—the way we perceive ourselves and the world—significantly impacts whether and how we will exercise our strengths. Our mind-set is created through the accumulation and interpretation of our experiences. The *strength mind-set* acknowledges and understands weaknesses within the self, but does so from the context of recognizing and embracing our strengths and viewing them as resources to draw upon when presented with difficult situations. This is in contrast to the *deficit mind-set*, which focuses on our deficiencies and weaknesses and tends to cause us to feel constrained and limited (Jones-Smith, 2014, pp. 50–51). Operating from a deficit mind-set, we tend to focus on weaknesses—such as our low grades or mistakes—without giving enough weight to our successes. Using strengths causes them to more fully develop, making strength development a process of internal talent and ability combined with awareness and practice. As Donald Hebb (1949) famously observed, the neural pathways we use more often become stronger, or more simply: neurons that fire together wire together. In the supervision process, this operates most effectively within the context of a supportive environment that permits the exploration and expression of strengths.

The ROPES Model

Graybeal (2001) proposed a model of strength development emphasizing the freedom and flexibility that can come from intentionally recognizing resources and possibilities. He suggested the ROPES model for identifying strengths, emphasizing a future-oriented perspective based upon the awareness of increased freedom and effectiveness through identifying Resources, Options, Possibilities, Exceptions, and Solutions. The following lists some of the components of each area:

Resources

Personal

Organizational

Social environment

Options

Present focus

Emphasis on choice

What can be accessed now?

What is available and hasn't been tried or used?

Possibilities

Future focus

Imagination

Creativity

Vision of the future

What have you thought of trying but haven't tried yet?

Exceptions

When is the problem not happening?

When is the problem different?

When is part of the hypothetical, future solution occurring?

How have you survived, endured, thrived?

Solutions

Focus on constructing solutions, not solving problems

What's working now?

What are your successes?

What are you doing that you would like to continue doing? (p. 237)

His model combines a solution-focused perspective with a strength-identification focus.

The next section will explore ways—both formal and informal—to identify supervisee strengths.

Identifying Strengths

The strength-based blueprint of supervision depends upon being able to accurately identify the core strengths of our supervisees from which to build. Similar to Michelangelo being able to see the potential of beauty hidden in the raw stone, effective strength-based supervisors are skilled at identifying and bringing to fruition the already existing strengths and sometimes hidden abilities or faint glimmers of talent within the supervisee. First, we'll look at some informal ways to do so and transition to two formal instruments to consider using as part of the supervision process.

From a strength-based perspective, it is essential as a supervisor to foster awareness of and help increase the use of strengths within our supervisees because it increases their effectiveness. Instead of trying to change weaknesses into strengths—which is often a frustrating and counterproductive process—we should attempt to bring areas of weakness into "functional competence," since trying to fix weaknesses generally leads to merely average performance (Jones-Smith, 2014, p. 23).

Often, we engage in "strength surveillance" in everyday life, a process of monitoring and judging ourselves, leading us to either recognize, minimize, or remain unaware of our strengths. If building upon strengths is a key component of the strength-based supervision approach, helping our supervisees recognize and acknowledge, claim ownership, and intentionally practice their strengths is critical. Strengths can be identified through using formal measures and also informally, through less structured, more conversational methods.

However, most people tend to be modest and reluctant to talk about strengths and find it difficult to name them if asked. Linley and Harrington (2006b) suggest that this may indicate that we often do not fully appreciate our strengths or know what they are. This probably also reflects the cultural upbringing that many of us—even from individualistic cultures—have experienced, being taught the value of modesty and humility. If you have ever asked a client struggling with low self-esteem to name personal strengths, more than likely you were met with a deer-in-the-headlights response as the client tried to mutter something to get the process over with as quickly as possible.

Like many attributes, strengths are often best inquired about indirectly and are often ascertained through subtle clues. For example, we tend to become more animated when talking about our strengths. Listening attentively to our supervisees for expressions of high energy and enthusiasm, stories of success, and challenges successfully navigated can give us clues as to our supervisees' strengths. Summarizing research from Donald Clifton and colleagues, Compton and Hoffman (2013) state that strengths share the following identifiable characteristics:

1. Yearnings—we feel a strong psychological pull toward interests, goals, and activities that connect to our strengths. These can serve as an internal compass.

2. Satisfaction—when we use or fulfill a strength, we experience intrinsic satisfaction; we feel good about ourselves and the activity.

3. Learning—we tend to learn more easily in areas of our strengths, and we are drawn to want to learn more. If we have a talent for golf or computer

science or ballet, we likely enjoy reading books and magazines about these topics. If these are not areas of strength, probably nothing could be more boring than reading about these topics.

4. Excellence or flow—when we activate a strength, we can exhibit consistently good performance, and at times will experience a flow state while engaged in the activity.

5. Less effort—we tend to both learn and execute more easily within our areas of strength. (p. 264)

These are all tell-tale indicators to be attuned to. We can also ask our supervisees about their strengths, through indirect questions such as:

- How would your friends describe you?

- What skills were you surprised to learn that you had at your last job?

- What does your partner say when your partner brags about you?

- What seemed to come easily for you during your recent sessions?

- Did you experience some moments when things seemed to be "clicking"? Tell me about these moments.

- Tell me about the parts of conducting therapy that have seemed easy for you.

A simple exercise that is often rich and revealing and can be used both in individual supervision or group supervision is to ask the supervisee to tell a story that illustrates a strength or virtue. As is true of almost everything in both therapy and supervision, the more specific and the more detailed the supervisee can make the story, the better. After the supervisee has told the story, the listener then reflects back the strengths or virtues revealed in the story. This typically makes it easier for the storyteller to "own" the strengths because the storyteller is simply hearing reflected back strengths that have already been revealed.

Interestingly, my (John Wade) informal observations suggest that a large percentage of stories of strengths involve hardship, difficulty, and adversity. Strengths often seem to emerge through the process of struggle, a very important message to illuminate when the supervisee is feeling unsure or inadequate. Very frequently, the listener identifies strengths the storyteller had not thought of as possessing. However, since the listener is merely labeling the characteristics the storyteller described, these additional strengths are more easily acknowledged and embraced.

Instruments for Identifying Strengths

In addition to being attentive to indications and clues from our supervisees as to their strengths, there also are empirically supported formal assessments that can be very useful in both identifying strengths and also providing a common understanding and language to discuss them. Two of the most widely used instruments are described in this section.

The Values Inventory of Strengths (VIA-IS; Peterson and Seligman, 2004) is a 240-item instrument that measures 24 character strengths (10 items for each strength) and can be completed in about 30 minutes. It is available free of charge online at www.positivepsychology.org and also as a paper-and-pencil measure. The VIA-IS was intended to serve as the antithesis to the Diagnostic and Statistical Manual for Mental Disorders (DSM) and to provide a common language for describing human strengths. After reviewing dozens of inventories of virtues and strengths, Peterson and Seligman arrived at a list of 24 strengths, organized under six overarching virtues (wisdom and knowledge, courage, humanity, justice, temperance, and transcendence) thought to "emerge consensually across cultures and throughout time" (Peterson and Seligman, p. 29). In order to leave no stone unturned as they and their associates explored character strengths for their classification, not only did they examine the literature in such fields as psychiatry and philosophy, they also looked at messages of character strengths in Harry Potter books, the profiles of Pokeman characters, and even the Klingon Code from the *Star Trek* television show (Peterson, 2006).

The other major strengths inventory—which is designed to more readily translate to organizational setting than the VIA-IS (and is consequently frequently used in business and academic settings)—is the Clifton Strengths Finder (Buckingham & Clifton, 2000). It is now in its second rendition, the Clifton Strengths Finder 2.0 (CSF 2.0; Asplund, Lopez, Hodges, and Harter, 2007; Rath, 2007). The Clifton Strengths Finder 2.0 is a 180-item instrument yielding information and ranking on 34 strengths, or "talent themes," that are common in society and predictive of educational and vocational success. The top five strengths are revealed to the respondent, along with suggestions for putting these themes into action and a "strength-based action plan" translating the talents into both short- and long-term goals. It is available online for a fee at www.strengthsfinder.com.

Strengths Applications

Using our strengths has been found to have a multitude of benefits. Operating from our strengths has been found to be an important predictor of well-being and lead to less stress and increased positive affect, vitality, and self-esteem at 3-month and 6-month follow-ups (Wood, Linley, Matlby, Kashdan, & Hurling, 2011). Using our strengths in a new way was found to increase happiness and decrease depression for 6 months (Gander, Proyer, Ruch, and Wyss, 2012). A qualitative study examining the use of VIA strengths by women in the workplace discovered that the use of strength led to a "virtuous circle" in which the use of strengths helped them overcome obstacles that had impeded their use of strengths (Elston & Boniwell, 2011).

Lopez and Edwards (2008, pp. 96–97) summarized that intentionally integrating the wise application of strengths with goals and motivation has been found to enhance the ability to reach goals. The following description more fully details the three main components necessary to reach goals: (1) setting goals, (2) using multiple strengths, and (3) increasing motivation.

Setting goals

- Set goals that will be difficult but achievable (think about stretching goals or operating in the learning zone, not the comfort zone or the panic zone).

- Be specific about your goals and define them operationally in tangible and measurable terms.

- Take time in setting your goals and allow yourself to adjust your goals once you have experiences to guide you.

Use multiple strengths

- Think about the steps involved in reaching your goal.

- Think about the different strengths that you can use to reach your goal.

- In your mind, rehearse what you will need to do during the pursuit of your goal to be successful in reaching it. Also, anticipate problems that you might have in reaching your goal and the personal strengths you can use to overcome the problems.

Motivation

- Think about the process of reaching your goal as a journey. Anticipating roadblocks that you might face can be helpful in reminding you that when you start to feel discouraged, it is a signal that you must increase your motivation and work harder.

- As you work toward your goal, remind yourself of how far you have come and think positively about progress toward the goal. Think about similar challenging situations where you were able to overcome the situation. (Lopez & Edwards, 2008, pp. 96–97).

Although it is important to identify and build upon strengths, for strengths to be effectively applied also involves discernment and wise application. Flexibility has often been regarded as the cornerstone of mental health. It is critically important to be able to adapt both the strengths used and the manner in which strengths are applied to fit the needs and expectations of a situation. Schwartz and Sharpe (2006) suggest that practical wisdom is necessary to discern when it is best to use your strengths and state that relevance, conflict, and specificity must be considered. One needs to consider what bearing a strength might or might not have on a situation, how different strengths may be in conflict with one another, and how they might be tailored to the specific situation at hand. Linley and Harrington (2006a) suggest that just as personality can fluctuate according to the demands of the situation but is stable and consistent over time, so, too strengths might also fluctuate according to situational demands but largely remain consistent (p. 88).

Too much (overuse) and too little (underuse) of character strengths has been shown to have a negative impact on well-being (e.g., Grant and Schwartz, 2011) and goal achievement. When I (John Wade) give workshops on strengths, I'll often use the adaptability we naturally employ as we communicate to illustrate this principle. For example, we typically talk a certain way at work, a slightly different way with our friends, another way still in the locker room, and a decidedly different way at church. For most of us, if we were to talk the same way in church as we do in the locker room it would cause problems, or at the very least, embarrassment. The same principle operates with the application of strengths—although operating from strengths is generally good, effective application typically involves nuance, flexibility, and awareness of the context and situation.

Even though using our strengths is typically advantageous, more is not always better. For instance, the overuse of the strength of leadership or relying upon it in the wrong situations will result in being regarded as bossy or controlling. Curiosity carried too far or used unwisely can morph into intrusiveness. If we overly rely upon empathy in our role as supervisors, the supervision process can unintentionally degrade into a one-trick-pony show, neglecting many important facets of supervision such as teaching, challenging, and probing. Although success will most likely come from recognizing and building upon strengths, it is also important for both supervisors and supervisees to recognize potential problems that using strengths may cause.

Most of us, however, are more likely to be prone to not recognizing and consequently underusing our strengths. This can sometimes be a consequence of the fact that our strengths come more easily and naturally for us, which can result in the lack of awareness of certain strengths precisely because they are less effort. Also, regardless of our cultural background, most people are taught not to be boastful, and consequently focusing on our strengths can feel uncomfortable.

In addition to the importance of judiciously using strengths, Wright and Lopez (2002) advocate for a balanced focus on both strengths and weaknesses, as well as the recognition of environmental resources and stressors. Practitioners (and supervisors) must be committed to examining all four areas, which serves to counterbalance the tendency to focus on pathology or weaknesses. Wright and Lopez (2002) urge practitioners (and presumably supervisors) to "remain on guard lest positives in the person and situation remain overlooked because of the intrusion of the fundamental negative bias and environmental neglect" (p. 38).

How we use and approach strengths is very dependent upon cultural factors. Heine (2012) reflected upon his two years of experience as a Canadian teaching English at a junior high school in rural Japan. He noted that the

Japanese teachers tended to motivate their students by telling them how difficult things would be and how poor their skills were, which seemed to inspire greater effort. Heine stated that he was often chastised for praising his students too much, which was regarded as a motivation killer (pp. 241–242). It appears that Westerners might be more culturally prone to naturally gravitate toward a strength orientation. Heine (2012) described that people with a *prevention orientation* focus their efforts on things they don't do well because correcting shortcomings will enable them to avoid failure. In contrast, people with a *promotion orientation* are concerned with advancement and promotion and focus their efforts on things they already do well because these areas provide more opportunities for success. Canadians, operating from a promotion orientation, have been found to persist longer on tasks after experiencing success, whereas Japanese, operating from a prevention orientation, persist longer at tasks after performing poorly, attempting to improve themselves in areas of weakness (pp. 252–254).

Niemiec (2013) describes a three-step model of strength development, termed the aware-explore-apply model. It was created for working with the VIA character strengths, but its principles seem to broadly apply to working with strengths in general. The three steps involve:

1. Aware: strength-spotting, combating strength blindness and cultivating strength awareness

2. Explore: exploring strength overuse, underuse, use across contexts, past use with problems and successes

3. Apply: taking action with goal setting, deploying and aligning strengths, and valuing strengths in others (Niemiec, 2013)

Knowledge of our strengths and tendencies as supervisors, combined with knowledge of the strengths and personality styles of our supervisees, can help guide the training process to be the most productive. Kitzrow (2002) provides an example of how knowledge of individual differences, as illustrated through the different Myers Briggs Type Indicator (MBTI) personality types, can guide and enhance clinical supervision. Her discussion uses the language and paradigm of the MBTI as one way that supervisors can tailor their supervision to best fit both the supervisor's and supervisee's natural strengths and characteristics. (For a detailed exploration, please refer to the article.)

There are also many useful books on the MBTI personality type and applications, such as *Please Understand Me* by Kiersey and Bates (1984). The personality types of introversion and extraversion will be used as examples here, as they are understandable even without familiarity or experience with the MBTI. This example, based on the MBTI, is used for the purposes of illustration, but even an informal basic understanding of the needs and personality styles of our supervisees can help us to tailor our supervision efforts.

Characteristics, Expectations, and Needs of Extraverted Supervisees

- They learn best through interaction and discussion. They may need help focusing their natural enthusiasm and curiosity and should be encouraged to slow down and engage in inner exploration and reflection.

- They approach new relationships with enthusiasm and are quick to open up. This applies to relationships with both supervisors and clients.

- They need and expect a high level of interaction and feedback in supervision.

- They tend to have a higher level of natural confidence and don't hesitate to take the initiative in new situations or to take risks. However, they may need help to slow down and reflect before plunging in and taking action.

Characteristics, Expectations, and Needs of Introverted Supervisees

- They learn best when allowed time for internal processing and reflection. May need help overcoming their natural reticence and should be encouraged to engage in interactive discussion and to express themselves in supervision.

- They approach new relationships without caution and need more time to feel comfortable and open up. This applies to relationships with both supervisors and clients.

- They often lack confidence in themselves and their abilities and hesitate to take the initiative in new situations or to take risks. They may need encouragement in new situations, to take action and appropriate risks, and to develop confidence.

Supervisory Style of the Extraverted Supervisor

- Active approach
- Open, expressive, and energetic
- Helps supervisees explore a broad range of interests and issues
- Processes information and solves problems externally through interaction and discussion

Supervision Skills to Work On

- Help supervisees explore issues and cases in depth
- Slow down and allow time for reflection and processing
- Talk less and listen more

Supervisory Style of the Introverted Supervisor

- Reflective approach
- Skilled at one-to-one communication

- Allows supervisees time to process information internally

- Helps supervisees explore issues and cases in depth

Supervision Skills to Work On

- Help supervisees focus on action as well as reflection

- Talk more and make more effort to be more open and expressive (pp. 142–144)

Although some of these points are fairly obvious, it is often easy to overlook and disregard the "obvious" unless we are consciously being mindful. Another example is working with supervisees who fall into the "sensing" as opposed to "feeling" category of the MBTI personality types. "Sensors" tend to focus more on practical details and are less drawn to "intuitive" information, such as patterns and more abstract meaning. Sensing supervisees tend to learn best through practical, step-by-step approaches. They expect and need clear, detailed information and want to discuss their cases in detail. They are most comfortable with specific problems that can be addressed with specific techniques but might need encouragement to work with problems and solutions that are less clearly defined (p. 144).

Questions to Consider:

- What strengths does your supervisee need to develop more and how can you help with that development?

- What strengths would you like to develop further?

- Consider choosing one strength to focus on and create a plan (specific steps) to bolster it.

- Who are your role models? What strengths do they exemplify? What is one specific behavior you could try to emulate?

- What have you been struggling with in your clinical work recently? How might you apply a specific strength to more effectively deal with it?

Using Strengths to Address Weaknesses

I can almost hear the anxiety radiating from some supervisors as you have been reading this chapter so far, especially those working with supervisees whose very real weaknesses have made themselves all too apparent. All this focus on strengths is well and good—but what about weaknesses?! One of the common misconceptions about positive psychology is that weaknesses should be ignored. Nothing is further from the truth. As any clinician or supervisor with any experience knows, weaknesses can cause very real problems. Many strength researchers (e.g.,

Buckingham, 2010) suggest partnering with others who are strong in those areas where you are weak and delegating to operate as much as possible from within your strength zone. While this is certainly wonderful advice, it works much more easily within a group or team setting than a primarily individual activity such as psychotherapy. However, the individual's strengths can be used to help manage personal weaknesses. *A strength-based approach to supervision isn't about ignoring weaknesses; instead, it is about using strengths to address weaknesses.*

Addressing weaknesses:

- Use your strengths to address weaknesses.
- Remember how you have worked with or overcome problem areas in the past.
- Think of specific ways these abilities can be applied to the present situation.

Conclusion

Having a focus on strengths and an orientation toward eliciting the abilities and wisdom of our supervisees does not at all mean that we should have low expectations or be "soft." Joanne Lipman (2013) notes that often the most successful in their field can trace the influences of their success to teachers and coaches who had high expectations and who would challenge them and consequently pull out their highest levels of performance. High expectations send a powerful and very positive message to those we supervise, namely, that we have faith in their abilities.

Questions to Consider

- Am I overly focusing on my supervisee's strengths that have quickly emerged? Are there some "glimpses" of strengths to be attentive to and try to find ways to amplify?
- Which of my strengths as a supervisor would I like to intentionally develop further? What are the first steps I need to take to do so?
- Is the agency providing facilitative conditions for strengths to develop for both supervisees and staff? Are there small changes that could make the setting even more conducive to a flourishing of strengths in both parties?

Recommended Readings

Books

Buckingham, M., & Clifton, D. O. (2000). *Now discover your strengths*. New York: Free Press.

Buckingham M. (2010). *Go put your strengths to work*. New York: Simon and Schuster.

Clifton, D. O., & Anderson, E. (2002). *Strengths quest: Discover and develop your strengths in academics, career, and beyond*. New York: Gallup Press.

Compton, W. C., & Hoffman, E. (2013). *Positive Psychology: The science of happiness and flourishing* (2nd ed.). Belmont, CA: Cengage Learning.

Jones-Smith, E. (2014). *Strengths-based therapy: Connecting theory, practice, and skills*. Los Angeles, CA: Sage Publications, Inc.

Saleebey, D. (1992). *The strengths perspective in social work practice*. New York: Longman Publishing Group.

Articles and Book Chapters

Baumeister, R. F., Bratslavsky, E., Finkenauer, C., & Vohs, K. D. (2001). Bad is stronger than good. *Review of General Psychology, 5*, 323–370.

Linley, P. A., & Harrington, S. (2006a). Playing to your strengths. *Psychologist, 19*(2), 86–89.

Linley, P. A., & Harrington, S. (2006b). Strengths-coaching: A potential-guided approach to coaching psychology. *International Coaching Psychology Review, 1,* 37–46.

Linley, P. A., Nielsen, K. M., Gillett, R., & Biswas-Diener, R. (2010). Using signature strengths in pursuit of goals: Effects on goal progress, need satisfaction, and well-being, and implications for coaching psychologists. *International Coaching Psychology Review, 5*(1), 6–15.

Lopez, S. J., & Edwards, L. M. (2008). The interface of counseling psychology and positive psychology: Assessing and promoting strengths. *Handbook of counseling psychology*, 86–99.

Lopez, S. J., Magyar-Moe, J. L., Petersen, S. E., Ryder, J. A., Krieshok, T. S., O'Byrne, K. K., et al. (2006). Counseling psychology's focus on positive aspects of human functioning. *The Counseling Psychologist, 34*, 205–227.

Wood, A. M., Linley, P. A., Matlby, J., Kashdan, T. B., & Hurling, R. (2011). Using personal and psychological strengths leads to increases in well-being over time: A longitudinal study and the development of the strengths use questionnaire. *Personality and Individual Differences, 50*, 15–19.

References

Adler, A. (1927). Understanding human nature.

Allport, G. (1937). *Personality: A psychological interpretation*. New York: Holt.

American Psychiatric Association. (2013). *Diagnostic and statistical manual of mental disorders* (5th ed.). Washington, DC: Author.

Asplund, J., Lopez, S. J., Hodges, T., & Harter, J. (2007). *The Clifton StrengthsFinder® 2.0 technical report: Development and validation.* Princeton, NJ: The Gallup Organization.

Baumeister, R. F., Bratslavsky, E., Finkenauer, C., & Vohs, K. D. (2001). Bad is stronger than good. *Review of General Psychology, 5,* 323–370.

Biswas-Diener, R., & Dean, B. (2007). *Positive psychology coaching: Putting the science of happiness to work for your clients.* Hoboken, NJ: John Wiley & Sons.

Brown, B. (2010). *The power of vulnerability.* Retrieved from http://www.ted.com/talks/brene_brown_on_vulnerability.html

Buckingham, M. (2010). *Go put your strengths to work.* New York: Simon and Schuster.

Buckingham, M., & Clifton, D. O. (2000). *Now discover your strengths.* New York: Free Press.

Compton, W. C., & Hoffman, E. (2013). *Positive psychology: The science of Happiness and Flourishing* (2nd ed.). Belmont, CA: Cengage Learning.

Davies, D. (2004). *Child development: A practitioner's guide* (2nd ed.). New York: Guilford Press.

Elston, F., & Boniwell, I. (2011). A grounded theory study of the value derived by women in financial services through a coaching intervention to help them identify their strengths and practice using them in the workplace. *International Coaching Psychology Review, 6,* 16–32.

Gander, F., Proyer, R. T., Ruch, W., & Wyss, T. (2012). The good character at work: An initial study on the contribution of character strengths in identifying healthy and unhealthy work-related behavior and experience patterns. *International Archives of Occupational and Environmental Health, 85*(8), 895–904.

Gelso, C. J., & Fretz, B. R. (1992). *Counseling psychology.* San Diego, CA: Harcourt Brace Jovanovich.

Gottman, J. (1994). *Why marriages succeed or fail.* New York: Simon & Schuster.

Grant, A. M., & Schwartz, B. (2011). Too much of a good thing: The challenge and opportunity of the inverted u. *Perspectives on Psychological Science, 6,* 61–76.

Graybeal, C. (2001). Strengths-based social work assessment: Transforming the dominant paradigm. *Families in Society, 82,* 223–242.

Hebb, D.O. (1949). *The organization of behavior.* New York: John Wiley & Sons.

Heine, S. J. (2012). *Cultural psychology* (2nd ed.). New York: WW Norton.

Jones-Smith, E. (2014). *Strengths-based therapy: Connecting theory, practice, and skills.* Los Angeles, CA: Sage Publications, Inc.

Jordaan, J. E., Myers, R. A., Layton, W. C., & Morgan, H. H. (1968). *The counseling psychologist.* Washington, DC: American Psychological Association.

Kiersey, D., & Bates, M. (1984). *Please understand me.* Del Mar, CA: Prometheus Nemesis Book Company.

Kitzrow, M. A. (2002). Applications of psychological type in clinical supervision. *The Clinical Supervisor, 20*(2), 133–146.

Linley, P. A., & Harrington, S. (2006a). Playing to your strengths. *Psychologist*, *19*(2), 86–89.

Linley, P. A., & Harrington, S. (2006b). Strengths-coaching: A potential-guided approach to coaching psychology. *International Coaching Psychology Review*, *1*, 37–46.

Lipman, J. 2013, September 27). Why tough teachers get good results. Wall Street Journal. Retrieved from http://www.online.wsj.com/news/articles/

Lopez, S. J., & Edwards, L. M. (2008). The interface of counseling psychology and positive psychology: Assessing and promoting strengths. *Handbook of Counseling Psychology* (4th ed.), 86–99.

Lopez, S. J., Magyar-Moe, J. L., Petersen, S. E., Ryder, J. A., Krieshok, T. S., O'Byrne, et al. (2006). Counseling psychology's focus on positive aspects of human functioning. *The Counseling Psychologist*, *34*, 205–227.

Maslow, A. (1954). *Motivation and personality.* New York: Harper & Row.

Niemiec, R. M. (2013). VIA character strengths: Research and practice (The first 10 years). In H. H. Knoop & A. Delle Fave (Eds.), *Well-being and cultures: Perspectives on positive psychology* (pp. 11–30). New York: Springer.

Peterson, C. (2006). *A primer in positive psychology.* New York: Oxford University Press.

Peterson, C., & Seligman, M. E. P. (2004). *Character strengths and virtues: A handbook and classification.* New York: Oxford University Press.

Rath, T. (2007). *Strengths Finder 2.0.* New York: Gallup Press.

Rogers, C. (1961). *On becoming a person.* Boston, MA: Houghton Mifflin.

Schwartz, B., & Sharpe, K.E. (2006). Practical wisdom: Aristotle meets positive psychology. *Journal of Happiness Studies, 7,* 377–395.

Saleebey, D. (1992). *The strengths perspective in social work practice.* New York: Longman.

Seligman, M. E. (2002). *Authentic happiness: Using the new positive psychology to realize your potential for lasting fulfillment.* New York: Simon and Schuster.

Snyder, C.R. (2000). *Handbook of hope.* San Diego, CA: Academic Press.

Terman, L. M., Buttenweiser, P., Ferguson, L. W., Johnson, W. B., & Wilson, D. P. (1938). *Psychological factors in marital happiness.* New York: McGraw Hill.

Terman, L. M., & Oden, M.H. (1947). *Genetic studies of genius . . . : The gifted child grows up; twenty-five years' follow-up of a superior group* (Vol. 4. Stanford, CA) University Press.

Thompson, A. S., & Super, D. E. (Eds.). (1964). *The professional preparation of counseling psychologists: Report of the 1964 Greyston Conference.* New York NY: Bureau of Publications, Teachers College, Columbia University: New York.

Weick, A., Rapp, C., Sullivan, W. P., & Kisthardt, W. (1989). A strengths perspective for social work practice. *Social Work, 34*(4), 350–354.

Wood, A. M., Linley, P. A., Matlby, J., Kashdan, T. B., & Hurling, R. (2011). Using personal and psychological strengths leads to increases in well-being over time: A longitudinal study and the development of the strengths use questionnaire. *Personality and Individual Differences, 50*, 15–19.

Wright, B.A., & Lopez, S.J. (2002). Widening the diagnostic focus: A case for including human strengths and environmental resources. In C.R. Snyder & S. J. Lopez (Eds.), *The handbook of positive psychology* (pp. 26–44). New York: Oxford University Press.

5

Evaluation and Feedback

"Everything that can be counted does not necessarily count; everything that counts cannot necessarily be counted."

—Albert Einstein

"Feedback is the breakfast of champions."

—Ken Blanchard

Imagine trying to learn archery without being able to see if you have hit the target. To say the least, it would be very difficult. Saptya, Riemer, and Bickman (2005) use this analogy to describe the importance of feedback to the learning process. Feedback is central to learning. Without feedback, mistakes can go uncorrected, bad habits can develop, positive behaviors might be dropped, and inaccurate assumptions about the quality of performance might be made (Westberg and Jason, 1993). Supervisees and students also seem to recognize the importance of feedback, ranking receiving supervisor observation and feedback as the most effective factor contributing to their skill development (Smith, 1984).

The importance of feedback to learning and performance has long been recognized. For example, in 1912, the pioneering educational researcher Edward Thorndike (cited in Westberg & Jason, 1993) had three groups of subjects draw lines of specific lengths. The group who received no feedback did not improve with practice; the group who received incomplete feedback improved slowly and inconsistently; but the group who received specific and thorough feedback was able to draw lines of precise lengths after only a few tries. Feedback is foundational for growth and learning, and has been identified by many supervisees as preferable to other supervisory methods, such as didactic instruction (Westberg & Jason, 1993). Referring back to the archery example, if we wanted to improve our archery skills, it's a good bet that most of us would hire an archery coach who would give us individualized attention and feedback, versus choosing an archery lecturer, no matter how good the lecturer was.

Regardless of the amount of training and experience providing supervision, most supervisors are more comfortable with providing feedback than evaluation. Cormier and Bernard (1982) state that evaluation "is typically a weak suit for most supervisors" (p. 490). Feedback and evaluation are related but serve different functions. The focus of feedback is to provide specific information on the supervisees' performance to assist them in learning clinical skills and judgment. Using the archery example again, the coach provides feedback (e.g., observations and comments regarding technique and execution) to help the student more accurately hit the target. However, there's no judgment regarding accuracy, and the main goal is simply improvement. Typically, therapists as supervisors are fairly comfortable in this role, since as clinicians, we are used to providing clients feedback. Bernard and Goodyear (2004) note that this is similar to psychotherapy, in which the individual's own progress is the measuring stick, not an external reference.

Evaluation differs from feedback because it adds the dimension of setting specific criteria that must be met. The measuring stick is not simply improving one's abilities with the self used as the referent but measuring progress against external criteria. For the purposes of evaluation, meeting externally defined criteria (e.g., agency expectations, licensure requirements, etc.) is the standard. To progress from beginning to intermediate archery, a student must demonstrate a certain level of proficiency by obtaining a minimum score during target practice. The same principle operates with the supervision of supervisees learning clinical skills. Institutions and training centers expect a certain level of competency before graduating supervisees to the next level. Ultimately, licensing agencies and accrediting boards expect supervisors and agencies to protect the public by monitoring progress and verifying the competence of those supervisees being passed to the next level by verifying that certain standards have been met.

While most mental health professionals are at least somewhat comfortable providing feedback, the pressure and responsibility inherent in passing judgment and making evaluation can be much more anxiety producing. As will be further discussed, if feedback is given consistently throughout the supervisory process, the evaluative function should naturally flow as a result of the foundation that has already been laid. Although providing evaluation can raise the anxiety of both supervisee and supervisor, especially if not done well, it is helpful to view feedback and evaluation as simply one of many components of effective supervision. In fact, effective evaluation practices appear to be positively associated with and predictive of a stronger working alliance (Lerhmann-Waterman & Ladany, 2001).

Although different from therapy in both purpose and form, supervision and therapy do share some key components, such as the importance of creating a strong working alliance based on safety, respect, and understanding. Within the context of therapy, the exploration of both strengths and weaknesses can be very therapeutic and facilitate change and growth, assuming that the proper conditions have been set. The same principle applies to supervision. Following from the establishment of a strong working alliance, raising awareness of both strengths and areas for growth can serve as the springboard for more targeted growth and development.

This chapter examines the theoretical underpinnings of goal setting and feedback, as well as criteria and measures for evaluation. Effective methods for providing feedback are explored in detail. If goal setting, providing feedback, and selecting criteria and measures for evaluation are each done carefully and thoughtfully, evaluation should flow seamlessly as a result.

Goals

Setting goals and providing feedback and evaluation are inherently connected. As Watkins (1997) noted reviewing the psychotherapy supervision literature, evaluation appears to consist of two primary activities: goal setting and feedback. Goals, whether identified by the supervisor or more hopefully, mutually agreed upon through a process of collaborative input between the supervisor and supervisee, serve as both the foundation and as the markers of evaluation. Evaluation informs supervisees about their progress, helps raise awareness of strengths and weaknesses, and is critical to the process of monitoring client care. Strength-based supervision depends upon incorporating best practices for providing evaluation and feedback, with the expectation that identifying and providing a roadmap to hit important targets is much more likely to help the supervisee attain competency and accuracy than an overemphasis on the pitfalls to be avoided. Goal setting from a strength-based perspective blends many important positive psychology constructs with fundamental supervision tasks and principles, which will be detailed in this section.

Goal-Setting Theory

Because goal setting is key to the foundation of feedback and evaluation, an overview of goal-setting theory will be given. Goal setting is intimately connected to both feedback and performance. Locke and Latham (2002) summarized 35 years of multidisciplinary empirical research on goal-setting theory and suggest that goals affect performance through four primary mechanisms:

1. Goals direct attention and effort toward goal-relevant activities and away from goal-irrelevant activities. We tend to give attention to activities and behaviors that have been identified through goals. For example, research investigating the impact of goals on performance discovered the surprising finding that people given feedback about multiple aspects of their performance on an automobile driving task improved their performance only on the dimensions for which they had set goals (Locke & Bryan, 1969). Goals help to focus attention and to guide learning.

2. Goals have an energizing function, and higher goals tend to lead to greater effort than lower goals.

3. Goals affect persistence, and challenging or "hard" goals tend to prolong effort.

4. Goals affect action indirectly by leading to the arousal, discovery, or use of task-relevant knowledge and strategies.

Locke and Latham (2002) also identified several principles and practical applications that should serve as a foundation as we collaboratively construct supervision goals with our supervisees:

- The highest levels of effort occurs when the task is moderately difficult; the lowest levels of effort occur when the task is either very easy or very hard. Ideally, the task is challenging but achievable with work and diligence.

- Goal specificity is important to effective goal setting and helps to reduce ambiguity, which can be the great enemy of effort and progress. As Heath and Heath (2010) observe, most supervisees have the motivation and willingness to work hard and challenge themselves as long as the "road map" is clear.

- When presented with a goal, people automatically apply the knowledge and skills they already have that are relevant to the situation. If the path to the goal is not a matter of simply using automatic skills, people draw from the range of skills they have used previously in related contexts and apply them to the present situation.

- For new tasks, people engage in deliberate planning to develop strategies that will enable them to attain their goals.

- People with high self-efficacy are more likely to develop effective task strategies.

- Assuming the person has been trained in effective strategies, those with high performance goals are more likely to use those strategies, leading to improved performance.

- Not surprisingly, simply urging people to do their best typically is less helpful than setting specific, increasingly challenging goals to stepwise lead to higher performance.

- However, when confronted with a complex task, urging people to do their best sometimes leads to better strategies than setting a specific, difficult performance goal. "This is because a performance goal can make people so anxious to succeed that they scramble to discover strategies in an unsystematic way and fail to learn what is effective. This can create evaluative pressure and performance anxiety. The antidote is to set specific, challenging learning goals, such as to discover a certain number of strategies to master the task" (p. 707).

Locke and Latham's (2002) analysis indicates that the concept of self-efficacy is important in goal setting. For self-defined goals, (1) people with high self-efficacy set higher goals, (2) are more committed to their goals, (3) find and use better strategies to attain their goals, and (4) respond more positively to negative feedback than people with low self-efficacy. This seems to underscore the importance of fostering the development of supervisee self-efficacy as integral to the supervision process, especially as supervisees mature and develop greater autonomy and begin to rely increasingly on self-defined goals. This also points to the benefit of establishing goals in a collaborative manner whenever possible, and striving to ensure "buy-in" and ownership from supervisees of goals that must be extrinsically set.

Higher self-efficacy is also positively correlated with enhanced goal commitment. Drawing from the research of Bandura (1997) and White and Locke (2000) on self-efficacy, Locke and Latham (2002) advise that leaders or supervisors can increase supervisee self-efficacy: (1) by ensuring adequate training that increases mastery by providing success experiences; (2) by role modeling or finding models with whom the supervisee can identify, and (3) through persuasive communication that expresses confidence that the person can attain the goal. Each of these will be described more fully.

Ensuring Adequate Training That Increases Mastery by Providing Success Experiences

Success experiences, in which true success is experienced versus just being told that one has done a good job, lead to increased self-efficacy (Bandura, 1997). It is important for supervisors to create opportunities for early success to energize motivation and instill hope and confidence. Heath and Heath (2010) note that forward progress and momentum is more likely to occur if it seems like the growth process has already started, a process they term "shrinking the change." (Piano bar musicians who put "seed money" in the tip jar know this principle well.) Heath and Heath also give the example that people are much more likely to use a punch card for a free sandwich if they are given one or two free punches than if they have to start with a blank card, even if the total number of sandwiches needed to be purchased to earn a free one is the same.

Applying this concept to supervision, a supervisor could ask the supervisee where the supervisee is on a scale of 1 to 10 in the development of a particular skill. If the supervisee responds with a 2 or 3, the needed progress is likely to feel rather daunting. However, imagine the difference if the supervisor responds with, "Great, you're already 20 or 30% of the way there!" The supervisor is focusing on the mastery that is already beginning and putting a couple of stamps on the supervisee's punch card.

Role-Modeling or Finding Models with Whom the Supervisee Can Identify

Mahrer and Boulet (1997) assert that the norm in clinical training is for seasoned professionals to listen to at least several hours of video recording of therapy sessions, but it seems to be the exception. They state that, "There is probably no other profession whose trainees are to learn their craft without seeing, studying, and learning from the actual work of exemplars. Students in other fields usually have rich opportunities to learn from studying the work of fine cellists, surgeons, plumbers, ballerinas, dentists, electricians, architects, and lawyers. Imagine a violinist who had never heard a violinist performing; this is the model we proudly follow and aggressively defend. What a pity. Learning how to do psychotherapy could and should include the careful study of the work of fine practitioners" (p. 179). No literature was located to identify reasons why clinical training so rarely involves supervisees observing the clinical sessions of more experienced or expert clinicians, but hopefully the identification of role modeling as an important component of training will lead more programs to adopt the practice.

Through Persuasive Communication That Expresses Confidence That the Person Can Attain the Goal

Persuasive communication can occur by giving information about strategies that facilitate goal attainment and by communicating inspiring messages and providing cognitive stimulation. Ken Blanchard and Spencer Johnson, authors of the *One-Minute Manager,* offer a very practical and easy way to do this, simply advising supervisors to catch their employees doing something right and to acknowledge them for it (1983, p. 44).

For goals to be effective, people need not only ongoing feedback, but also *summary feedback* (evaluation) that reveals progress in relation to their goals. Clinicians, like other professionals, tend to be self-directed in their learning (Riemer, Rosof-Williams, & Bickman, 2005). Given accurate feedback, the awareness of discrepancy between the desired outcome and the current state will prompt supervisees to strive and problem solve to narrow the gap. When people find they are below their target, they typically increase their effort or try a new strategy, assuming they are committed to the goal and improvement is believed to be achievable (Saptya et al., 2005).

Strength-Based Goal Setting

Most models of psychotherapy begin with carefully listening to the needs of the client and developing an individualized treatment plan. This is done with varying degrees of collaboration with the client depending upon the theoretical orientation, and with varying degrees of detail depending upon the approach. Similarly, just as clients have individualized treatment plans, therapists in training also need a plan to promote their skill development. Ideally, these written goals should include the purpose, goals, and objectives of supervision, and specify timelines for change (Center for Substance Abuse Treatment, 2009). Cocreating and tailoring individual goals for each supervisee reflect what Snyder and Lopez (2007) refer to as the "positive-schooling approach to education," where "teachers develop tailored goals for each student to engender learning, and then work with him or her to develop the plans and motivation to reach their goals" (p. 384).

Appreciative Inquiry

Appreciative Inquiry (AI) is a model that works well within a strength-based approach to supervision to collaboratively create supervisee goals. Appreciative Inquiry (e.g., Cooperrider & Srivastva, 1987; Cooperrider & Whitney, 1999) arose as a model to facilitate change in organizations. AI is grounded in the principles of appreciating the strengths already present in an organization or individual and the intentional use of questions as a method to identify and illuminate and build upon the positives. Many of AIs' guiding philosophies and techniques can be recognized as a blending of positive psychology and solution focused therapy. Bloom, Hutson, and He (2008) have expanded the traditional AI model, extending the four-stage AI model to a six-stage process, adding an extra stage at the beginning and end. The aspirational nature of the early stages of the model is combined with the practicality and concreteness of the later stages. Their model, slightly adapted to more accurately reflect the needs and process of supervision, is as follows:

1. *Disarming stage*—create a safe, welcoming environment. This should be a given for anyone serving as a supervisor in a mental health profession, applying the relationship-building skills learned for clinical work to creating a trusting and secure supervisory alliance. Possible discussion prompts for the disarming stage could include:

   - "I'm really glad you're here. Your references talked about (name two to three specific, positive qualities). These attributes should be very helpful in your work here."
   - "What strengths would you like to further develop during your training?"
   - "Most people experience some anxiety when they start a new program. I'm curious about what you might be feeling apprehensive about?"

2. *Discovery stage*—use positive, open-ended questions to elicit the supervisee's preferences, passions, and strengths. Possible questions to ask in the discovery stage include:

   - "Describe three life events that have made you into the person you are today."
   - "Since starting in the program, what is something that you have accomplished and are proud of?"

- "What therapists are your role models? Why? What qualities do you hope to emulate?" (Habley & Bloom, 2007)

During the discovery stage, the supervisor encourages the supervisee to be open to possibilities—and similar to the expansive intention of narrative therapy—communicates that there are multiple possibilities, which serves to both relieve the pressure from having to find the one "correct answer" and encourage deeper self-inquiry.

3. *Dream stage*—the supervisor collaborates with the supervisee to formulate a vision of what the supervisee might become through the learning process and then assists in developing goals. During this stage, the focus is more on aspirations and ideals; the next stage will focus on developing concrete strategies to begin to make the ideal possible and achievable. The dream stage builds upon the exploration of the discovery stage and creates images of possibilities, with the understanding that the more detailed the image, the more powerful it will be. Bandura (1997) also notes the importance of ownership, observing that when people select their own goals, they are likely to have greater self-involvement in achieving them. Possible questions to ask include:

- "What is the inspiration for your clinical work?"
- "Thinking about your best therapy so far (or best helping experiences if this is the supervisee's first clinical experience), what do you want to carry forward into the future and expand upon?"
- "What do your mentor or advisor want for you as a developing therapist?"

4. *Design stage*—this is when reality and practicality meet. Practical steps are formulated to begin to implement the previously identified aspirations and goals. During the design stage, the supervisor questions and collaborates with the supervisee to devise concrete, incremental, and achievable goals. Possible questions to ask include:

- "What can you do in the next week to move one step closer to at least one of your goals?"
- "What is a small step you can take?"
- "Let's brainstorm about what you will need to do to accomplish these goals and objectives."
- "What is the first step you need to take to make progress toward your goal?"

5. *Deliver stage* (This stage is also commonly referred to as the "destiny" stage in the AI literature)—the supervisee follows through on the plans. The supervisor offers constancy and support as the supervisee is learning—at

times fitfully—viewing it as part of the developmental learning process, and assists the supervisee in continuing to update and refine goals. Possible questions to ask include:

- "What will you do if you run into roadblocks?"
- "How have you successfully managed challenges previously in your professional or academic life?"
- "How will you track your progress?"

6. *Don't settle stage*—the supervisor challenges the supervisee to proactively raise the supervisee's internal bar of self-expectations. Successes are acknowledged and highlighted and serve as the incrementally rising foundation from which to attempt new challenges. Possible questions to ask include:
   - "You have done great so far, but what is one thing you can do even better?"
   - "If you were going to raise your own internal bar of expectations, what would that mean?"
   - "What would happen if I challenged you to become the best you that you could possibly become? What would you need to do differently?" (Bloom et al., 2008)

Feedback

Feedback Theory and Historical Review

Ende (1983) observed that the concept of *feedback,* which can be defined as information that an individual or system uses to make adjustments in reaching a goal, was first applied in a meaningful way by rocket engineers in the 1940s and has consequently been applied in many other fields. Norbert Weiner (1950), the father of cybernetics, extended the concept to the humanities and described that learning may occur if information proceeds backward from the performance and is able to change the pattern of the performance. Feedback occurs when insight is offered as to what the supervisee actually did, as well as the consequence of those actions. The dissonance highlighted between the intended outcome and the actual result provides the impetus for change and growth.

Kluger and DeNisi (1996) conducted a historical review of feedback theory, and noted that the general wisdom is that knowledge of performance increases learning and motivation. However, a more careful examination of the research evidence indicates that the effects of feedback interventions actually are quite variable. Depending upon the situation and the nature of the feedback, feedback does improve performance in the majority of instances; however, at times it has no impact, and in about one-third of the cases, feedback actually interferes with or decreases performance. Therefore, it is important to be familiar with both the general principles of feedback, as well as the exceptions and nuances.

The feedback intervention theory (FIT) helps summarize established feedback theory and explain the impact of feedback on performance and learning (Kluger & DeNisi, 1996). The basic assumptions of FIT are:

1. Behavior is regulated by comparisons of feedback with goals or standards (and identification of gaps between the two).

2. Attention is limited, and only those feedback-standard gaps that receive attention actively participate in behavior regulation.

3. Feedback interventions change the locus of attention and therefore affect behavior.

When a person detects or is made aware of a discrepancy between performance and goals, the individual is motivated to narrow the discrepancy. Feedback causes attention to be shifted, i.e., the person will be thinking about something else after the feedback. However, when feedback causes attention to be directed to the self, the risk increases that feedback will detract, rather than enhance, performance (Kluger & DeNisi, 1996, 1998). Feedback that directs attention to the self, especially on complex tasks, depletes cognitive resources needed for task performance and directs some of these resources to self-related goals, such as self-enhancement. Developmentally oriented feedback focusing on various performance dimensions that highlight weaknesses and strengths appear to be more effective (Marsh & Roche, 1997).

Feedback interventions can be categorized into two broad classifications: knowledge of results (KR) and knowledge of performance (KP) (Kluger & DeNisi, 1996). It is possible to know the results or outcome without knowing about the effectiveness of one's performance. For example, a clinician might know that a client's social anxiety symptoms are decreasing, but not know what aspects of the treatment approach or personal qualities as a therapist contributed to this outcome. Interestingly, knowledge of performance generally has little impact on an individual who is already performing at a high level and can actually decrease motivation if one is doing poorly. The effects of feedback grow more positive either as the task becomes more subjectively familiar or as it becomes more objectively simple (Kluger & DeNisi, 1998). Ironically, the people who probably need feedback the most benefit the least from typical feedback interventions.

Kluger and DeNisi (1996) summarize their meta-analysis on feedback intervention, noting that feedback appears to be psychologically reassuring and people generally like to obtain feedback and will even seek it when it does not affect their performance. However, they caution that although in certain situations feedback can produce a large, positive effect on performance, given the potential of feedback attracting attention to the self and away from the task, supervisors need to be aware to minimize the potential risks associated with it. It is helpful to relate feedback to previously established goals, which is more likely to direct attention to the task at hand and not to the self. Cues that foster high self-efficacy tend to direct attention to the task and cause people to invest more effort. Performance is increased to the degree that cognitive attention is focused on the task and the situation rather than on the self. This principle operates at the fullest expression during experiences of peak performance or "flow" (Czikszentimihalyi, 1990), which are characterized by a lack of awareness of one's emotional state and the experience of being totally engaged and immersed in the activity. Conversely, when cognitive energy is directed to the self, such as self-doubt or self-blame, it tends to interfere with the inhibition and concentration required for optimal performance.

Providing Effective Feedback

Not all feedback is equally effective, and the quality of feedback is influenced by the timing, nature, and appropriateness of the feedback given. This section details the characteristics associated with the best practices of effectively providing feedback. We examine and offer feedback from a variety of disciplines as suggestions on how to give feedback effectively.

The terms "feedback" and "evaluation" are often used interchangeably but are distinct in both form and function. Feedback presents information and is based on observations, not judgment (Ende, 1983), and helps the student remain on course in reaching a goal. Evaluation, on the other hand, is summative. It comes after the fact and presents a judgment (from the supervisor) about how well or poorly a supervisee has met a given goal in relation to established criteria or measured against the performance of peers. Ende suggests that feedback is neutral, spoken in nouns and verbs, whereas evaluation is expressed in normative statements, with adverbs and adjectives. For example, "I notice that you were reflecting more in your last session" is simple feedback, whereas, "You have shown a lot of improvement using reflection this semester" is evaluative. Ende, however, acknowledges that in practice, judgment is almost always perceived to be attached to feedback received by the recipient, and positive feedback is often appraised as "good" and negative feedback as "bad."

The following are guidelines for giving feedback based on compilations of standard practices from the fields of personnel management, group dynamics, and education (Ende, 1983):

- Supervisor and supervisee should work as allies with common goals

- Should be well-timed and expected

- Based on first-hand data

- Regulated in quantity and limited to behaviors that are remediable

- Phrased in descriptive, nonevaluative language

- Deals with specific performances, not generalizations

- Offers subjective data, labeled as such

- Deals with decisions and actions, rather than assumed intentions or interpretations

Ende also suggests:

- Feedback should deal with specifics, making use of real examples; generalizations are too broad to be helpful as feedback.

- Not only are data based on actions more accurate, but they allow for psychological distance, which is important if the feedback is negative or the supervisee is insecure.

- Subjective data are also very appropriate for feedback about clinical skills, because therapists are often judged by clients by these factors, but subjective data needs to be identified as such. Better to say that you saw the supervisee's hand shaking on the video than state that the supervisee looked nervous.

Ende (1983) asserts that personality traits should not be the topic of feedback unless they are manifested in behaviors that can be observed and reviewed. However, we would suggest that given the powerful impact that the clinician's personality can have on the therapeutic process, that personality factors are appropriate for feedback and exploration within the context of clinical supervision. It is important, though, for care to be taken to limit feedback only to behaviors that are remediable, within the supervisees' power to change.

Examining the literature addressing discussing clinical supervision of lawyer competence, Kreiling (1980) outlines factors that might increase supervisees' receptivity to feedback. Feedback must be perceived as relevant to what the supervisee is trying to accomplish to be considered useful. By focusing on learning dilemmas where there are no easy answers (there are many of these situations in clinical supervision), the supervisor can help assure that the feedback will be perceived as relevant. Feedback should be focused on information that is directly observable. Kreiling states that "more specific feedback does not demoralize because it describes behavior that both the actor and the observer can agree has occurred and about which some action to change can probably be taken" (p. 299). But focusing on observable behavior doesn't mean that the supervisor can't offer an opinion. Much like the clinicians' judgment is a valuable tool in the therapeutic process, the supervisors' judgment and expertise should be used as one of many important supervision assets. Kreiling also advises that any feedback given should be checked to ensure the supervisee understands what the supervisor is trying to convey, as poorly conveyed or misunderstood feedback can have destructive consequences in spite of the sender's good intentions. Asking the supervisee for an understanding of the feedback provides the opportunity to clear up any misconceptions, and conveys a message of care and concern.

Process of Giving Feedback

Supervisors are often concerned that feedback will have unintended consequences, namely, that critical feedback may result in more harm than good because the supervisee might be hurt by negative feedback, causing the supervisory relationship to be strained. These concerns and misconceptions often result in what the field of personnel management refers to as "vanishing feedback." Well-meaning supervisors can be so indirect and vague that nothing of value is transmitted and supervision is not helpful (Ende, 1983). However, without feedback, mistakes go uncorrected and good performance is not reinforced.

The lack of clear feedback can also result in unintended consequences, such as the supervisee attaching inappropriate importance to external cues to try to get a "read" on the supervisor's appraisal, so that a raised eyebrow is thought to imply substandard performance, or a pregnant pause prompts anxiety. Trying to avoid difficult feedback may be well-intentioned, but even constructive criticism is often welcome, as feedback "conveys an attitude of concern for the progress and development of the person in a real sense" (Ende, 1983, p. 779). Although supervisors are at times wary of providing direct or "constructive" feedback, supervisees tend to equate a collaborative supervisory approach with being provided sincere, direct feedback, and frequently desire more feedback than they receive (Lietz & Rounds, 2009, pp. 129–130).

Several variables impact the comfort and ease with which supervisors experience the process of giving feedback, including the receptivity of the supervisee to feedback in general, and the scope and topic of the feedback. Hoffman, Hill, Holmes, and Freitas (2005) examined the supervisor experience of the process of giving easy, difficult, or no feedback to supervisees. Supervisors found it easier to give feedback about clinical issues (e.g., clinical skills, client welfare) than to give feedback about issues such as the supervisory relationship, the supervisee's personality, or professional behavior. It was also easier to give clinical feedback in situations when there was a clear need for the feedback, and it fit within the domain of supervision (e.g., the feedback was clear-cut or situation specific, or the supervisor had observed the supervisee's behavior on videotape.) In these instances, the supervisor typically gave the feedback directly and processed it thoroughly with the supervisee. When the supervisor gave feedback based on something the supervisor clearly felt could improve or enhance the supervisee's clinical work, even if the supervisee did not like hearing the feedback at the time, supervisors generally reported that supervisees later told them that it helped their clinical work.

In contrast, supervisors felt it was more difficult to give feedback when the clinical issues were subjective (e.g., a difference of opinion about how therapy "should" be conducted). Nonclinical issues, such as personality and professional issues, were more likely to be viewed as subjective and more difficult than clinical issues to provide feedback on (Hoffman et al., 2005). Giving feedback about supervisee personality traits was also seen as difficult because supervisors wondered whether they had the right or responsibility to try to change things about the supervisee's personality. Feedback is more easily given to some supervisees than others, depending on the supervisory relationship and the openness of the supervisee. The strength of the supervisory–supervisee relationship seemed to play an important role in how the feedback was received, integrated, and used. Also, (1) the belief that the supervisor had something to offer (expertise), (2) the use of videotape or audiotape to demonstrate or support the feedback, and (3) appropriate timing eased the process of giving feedback.

Applying Motivational Interviewing Concepts to Feedback

In the abstract, it seems very reasonable and logical that supervisees would want their unsuccessful interventions and misguided efforts illuminated and examined and that they would be overflowing with gratitude for the learning opportunity. However, as human beings with our inherent sensitivities and defenses, we often have trouble hearing and accepting feedback even when it is constructively and diplomatically presented. Noticing that many of the factors associated with good supervision (e.g., empathy, respect, normalizing, encouraging the supervisee to take an active role, etc.) are inherent in *motivational interviewing* (e.g., Miller & Rollnick, 2002; Rollnick & Miller, 1995), Sobell, Manor, Sobell, and Dum (2008) created a motivational procedure for facilitating feedback during supervision. They posit that the "less desirable" supervisor qualities can be seen as representative of reasons why motivational interviewing was developed as an interviewing style designed to manage resistance.

Motivational Interviewing (MI) is defined as a directed, client-centered counseling style for eliciting behavior change by helping clients explore and resolve ambivalence (about both wanting to change and wanting to continue the behavior; Rollnick and Miller, 1995). It is a therapeutic style developed for discussing sensitive issues with clients who might be at varying levels of openness or receptivity and is frequently used for issues in which resistance is typical, such as substance abuse or smoking cessation (e.g., Miller, 2004; Miller & Rollnick, 2002). The primary goal of motivational interviewing is to minimize or decrease resistance and to enhance motivation to change the target behavior. This would certainly seem to transfer well to supervision, in which supervisees, especially when beginning or unsure of themselves, are likely to feel vulnerable and anxious.

To briefly summarize the principles of Motivational Interviewing in a simplified manner, it is a very client-centered approach, grounded in the therapeutic stance of collaboration, respect, and respecting autonomy. Change is believed to occur not through knowledge alone but through illuminating the connection with the individual's goals and values. Ambivalence is to be expected when change is being considered. The primary tasks and principles of the change facilitator are to: (1) express empathy, (2) develop the discrepancy between the current behavior and important goals or values, (3) "roll" with resistance, and (4) support self-efficacy and optimism.

The goal of MI-based supervision is for supervisors to use MI techniques to construct a conversation with supervisees that minimizes their resistance by being nonconfrontational, nonjudgmental, and empathic. Supervisors encourage supervisees to be full collaborators in the feedback discussion process. Thus, the supervisor might say, "Tell me a bit about what you heard on your tape, and how might you phrase things differently in a similar situation next time?" This could be followed with open-ended questions that are also part of MI (e.g., "What other things might you do differently?" or "What do we need to work on in supervision to get you to a higher level?"; Sobell et al., 2008, p. 152).

From an MI perspective, getting supervisees to "give voice" to the need to make changes is viewed as more likely to get them to consider making a serious change attempt than the supervisor telling supervisees what they must change. MI can be used to increase supervisees' motivation for change by giving them personalized feedback in a nonthreatening, nonjudgmental way (e.g., "So, it sounds like you were trying to reflect back what the client said. This is very different from when you first started seeing clients. How were you able to do that?" or "I noticed you said you asked several back-to-back questions during your session. What do you know about how patients respond when you ask them multiple questions in a row?"; Sobell et al., 2008, p. 152).

The following example will be used to more fully describe MI and demonstrate how it might be applied to supervision. Consider the case of Tonya, a first-year practicum student who tends to "talk too much" during sessions to the point of disrupting the flow of the sessions and making it difficult for some clients to fully express themselves. Tonya describes her theoretical orientation as a combination of CBT and client-centered and is conflicted between valuing the clients' story but also wanting to share her insightful observations and practical suggestions. She is also beginning to realize that her anxiety might play a role in her excessive talking but is uncomfortable acknowledging this, even to herself. The following are examples of MI-based questions that may be useful to use:

1. Reflective listening: simply reflecting back the main points heard by the supervisee, typically focusing on the most meaningful or emotionally charged

- "I hear your frustration that your clients don't seem to be buying into your suggestions."

- "It seems that you are feeling confused about where to go with this client."

- "It seems really hard to want to listen intently but also share your insights before you forget them."

2. Develop discrepancy: questions designed to note the discrepancy between intention and outcome

- "Tell me how you are feeling about your work with this client."

- "Where are you with the idea of incorporating silence?"

- "What do you make of your clients tendency not to go into much detail with their responses?"

3. Eliciting change talk: questions designed to help the supervisee start thinking about practical steps to begin positive change

- "If you did decide to try to give the client more room for fully expression, how would you do it?"

- "What would be the good things about simply reflecting more with the client?"

- "Why would you want to talk somewhat less in your next session?"

- "What are the good things about being more selective with your comments and what are the bad things?"

4. Responding to change talk: reflecting back change talk from the supervisee, asking for examples and elaboration, and offering affirmation

- "What else?"

- "Are there other reasons?"

- "I think you're right about that."

- "When was the last time you tried something along these lines?"

- "It is hard to think of offering less advice because it is difficult for you to see your client struggle, but you worry at times that your client feels talked down to."

5. Rolling with resistance: nonjudgmentally acknowledging the ambivalence

- Reflection—simply acknowledge it by reflecting it back

- Amplified reflection—overstate it a bit. "I can see that she is likely to make a week of terrible decisions if you hold back some of your observations."

- Double-sided reflection—"On the one hand, you see the value of being client-centered. On the other hand, it is difficult to trust your client to make good decisions."

6. Enhance confidence: questions focused on illuminating actual successes and strengths to foster increased self-efficacy

- "What gives you some confidence that you can do this next week?"

- "What is there about you that could help you succeed in making this change?"

The Role of Positive Emotions in Feedback

Positive emotions have a significant impact on widening our scope of attention and increasing intuition and creativity (e.g., Fredrickson, 2001), and the priming of positive emotions has been found to increase cognitive flexibility, speed, and accuracy. In fact, medical internists primed to feel good with a small gift of candy to increase their positive affect demonstrated more flexible thinking and made diagnoses more accurately and quickly (Isen, Rosenzweig, and Young, 1991). The take-home message might be that we should stop by the candy store before we visit the doctor the next time.

Eliciting positive emotions has been found to be useful for cognitive processing, problem solving, and for learning, but how much positivity? Can there be too much of a good thing? Fortunately, research has been conducted addressing this very question, namely, investigating the optimal ratio of positive to negative or critical feedback. Losada (1991) studied business teams and found that positive emotion played a primary role in how well the teams functioned. Looking at moment-to-moment group interactions, high-performance teams had a much wider range of behavior, and their discussions were more fluid and flexible. Although there were more positive comments, there were also strong criticisms and challenges. The ample focus on successes and strengths seemed to make possible the room to hear constructive feedback. However, as Aristotle advised over two millennia ago, balance is the measure of all things; too much "positivity" is not good for work or performance. When negative feedback occurred in the context of high amounts of support and approval (e.g., a ratio of approximately 3:1), workers bounced back quickly after being criticized (Losada & Heaphy, 2004). Highlighting problems or challenges actually served to ignite performance and inspire thinking with greater clarity and effectiveness. However, in groups where the positive/negative ratio was below 3:1, there was less resiliency and a narrower range of behavior, and in particular after negative comments, people seemed to lose creativity and authenticity.

This seems to refute the assumption that is sometimes erroneously attributed to positive psychology or the strength-based paradigm that the goal is all positivity all the time. When feedback is only supportive and approving, without a healthy balance of authenticity and, at times, focusing on areas that need improvement, the behavior range becomes constricted, just as it does with too much negative feedback. According to Fredrickson and Losada (2005), if the ratio of positive to negative comments goes above about 12:1, behavior becomes rigid and unresponsive. Similar to the need to be flexible within therapy (Lopez, Snyder, and Rasmussen, 2003), the goal of effective feedback within supervision is to shift our attention back and forth to strengths and weaknesses as necessary. As with mental health, flexibility is the key for good supervision.

Feedback Learning

It is commonly assumed that mental health professionals become better therapists with experience. This assumption certainly seems to make intuitive sense. Undoubtedly, many supervisors—myself included—have written reference letters for clinicians entering the job market using the phrase that they would "benefit from continued experience" as a way to imply that we realize that our supervisees are not perfect but without really diminishing their glow. But how true is this assumption? Does experience make us better therapists? Bickman (1999) carefully examines this question and draws some disturbing conclusions. He notes that research on the question of whether clinician experience affects client outcomes is mixed. Some research indicates that the role of experience has almost no impact on client outcomes (e.g., Luborsky et al., 1980; Smith and Glass, 1977; Stein and Lambert, 1984; Strupp and Hadley, 1979), whereas other analyses do report that the therapists' level of experience does positively impact therapeutic outcome (e.g., Dush, Hirt, & Schroeder, 1989; Stein & Lambert, 1995).

Bickman (1999) suggests that the lack of a consistent relationship between a clinician's experience and clients' outcomes is because several variables make it difficult to learn from experience. Borrowing the term "feedback learning" (Sperry, Brill, Howard, & Grissom, 1996), he asserts that receiving feedback on successes and failures of treatment is critical for learning to occur. Although simple in theory, feedback learning with counseling skills is complex and difficult to achieve. For the feedback loop to operate, several conditions must be met (Bickman, 1999, pp. 969–970):

1. *Know the outcomes of treatment.* To learn from experience, clinicians must have knowledge of the outcomes of therapy, but clinicians tend not to receive systematic information about clients' outcomes either during or after treatment.

2. *Receive quick, continuous, and correct feedback.* Those of us who have either children or pets know this well. However, feedback from clients is often informal and unsystematic, making it difficult to become better practitioners based on feedback.

3. *Be aware of the processes and tactics used in sessions.* Unfortunately, clinicians have great difficulty accurately recalling their behaviors in sessions.

4. *Know the relationships between process and outcomes.* Because clinicians have little knowledge of their own behaviors and client outcomes, it is very difficult to know the relationships between processes and outcomes.

5. *Tailor treatments. Apply* general knowledge to specific individual clients and clinical situations.

Awareness of the ever-changing progress of the client and of the therapist's role in the change process is vital if learning is to occur. Supervisors should give time and attention to raising awareness of the processes used in sessions. A general truism of psychotherapy is that power is in the specifics; the same applies to supervision. An effective supervisor helps focus on specific processes and tactics (the use of video recording can be very instrumental) and to illuminate the often murky relationship between process and outcome. The need for appropriate feedback and being able to reference useful criteria leads into the next section, which examines criteria and measures for feedback and evaluation.

Criteria and Measures

Client-Outcome Measures

This chapter has stressed that feedback is the foundation for learning from experience; that is, supervisees need to know client outcomes. Referring back to the example of learning archery (Saptya et al., 2005), providing corrective feedback to the supervisee about what is being done right and wrong adds information that can't be obtained solely on the basis of self-observation. The feedback from the supervisor must also be combined with information about knowing the outcome of the supervisee's actions, with an objective measure of whether these actions are "on target." For learning to occur, both the supervisee and the supervisor need to know where the arrow lands. If neither can see the target, learning is severely hampered. Client-outcome data can be used to inform treatment and discuss progress with clients, and also to inform supervision (Lambert and Hawkins, 2001). Tracking outcome data can provide objective information to both supervisee and supervisor regarding therapeutic progress, and this increased, additional information can facilitate training.

The true test of supervision is the impact on client outcomes (Reese et al., 2009). However, in practice, therapists are often trained and supervised with only limited knowledge of client outcomes and with a lack of information about client-treatment responses from objective measures. Not surprisingly, clinicians have limited ability to make accurate judgments; however, most professionals are typically very confident of their clinical decisions even if operating without feedback (Garb, 1989), which is potentially problematic for both openness to learning from experience and client care. This seems to reflect the more general trait of the "above average" effect, in which people tend to rate themselves as above average as compared to their peers, especially on more ambiguous abilities such as driving or leadership qualities (Dunning, Meyerowitz, & Holzberg, 1989). Clinicians who do not receive systematic feedback may learn little about the impact of their decisions and actions and assume no changes in their treatment approaches are needed when, in fact, they are, or conversely, assume that change in treatment tactics is indicated when it is not needed (Lambert, Hansen, and Finch, 2001). Client-outcome data can provide a quick "dashboard indicator" to both supervisee and supervisor and help identify clients who might need more attention during supervision (Reese et al., 2009).

It appears that receiving client-outcome feedback is especially important for good clinical care involving clients who are not doing well in therapy. Saptya et al. (2005) conducted a meta-analysis of 30 randomized clinical trials that evaluated the effectiveness of feedback on the health status of clients to health professionals in community settings. Clinicians receiving client feedback did better compared to the control group of those not receiving feedback. However, more careful examination of the results indicated that "flagged clients"—those not progressing well in therapy—responded much better to feedback intervention compared to clinicians receiving feedback on "non-flagged" clients. Feedback provides both the long-term benefit of learning from experience and the short-term benefit of being informed of problem cases that need additional attention.

Many client-outcome measures exist, but here are three commonly used measures:

1. *The Outcome Questionnaire 45* (OQ45; Lambert et al., 1996) is a 45-item instrument, completed by the client before each session, that provides feedback to the therapist on the client's progress.

2. *Session Rating Scale* (SRS; Duncan et al., 2003) is a four-item scale that assesses the therapeutic relationship, goals and topics covered in therapy, the approach used in therapy, and the overall rating of the session.

3. *The Outcome Rating Scale* (ORS; Miller, Duncan, Brown, Sparks, and Claud, 2003) is a four-item measure designed to assess client progress in treatment.

Supervisees who received continuous feedback from their clients and used the ORS combined with the SRS over the course of an academic year with their clients during each session were found to be approximately twice as effective as those who did not receive feedback over the course of therapy. Therapists who received continuous feedback had 28 % of their clients demonstrate significant improvement versus 15% with therapists in the no-feedback condition (Reese et al., 2009). Interestingly, although supervisees who used the ORS combined with the SRS demonstrated better client outcomes, they did not report a better supervisory alliance or more satisfaction with supervision. However, therapists receiving feedback reported satisfaction in being able to monitor how they were doing with clients. They felt that client feedback gave them more structure and better places to start with new or "difficult" clients. Supervisors generally felt that client feedback was less useful, but did agree that client feedback assisted them with challenging feedback and helped to identify clients who needed more attention in supervision.

We would suggest that although using formal outcome measures as part of training is certainly ideal for getting the most objective client-outcome data, depending upon the orientation and approach of the therapist and setting, such a formalized procedure might not be regarded as preferable in all situations. We would, however, strongly encourage supervisees to at least check in verbally with clients at the end of each session and ask how they felt the session went; whether they addressed the concerns they wanted to address during the session; how they felt about the working relationship that session; and how their symptoms are doing compared to the previous session.

Evaluation of the Supervisory Process

Just as clinicians need feedback to serve as "dashboard indicators" of how the process of therapy is going, so, too can supervisors benefit from feedback on the supervisory process. This feedback, if incorporated, can serve to strengthen and improve the supervisory relationship and process. Several structured measures exist. Here are three commonly used empirically validated scales:

1. *Supervision Outcomes Survey* (SOS; Worthen & Isakson, 2003) is a 20-item measure designed to assess the supervisee's satisfaction with the supervisory process.

2. *Supervisory Working Alliance Inventory* (supervisee version: SWAI-T; Efstation, Patton, and Kardash, 1990) is a 19-item measure designed to measure supervisees' perception of the supervisory relationship.

3. *Counseling Self-Estimate Inventory* (COSE; Larson et al., 1992) is a 37-item designed to measure a counselor's self-efficacy on five counseling areas: (1) microskills, (2) counseling process, (3) dealing with difficult client behaviors, (4) cultural competence, and (5) awareness of one's own values.

Conclusion

A core principle in good assessment is that a diagnostic evaluation should never be made on the basis of a single type of data. One would never want to diagnose a child with ADHD based simply on the teacher's report of classroom behavior or the child's self-report scores. The greater the types and sources of information, the more confident one can be in the diagnosis; multiplicity of methods yields better information. The same principle applies to supervision. Good feedback and evaluation should be based on as many sources of data as possible: knowledge of clinical skills based on watching video-recorded sessions; progress toward mutually determined therapy goals; examination of conceptual and decision-making ability through examination of critical incidents; unobtrusive data, such as client-satisfaction surveys and client attendance and cancellation rates, et cetera. Feedback not only helps to guide the supervision and clinical-learning process, feeding back information about client outcomes also is a form of evidence-based practice. Moreover, from the perspective the local clinical scientist model (Stricker & Trierweiler, 1995), in which the clinical setting is regarded as analogous to a scientific laboratory, feedback from both clients and supervisor helps to bridge the challenging gap between science and practice.

It has been suggested that there are nearly as many evaluation instruments as there are training programs (Bernard & Goodyear, 2004). Many institutions have developed their own instruments—often Likert-Scale measurements—to use for summative evaluation. When developing and using homegrown evaluation measures, we encourage you to make sure that your evaluation instrument provides a clear road map. We tend to make forward progress only when the path is clear (Heath & Heath, 2010). Can we provide the supervisee clear examples of the difference between a 3 and a 4 and a 6 and a 7 on each of the items on our Likert Scale? If not, the measures have no value, and can, in fact, do damage to supervisee morale and the supervisor–supervisee relationship. And do we share these with our supervisee, ideally at the beginning of the evaluation period, to serve as a target to aim for? Even well-intended measures can be perceived and be subjective if they can't be operationalized in clear, concrete terms or tied to descriptive examples and have little value in providing guidance and direction. Effective evaluation not only identifies where the supervisee is, but provides clear examples and a road map for the next step.

Questions to Consider

- What am I doing to help my supervisee direct attention away from being overly self-conscious to being more fully immersed in learning and challenging growth?

- What am I role-modeling for my supervisees?

- Think of the best experiences I have had receiving feedback or evaluation. What made these such good experiences? How can I incorporate some of these elements into the feedback and evaluation I am providing?

- Does the time allocation in our supervision sessions roughly mirror the supervisory goals? If not, what changes would be helpful to make?

- What is the one "take home" feedback message I want my supervisee to really hear this week? How can I convey this most effectively? Are there ways we can work with this concept (role playing, etc.) to help the supervisee incorporate it more fully?

- Is there feedback that would be beneficial but I am hesitant to give? What can I do to make it a more comfortable process? For the supervisee? For myself as the supervisor?

Recommended Readings

Books

Bandura, A. (1997). *Self-efficacy: The exercise of control.* New York: Freeman.

Dweck, C. S. (2006). *Mindset: The new psychology of success.* New York: Random House.

Heath, C., & Heath, D. (2010). *Switch: How to change things when change is hard.* New York: Broadway Books.

Orem, S. L., Binkert, J., & Clancy, A. L. (2007). *Appreciative coaching.* San Francisco, CA: Jossey-Bass.

Articles

Bickman, L. (1999). Practice makes perfect and other myths about mental health services. *American Psychologist, 54,* 965–978.

Ende, J. (1983). Feedback in clinical medical education. *Journal of the American Medical Association, 250*(6), 777–781.

Fredrikson, B. L., & Losada, M. (2005). Positive affect and the complex dynamics of human flourishing. *American Psychologist, 60,* 678–686.

Kluger, A. N., & DeNisi, A. D. (1996). The effects of feedback interventions on performance: A historical review, a meta-analysis, and a preliminary feedback intervention theory. *Psychological Bulletin, 119,* 254–284.

Locke, E. A., & Latham, G. P. (2002). Building a practically useful theory of goal setting and task motivation. *American Psychologist, 57,* 705–717.

Saptya, J., Riemer, M., & Bickman, L. (2005). Feedback to clinicians: Theory, research, and practice. *Journal of Clinical Psychology, 61*(2), 145–153.

References

Bandura, A. (1997). *Self-efficacy: The exercise of control.* New York: Freeman.

Bernard, J. M., & Goodyear, R. K. (2004). *Fundamentals of clinical supervision* (3rd ed.). Boston, MA: Allyn and Bacon.

Bickman, L. (1999). Practice makes perfect and other myths about mental health services. *American Psychologist, 54,* 965–978.

Blanchard, K., & Johnson, S. (1983). *The one-minute manager.* New York: Berkley Books.

Bloom J. L., Hutson, B. L., & He, Y. (2008). *The appreciative advising revolution.* Champaign, IL: Stipes Publishing.

Center for Substance Abuse Treatment. (2009). *Clinical supervision and professional development of the substance abuse counselor.* Treatment Improvement Protocol (TIP) Series 52. Rockville, MD: Substance Abuse and Mental Health Services Administration.

Cooperrider, D. L., & Srivastva, S. (1987). Appreciative inquiry in organizational change. In R. W. Woodman & E. Pasmore (Eds.), *Research in organizational change and development: An annual series featuring advances in theory* (pp 129–169). San Francisco, CA: Berrett-Koehler.

Cooperrider, D. L., & Whitney, D. (1999). Appreciative inquiry: A positive revolution in change. In P. Holman & T. Devane (Eds.), *The change handbook: Group for shaping the future* (pp. 245–261). San Francisco, CA: Berrett-Koehler.

Cormier, L. S., & Bernard, J. M. (1982). Ethical and legal responsibilities of clinical supervisors. *The Personnel and Guidance Journal, 60,* 486–491.

Czikszentimihalyi, M. (1990). *Flow.* New York: Harper & Row.

Duncan, B. L., Miller, S. D., Sparks, J. A., Claud, D. A., Reynolds, L. R., Brown, J., et al. (2003). The session-rating scale: Preliminary psychometric properties of a "working" alliance measure. *Journal of Brief Therapy, 3,* 3–12.

Duncan, B. L., Miller, S. D., Wampold, B. E., & Hubble, M. A. (2009). *The heart and soul of change: Delivering what works in therapy* (2nd ed.). Washington, DC: American Psychological Association.

Dunning, D., Meyerowitz, J. A., & Holzberg, A. D. (1989). Ambiguity and self-evaluation: The role of idiosyncratic trait definitions in self-serving assessments of ability. *Journal of Personality and Social Psychology, 57,* 1082–1090.

Dush, D. M., Hirt, M. L., & Schroeder, H. E. (1989). Self-statement modification in the treatment of child behavior disorders: a meta-analysis. *Psychological Bulletin, 106,* 97–106.

Ende, J. (1983). Feedback in clinical medical education. *Journal of the American Medical Association, 250* (6), 777–781.

Efstation, J. F., Patton, M. J., & Kardash, C. M. (1990). Measuring the working alliance in counselor supervision. *Journal of Counseling Psychology, 37,* 322–329.

Fredrickson, B. (2001). The role of positive emotions in positive psychology: The broaden-and-build theory of positive emotions. *American Psychologist, 56,* 218–226.

Fredrikson, B. L., & Losada, M. (2005). Positive affect and the complex dynamics of human flourishing. *American Psychologist, 60,* 678–686.

Garb, H. N. (1989). Clinical judgment, clinical training, and professional experience. *Psychological Bulletin, 105,* 387–396.

Habley, W. R., & Bloom, J. L. (2007). Giving advice that makes a difference. In G.L. Kramer (Ed.), *Fostering success in the campus community* (pp. 171–192). San Francisco, CA: Jossey-Bass.

Heath, C., & Heath, D. (2010). *Switch.* New York: Broadway Books.

Hoffman, M. A., Hill, C. E., Holmes, S. E., & Freitas, G. F. (2005). Supervisor perspective on the process and outcome of giving easy, difficult, or no feedback to supervisees. *Journal of Counseling Psychology, 52,* 3–13.

Isen, A. M., Rosenzweig, A. S., & Young, M. J. (1991). The influence of positive affect on clinical problem solving. *Medical Decision Making, 11,* 221–227.

Kluger, A. N., & DeNisi, A. (1998). Feedback interventions: Toward the understanding of a double-edged sword. *Current Directions in Psychological Science, 7,* 67–72.

Kluger, A. N., & DeNisi, A. D. (1996). The effects of feedback interventions on performance: A historical review, a meta-analysis, and a preliminary feedback intervention theory. *Psychological Bulletin, 119,* 254–284.

Kreiling, K. R. (1980). Clinical education and lawyer competency: The process of learning to learn from experience through properly structured clinical supervision. *Maryland Law Review, 40,* 284–337.

Lambert, M. J., Burlingame, G. M., Umphress, V. J., Hansen, N. B., Vermeersch, D., Clouse, G., et al. (1996). The reliability and validity of the outcome questionnaire. *Clinical Psychology & Psychotherapy, 3,* 106–116.

Lambert, M. J., Hansen, N. B., & Finch, A. E. (2001). Patient focused research: Using patient outcome data to enhance treatment effects. *Journal of Consulting and Clinical Psychology, 69,* 159–172.

Lambert, M. J., & Hawkins, E. J. (2001). Using information about patient progress in supervision: Are outcomes enhanced? *Australian Psychologist, 36,* 131–138.

Larson, L. M., Suzuki, L. A., Gillespie, K. N., Potenza, M. T., Bechtel, M. A., & Toulouse, A. L. (1992). Development and validation of the counseling self-estimate inventory. *Journal of Counseling Psychology, 39,* 105–120.

Larson, L., Suzuki, L., Gillespie, K. et al. (1992). Development and validation of the Counseling Self-Estimate Inventory. *Journal of Counseling Psychology, 39*(1), 105–120.

Lehrman-Waterman, D., & Ladany, N. (2001). Development and validation of the Evaluation Process Within Supervision Inventory. *Journal of Counseling Psychology, 48,* 168–177.

Lietz, C. A., & Rounds, T. (2009). Strengths-based supervision: A child welfare supervision training project. *The Clinical Supervisor, 28,* 124–140.

Locke, E. A., & Bryan, J. (1969). The directing function of goals in task performance. *Organizational Behavior and Human Performance, 4,* 35–42.

Locke, E. A., & Latham, G. P. (2002). Building a practically useful theory of goal setting and task motivation. *American Psychologist, 57,* 705–717.

Lopez, S. J., Snyder, C. R., & Rasmussen, H. N. (2003). Striking a vital balance: Developing a complimentary focus on human weaknesses and strength through positive psychological assessment. In S. Lopez & C. R. Snyder (Eds.), *Positive psychological assessment: A handbook of models and measures.* Washington, DC: American Psychological Association.

Losada, M. (1991). The complex dynamics of high performance teams. *Mathematical and Computer Modelling, 30,* 179–192.

Losada, M., & Heaphy, E. (2004). The role of positivity and connectivity in the performance of business teams: A nonlinear dynamics model. *American Behavioral Scientist, 47*(6), 740–765.

Luborsky, L., Mintz, J., Auerbach, A., Cristoph, P., Bachrach, H., Todd, T., Johnson, M., Cohen, M., & O'Brien, C. P. (1980). Predicting the outcome of psychotherapy: Findings of the Penn psychotherapy project. *Archives of General Psychiatry, 37,* 471-481.

Mahrer, A. R., & Boulet, D. B. (1997). The experiential model of on-the-job teaching. In C. E. Watkins, Jr (Ed.), *Handbook of psychotherapy supervision* (pp. 164-183). Hoboken, NJ: John Wiley & Sons, Inc.

Marsh, H. W., & Roche, L. A. (1997). Making students' evaluations of teaching effectiveness effective: The critical issues of validity, bias, and utility. *American Psychologist, 52,* 1187–1197.

Miller, S. D., Duncan, B. L., Brown, J., Sparks, J., & Claud, D. (2003). The outcome rating scale: A preliminary study of the reliability, validity, and feasibility of a brief visual analog measure. *Journal of Brief Therapy, 2*(2), 91–100.

Miller, W. R. (2004). Motivational interviewing in service to health promotion. *American Journal of Health Promotion, 18,* A1–A10.

Miller, W. R., & Rollnick, S. (2002). *Motivational interviewing: Preparing people for change* (2nd ed.). New York: Guilford Press.

Reese, R. J., Usher, E. L., Bowman, D. C., Norsworthy, L. A., Halstead, J. L., Rowlands, S. R., et al. (2009). Using client feedback in psychotherapy training: An analysis of its influence on supervision and counselor self-efficacy. *Training and Education in Professional Psychology, 3,* 157–168.

Riemer, M., Rosof-Williams, J., & Bickman, L. (2005). Theories related to changing clinician practice. *Child and Adolescent Psychiatric Clinics of North America, 14,* 241–254.

Rollnick, W., & Miller, W.R. (1995). What is motivational interviewing? *Behavioural & Cognitive Psychotherapy, 23,* 325–334.

Saptya, J., Riemer, M., & Bickman, L. (2005). Feedback to clinicians: Theory, research, and practice. *Journal of Clinical Psychology, 61*(2), 145–153.

Smith, H. D. (1984). Moment-to-moment counseling process feedback using a dual-channel audiotape recording. *Counselor Education and Supervision, 23,* 346–349.

Smith, M. L., & Glass, G. V. (1977). Meta-analysis of psychotherapy outcome studies. *American psychologist, 32,* 752–760.

Snyder, C. R. & Lopez, S. J. (2007). *Positive psychology: The scientific and practical explorations of human strengths.* Thousand Oaks, CA: Sage Publications, Inc.

Sobell, L. C., Manor, H. L., Sobell, M. B., & Dum, M. (2008). Self-critiques of audiotaped therapy sessions: A motivational procedure for facilitating feedback during supervision. *Training and Education in Professional Psychology, 2,* 151–155.

Sperry, L., Brill, P., Howard, K. I., & Grissom, G.(1996). *Treatment outcomes in psychotherapy and psychiatric interventions.* New York: Brunner.

Stein, D. M., & Lambert, M. J. (1984). On the relationship between therapist experience and psychotherapy outcome. *Clinical Psychology Review, 4,* 127–142.

Stein, D. M., & Lambert, M. J. (1995). Graduate training in psychotherapy: Are therapy outcomes enhanced?. *Journal of Consulting and Clinical Psychology, 63,* 182–196.

Stricker, G., & Trierweiler, S.J. (1995). The local clinical scientist: A bridge between science and practice. *American Psychologist, 50,* 995–1002.

Strupp, H. H., & Hadley, S. W. (1979). Specific vs nonspecific factors in psychotherapy: A controlled study of outcome. *Archives of general psychiatry, 36,* 1125-1136.

Wagner, R., & Harter, J. K. (2006). *12: The elements of great managing.* New York: Gallup Press; 2006.

Watkins, C. E. Jr. (Ed.). (1997). *Handbook of psychotherapy supervision.* New York: John Wiley & Sons.

Weiner, N. (1950). The human use of human being. In *Cybernetics and society.* Boston, MA: Houghton Mifflin Company,: p 71.

Westberg, J., & Jason, H. (1993). Providing constructive feedback. In J. Westberg & H. Jason (Eds.), *Collaborative clinical education: The foundation of effective health care* (pp. 297–318). New York: Springer Publishing.

White, S., & Locke, E. (2000). Problems with the Pygmalion effect and some proposed solutions. *Leadership Quarterly, 11,* 389–415.

Worthen, V. E., & Isakson, R. L. (2003). Enhancing Supervisory Relationships.

6

Diversity: Searching for Higher Ground, Not Just Common Ground

"We are each of us angels with only one wing, and we can only fly by embracing one another."
—I. F. Chamberlain, *Abdu'l-Baha on Divine Philosophy*, 2007, p. 83

"Diversity is not about how we differ. Diversity is about embracing one another's uniqueness."

—Ola Joseph

In the book, *Outliers: The Story of Success,* Malcolm Gladwell (2008) grippingly tells the story of the 1990 flight of a Columbian airliner that crashed onto Long Island, killing 73 of the 158 passengers on board. The tragedy occurred because the New York air traffic controllers did not grasp that the Columbian pilot was trying to communicate that the plane was almost out of fuel when he was instructed to remain in a holding pattern for over an hour because of air traffic delays. The pilot was trying to convey the urgency of the situation about the diminishing fuel supply, but given his understated communication style, the plane's imminent danger of crashing did not register with the New York air traffic controllers. Used to very direct communication, the air traffic controllers in New York simply thought the pilot was communicating the very common situation that many planes are running low on fuel as they approach landing. The plane ran out of fuel and crashed simply because both the pilot and the air traffic controller were attempting to communicate from their own cultural perspective and were unable to cross the cultural divide and understand each other.

Obviously and regrettably, the crash was very avoidable. If the pilots had just been able to communicate that they needed to be moved up to the front of the line for landing, or if earlier in the process, they had asked to be rerouted to land at Philadelphia, these flight plan changes could have been easily made and

123

catastrophe avoided. Gladwell also recounted a similar situation with a Korean Airlines flight in 1997 that crashed on its approach to the airport in Guam, one of several crashes over a several-year period for the airline. At the time, the loss rate for Korean Airlines was 17 times higher than the industry average—so bad that the United States Army, which has thousands of troops in South Korea, forbade its personnel from using the carrier. Fortunately, Korean Airlines began implementing cultural training shortly after the 1997 crash, and now has an unblemished safety record, illustrating that change is possible.

Although there were several contributing factors to both crashes (as with most tragic outcomes), Gladwell attributes much of the difficulty in both catastrophes to the breakdown in communication due to cultural misunderstanding between the air traffic controllers and the pilots. Western communication typically has a "transmitter orientation," which means that it is considered the speakers' responsibility to communicate information clearly and unambiguously. Conversely, many Asian and other collectivist countries tend to have a "receiver orientation," in which it is the responsibility of the listener to make sense of what is being said, even when communication is presented indirectly.

In mental health, the failure to empathically and appropriately respond to cross-cultural interactions will not likely result in mass transportation crashes, but the results can be tragic nonetheless. Effective supervision, as well as good clinical work, is dependent upon truly appreciating the differences of perspective and worldview that permeate every therapeutic and supervisory interaction. But appreciating diversity and effectively navigating differences does not merely mean that problems and bad outcomes can be minimized; it also can add richness and increased perspective to interpersonal interactions and clinical and supervisory work, which will be highlighted throughout the chapter.

Trevino (2012), a native Mayan woman from Guatemala, illuminates some of the potential possible in adopting a perspective of embracing diversity. She explains that in the Mayan vision of the cosmos, the focus is on the interconnectedness among all living things and attunement with all that surrounds us. In fact, the greeting of "*In Lak'ech Ala K'in*" is used to convey honor and means "I am another yourself" or "I am you, and you are me" (p. 36).

This chapter will focus on practical ways to use the strength and potential of diversity in supervision, while also addressing the challenges that differences can impose. Diversity is evident in all aspects of people's interactions and is involved (either explicitly or implicitly) in every therapeutic and supervisory interaction. Although much of the research on diversity focuses on race and ethnicity, we will take a broad perspective of diversity in this chapter, choosing to think of diversity as any meaningful way in which the clinician and client or supervisee perceive themselves to be different from each other and have a different perspective on life and the world. The goal of this chapter is not to try to provide all of the answers needed when working with clients and supervisees from backgrounds different from our own, but rather to provide opportunities for reflection, food for thought, and some ideas on working within a diverse population using a strength-based perspective, all the while recognizing the potential and opportunities contained through diversity.

Importance of Diversity Training

One only needs to fill out an application or respond to a census taker's questions to realize that we are frequently grouped into categories as people. And we have all heard the statistics that in the coming decades no single ethnic group will be in the majority in the United States, increasing the need for multicultural competence. But the need for skill and sensitivity with issues of diversity isn't merely a numbers issue based on the fact that visible diversity status is growing in the United States; rather, a true diversity perspective appreciates both the shared human commonalities and also the unique differences held by any two people, regardless of the initial appearance of similarity or difference.

For many, many people, checking a single identifier box to describe oneself is a difficult and very inaccurate task that often requires the person to lop off important parts of one's identity or "swallow" some ethnic pride to fill in the right bubble. The United States is rapidly becoming a population that does not fit neatly into little boxes; we are a complex and diverse people who cannot be accurately described in constricting categories. We are becoming more of an "other" rather than the "same." As supervisors, it is increasingly important that we examine ourselves and our "otherness" and then, in kind, work with our supervisees to help them see that within themselves.

Torres, Solberg, and Carlstrom (2002) highlighted one example of the myth of sameness within the Latino population, surveying Latino male participants about machismo. The results indicated that machismo is a multidimensional construct, and that only 10% of the population responded to ideas about machismo that included authoritarian, emotionally restrictive, and controlling behaviors. The majority of the participants reported they were emotionally responsive, collaborative, and flexible. Implications of this study indicate the need to change the stereotypes that we hold about this population in order to be more consistent with the current Latino male identity. Ideas that we stereotypically hold about certain populations (often even our own) clearly hold us back from fully appreciating and experiencing all that various populations have to offer.

The importance of being able to work effectively with issues of diversity is very clear. Constantine (2002) found that the shared variance between clients' perception of counselors' general counseling competence and clients' perceptions of counselors' multicultural-counseling competence was approximately 60%, indicating that it is not a stretch to say that "multicultural competence is synonymous with general counseling competence" (Coleman, 1998, p. 153).

Effective multicultural counseling skills are beneficial in building positive rapport and trust within the helping relationship (the most important of the common therapeutic factors), and multiculturally aware therapists strengthen the therapist–client relationship through cultural understanding (Pedersen, 2000). Even if not always explicit, "culture is an inevitable silent participant in all counseling because counseling is a culture-specific human intervention" (Das, 1995, p. 50).

Falender and Shafranske (2004) note that the majority of attention to diversity in both research and theorizing has focused on multiculturalism—just one particular aspect—rather than to the broader realm of diversity and advocate for consideration of the entire spectrum of diversity (pp. 117–118). Throughout this chapter, although some of the references refer specifically to culture and multiculturalism because that is by far the most heavily studied area of diversity, we will be working from a framework of understanding diversity in the broadest sense. This is not at all to minimize the importance of cultural and racial or ethnic differences, but to also be inclusive of other important aspects of diversity and human experience such as gender, age and generation, ability status, and sexual orientation, to name just a few. It is also essential that a diversity perspective be attuned not only to differences between groups but also to within-group differences, which have been shown to exceed between-group differences (Suzuki, McRae, & Short, 2001).

We propose that a worldview perspective is a useful way to think about diversity and a guide for both therapy and supervision. Jones-Smith (2012) conceptualizes *worldview* as a frame of reference that an individual holds about life that includes the individual's assumptions, understandings, interpretations, and beliefs about one's relationship to the people, institutions, and phenomena within the individual's environment (p. 295). Baruth and Manning (2003) succinctly define worldview as "a person's value-laden beliefs and assumptions about life aspects, such as relationships with others and the broader world, as well as perspectives of past and present events and outlook about the future" (pp. 58–59). Obviously, many factors impact one's worldview, ranging from race, gender, and sexual orientation to family experiences, educational attainment, socioeconomic status, and even professional identity and the types of literature one reads. A diversity-sensitive therapist must explore and conceptualize client and supervisee problems and potential solutions within the context of their worldview.

Strength-Based Approach to Diversity

Multiculturalism and diversity often seem to be approached from a deficit perspective, raising images of a minefield to be crossed, filled with perils such as premature termination for clients and cultural impasses in supervision, which of course are real possibilities if cultural and diversity issues are handled poorly. However, as with many things, the challenges of bridging potential gaps of understanding and perspective can also provide great opportunities. Butler (2003) notes that many professionals are unsure or seem to fear multiculturalism; however, he suggests that "it should be envisioned as another tool that enhances the profession and its ultimate goal of helping people" (p. 127). Sue, Ivey, and Pedersen (1996) echo this sentiment, noting that multicultural counseling is truly a strength-based approach by adding to the tools in the clinician's or supervisor's toolbox. They explain in their Theory of Multicultural Counseling that the ultimate goal of a culture-centered approach is to expand the repertoire of counseling responses available, and that conventional roles of counseling constitute only some of many alternative helping roles available from other cultural contexts.

Torrey (1986) advises that although it can appear that healing methods are radically different across cultures, the techniques of therapy used throughout the world are quite similar. However, the differences of expression can often help broaden our perspective and offer us additional methods for approaching common situations. The Quaker tradition of the "clearness committee,"—which role is to assist any member struggling for clarity—is an excellent example of increasing our possible tools by going beyond our traditional cultural perspective. In the Quaker tradition, an individual who is seeking clarity and perspective invites half a dozen friends, colleagues, mentors, or even strangers to gather and meet (Levoy, 1997). The committee first observes a period of meaningful silence. The rules of the clearness committee are simply to ask questions only; advice giving, storytelling, problem solving, or challenging are strictly prohibited. The guidelines are to "simply pose questions in a spirit of caring rather than even curiosity, evocation rather than imposition. The goal is not so much to comprehend as to apprehend" (p. 41). The Western tendency is to be proactive and action oriented, and when confronted with uncertainty, it is very tempting to try to problem solve and reduce the anxiety inherent to the process. However, by assuming that the answers for important life questions reside within the person seeking clarity, asking questions can engage the focus of the person in a way that makes it more possible to hear one's own inner guidance. This Quaker-inspired tradition could be a wonderful approach to add to traditional group supervision, especially if a problem-solving, advice-giving pattern seems to be starting.

Embracing a true diversity perspective, which compels us to intentionally explore and try to more fully understand the client's or supervisee's perspective and worldview, forces us to be better clinicians and supervisors. A worldview or diversity perspective acknowledges each person's perspective within the therapeutic process as different ways of constructing meaning out of life experiences. Gonzalez, Biever, and Gardner (1994) draw similarities between multicultural counseling and social constructivist views, noting that Social Constructivism is a mechanism to obtain culturally or worldview-based information from the client's situation to assist in comprehending the role of the worldview in the client's life. They emphasize the following points, reflecting how Social Constructivism and diversity counseling complement each other:

- *Therapist as learner.* The therapist must become sensitive to the client's understandings of the impact of the client's culture on the client's behavior.

- *Entertainment of all ideas.* The therapist should look for more than one answer to a client's problem and for different ways to arrive at a solution.

- *Maintenance of curiosity.* The therapist endeavors to avoid learning too quickly or assuming an answer before asking a question. The therapist makes sure that the client's self-stated problem is the problem and avoids prematurely assuming knowledge of the answer(s) to the client's presenting problem.

- *Collaboration between client and therapist.* The therapist has confidence in the client's ability to incorporate different descriptions and explanations that might be useful in creating solutions to the client's problems.

- *Therapist's understandings as "grist for the mill."* Therapist introduces the therapist's understanding of a client's story as tentative hypotheses rather than as better stories, better descriptions, or better options.

- *Creation of a space for the client's story.* Clients from an ethnic minority group sometimes understand and explain their world significantly differently than a person from a majority culture.

- *Seeing opportunities rather than barriers.* The therapist emphasizes opportunities in the form of strengths, skills, and competencies rather than emphasizing barriers in the form of weaknesses, deficits, and incompetence.

Intentional attunement to and exploration of areas of diversity can often help lead to the identification of strengths. Racial and ethnic minorities have been found to often develop better coping strategies than individuals from nonminority groups, possibly as a result of having to learn to deal with prejudice and discrimination (Ong & Edwards, 2008). Although being a member of any nonmajority group can at times involve prejudice, discrimination, and unique hardships, strengths are often borne through adversity and can become resources to use. It is important, however, to be able to view strengths and weaknesses from the perspective of the client or supervisee, not from just our own perspective, as various "strengths" may be perceived or expressed differently depending upon the culture (e.g., Chang & Banks, 2007).

It is important to be attuned to group and cultural differences of the meaning and expression of "strengths" and "weaknesses." For example, Chang (1996) found that Asian Americans scored higher in pessimism than Caucasian Americans; however, no differences were found in levels of depression, which would have been expected from a traditional Western or Caucasian perspective. A closer look at the data revealed that negative correlations were found between optimism and general psychological and physical health in the Asian American sample, whereas positive correlations existed between these variables in the Caucasian American group. However, positive correlations existed between pessimism and increased problem solving in the Asian American sample, while the reverse was found in the Caucasian sample, illustrating that it is important to view strengths and weaknesses from the perspective of the client or supervisee and be attuned to nuances of the expressions of strengths.

Although almost every research article ends with an obligatory statement that more research is needed, and more research that incorporates culturally representative sampling is truly very much needed. It is often assumed that the results of research studies reveal universal psychological principles that can generalize across cultures, races, and ethnicities. An analysis of the top journals in psychology found that 68% of the participants were American and 96% were from Western industrialized countries (Arnett, 2008). The characteristics of the typical psychological study participant (Western, educated, industrialized, rich, and democratic), captured in the acronym WEIRD (Henrich, Heine, & Norenzayan, 2010), are far from representative of most of the world's population. Imagine how Western readers would view the results and applicability to their lives if the vast majority of research knowledge came from third- world or nondemocratic countries. Moreover, approximately 70% of all psychological research is conducted on undergraduate students (Arnett, 2008), not even a representative sample of the American population. Heine (2012) notes that the typical American college student is 4,000 times more likely to participate in a research study than a randomly selected person outside of the West. Convenience of sampling often wins out over representativeness, and truly representative sampling is difficult, time-consuming, and costly, but it is important to keep in mind that the ability to generalize most psychological study findings might consequently be very limited.

Leong and Wagner (1994) challenged the field to examine ideas and values held firm by White, middle-class males as inappropriate for minority populations in America, as these populations probably do not hold the same worldview. Cross-cultural supervision is defined by Leong and Wagner (1994) as a supervisory dyad in which the supervisee and supervisor are from two culturally distinct groups, such as an African American supervisor and an Asian

American supervisee, or a White supervisor and a Latino(a) supervisee. Bernard and Goodyear (1992) conceptualize the development of cross-cultural awareness as beginning with the supervisee never having thought about cultural issues and ending with the supervisee having a cross-cultural awareness that is second nature and that has been internalized. Butler (2003) suggests that culturally competent clinical supervisors display these qualities (which can serve as a positive model to aspire to emulate):

1. Flexibility—the ability to work with a wide range of supervisees and give each of them the culturally specific tools they need in order to succeed

2. Critical thinking—the ability to understand and put into perspective the worldviews of their diverse supervisees; they are able to create a positive environment during supervision for supervisees to have an opportunity to address and discuss issues of diversity in an open and explicit manner

3. Ability to work across cultures and worldviews and have developed working knowledge of the historical backgrounds, cultural heritages, and life experiences of their supervisees

4. Ability to manage their own anxiety, modeling that uncomfortable situations can be addressed directly and challenging themselves to overcome these possible obstructions to the counseling or supervision relationship

5. Have a well-established sense of identity and do not have an air of superiority toward their supervisees, which could easily prompt defensiveness

6. Possess humor, humility, and patience, and view themselves as life-long learners. (pp. 131–132)

Inherent Challenges

An empathic appreciation of diversity and awareness of the limitations of our own perspective can greatly help therapeutic and supervisory relationships, and the attunement and commitment to truly understanding the client or trainee from a specific worldview can help us be better therapists and supervisors in all aspects. However, even if we are well intentioned, it does not necessarily come naturally or easily. Our brains are wired to be "cognitive misers," or put more bluntly, to be "lazy" (DiSalvo, 2011, p. 80), and we tend to selectively process information in a manner that is consistent with our own worldview (Pitner and Sakamoto, 2005, p. 686).

In the book *What Makes Your Brain Happy and Why You Should Do the Opposite* by Frank DiSalvo (2011), he discusses a study by Yamagishi, Hashimoto, and Schug (2008) regarding the strong appeal of perceived "in-group" trustworthiness. Not surprisingly, people typically judge those perceived to be more like them as nicer, more generous, trustworthy, and fair. People also tend to expect better treatment from in-group members because they are thought to value, and want to further, in-group member interests. When participants were offered the choice between receiving an unknown sum of money controlled by either an in-group or "out-group" member, people overwhelmingly chose the in-group member option. Interestingly, this even held true when the out-group stereotype was more positive than the in-group stereotype (DiSalvo, p. 143). This suggests that when there is awareness of mutual "in-ness" between the client and therapist or the supervisor and supervisee, there is an expectation of better treatment than would be received from an out-grouper, meaning that care and effort must be taken by both parties to overcome our natural tendencies.

It is clear that it can be helpful for clinical providers to examine their own cultural and diversity backgrounds as part of the process of becoming more attuned to and proficient conducting therapy in a diversity-competent manner, and that becoming aware of our own biases and assumptions will make it less likely that we will impose our values or beliefs onto our clients or engage in stereotypical thinking (Pitner and Sakamoto, 2005, p. 684). Although the literature is replete with admonitions to examine one's own attitudes and beliefs and discussions of the benefits of doing so (e.g., Anderson and Carter, 2003), the naturally occurring cognitive and affective barriers that can easily arise as part of this process are seldom acknowledged or discussed. Pitner and Sakamoto (2005) challenge clinicians to engage in "critical consciousness," moving away from their own worldviews and becoming attentive to their clients' worldviews, but also acknowledge that it does not come without a cognitive cost and even the risk of backfiring. Because critical, conscious awareness is not an automatic process, it requires more cognitive expenditure than does automatically processing information from one's own perspective, with a possible end result of the increased cognitive load being the inadvertent automatic use of heuristics to lessen the cognitive drain (p. 691). In other words, because exercising higher awareness about biases and stereotypes can be so cognitively taxing, it can result in the unwitting default to biases and stereotypes.

Social psychological literature also suggests that when an individual's self-image is challenged to the point that it produces anxiety, the individual is more likely to hold onto those worldviews to reduce the anxiety (e.g., Fiske & Taylor, 1991). No wonder resistance occurs! Bottom line (as probably many supervisors have experienced): diversity training and the process of self-discovery and acknowledging one's biases and prejudices (just consider how negatively loaded these terms are!) can arouse resistance and defensiveness (Abreau, 2001). This might cause clinicians to resort to cultural heuristics, relying too much on commonly learned and often stereotypical cultural characteristics of clients' social group memberships (e.g., "Asian clients often do not make eye contact with you, but when they do, they are angry at you"). Although some anxiety can prompt increased perspective and growth, too much anxiety can cause supervisees to ignore the diversity within any given group and resort to a cookbook approach to clients. So, what to do? The need to artfully manage the inherently dicey process of honest self-reflection and discussion of perspectives and attitudes will be the topic of the next section.

Creating Trust in the Supervisory Relationship

Establishing trust in the supervisory relationship regarding diversity entails two main aspects: One is for the supervisor to create an open, affirming atmosphere so that cultural and worldview differences between the supervisor and supervisee can be acknowledged, affirmed, and discussed. This component has been the focus so far in this chapter. The other important, and often-challenging component, is for the supervisor to create an inviting and nonjudgmental space for the supervisee to engage in the sometimes anxiety-provoking process of examining personal preconceptions and biases. Like most things, the effectiveness of self-examination seems to lie in the balance, and too much anxiety and discomfort will likely cause the process to shut down and supervisees to become defensive and resistant. It seems imperative to normalize this process for supervisees and to view the journey toward diversity competence as a task, making explicit to the supervisee that the final destination will be different from the beginning.

The focus of feedback needs to be on reinforcing the supervisee's willingness to engage in the vulnerability of the process and to acknowledge the inherent struggle of being willing to examine and confront potentially disconcerting attitudes and beliefs, which may at times be tied to messages from loved ones and respected and valued institutions. As much as possible, the process of critical consciousness should be offered as an invitation to supervisees, rather than as a task imposed in a blunt manner, which may cause a rebound effect. Potential defensiveness can be exacerbated if the supervisor sends the all-too-human message of asking the supervisee to acknowledge and explore personal prejudices or lack of awareness (again, these obviously are not value-neutral terms), but shuts down the process by explicitly or implicitly conveying negativity regarding the trainee's current place in the diversity-awareness journey.

Much care needs to be taken by supervisors and trainers to truly provide a safe and nonpunishing space if supervisees are asked to explore such sensitive topics. Care needs to be taken to try to normalize the process and help supervisees to feel enthusiasm about the possibility of growth in another important area of clinical effectiveness, instead of unwittingly fostering a "fixed" learning perspective (e.g., Dweck, 2006), causing supervisees to focus on trying to convey the impression of instant diversity competence. Gonzalez (1997) emphasizes the need for supervisees to be given permission to be imperfect when it comes to multicultural competency. Often supervisees become resistant during the training process, usually brought on by the persistence supervisors use when pushing or challenging supervisees to become more culturally competent (Butler, 2003). Supervisors should model that diversity awareness is always a work in progress, and that continuous growth, not perfection, is the standard.

Embracing a phenomenological perspective can be a very useful way to normalize and "de-shame" the process. The Phenomenological approach (which is often used with research but certainly seems to fit with supervision and therapy as well) starts with acknowledging our biases and filters, recognizing that as humans we all have perceptual filters. The goal is not to free ourselves from our perspective and become totally neutral, which is an impossibility, even in the more abstracted arena of research. Rather, the intent is that by acknowledging our limitations of perspective and blind spots we will be less negatively impacted by them. Acknowledging our biases and the constrictions of our perceptual filters can limit the adverse effects because we can better manage what we are aware of, and thus we can lessen the powerful impact of unacknowledged or examined preconceptions. The Phenomenological approach helps to reframe the invitation of diversity awareness from the potentially shame-inducing task of admitting prejudices to simply acknowledging one's preexisting perceptions and reflecting on how our particular perceptual filters might impact the supervision or clinical relationship.

Credibility as a culturally competent supervisor is imperative for trust to develop between a supervisor and a supervisee who have diverse backgrounds. Trust is the primary building foundation of all successful relationships, as exemplified by Erik Erikson's stages of development in which the foundational stage is trust versus mistrust. How do supervisors and supervisees build a trusting relationship? Typical "getting to know you" kind of questions will likely occur during the initial sessions of supervision. But the important work begins when the supervisor and supervisee start to explore the worldview held by each other and dissect how that worldview is going to impact the work that is being done with clients.

Reynaga-Abiko (2010) reflects on her experiences as a Latina supervisor working with supervisees of the dominant culture. Her reflections include the need for an understanding of different cultural issues that she has found to play key roles in her developing trusting relationships with supervisees, which included cultural norms, trust, communication, time, socioeconomic status, and spirituality. Gaining a better understanding of how each person in the supervisory relationship internalizes these issues can increase the comfort and trust in the relationship. Discussing ethical issues, which can be heavily impacted by perspective and culture, such as boundary issues, gift giving, and the nature of the relationship are all areas to be discussed and determined as to how the ethical codes are interpreted when participating in cross-cultural supervision (Reynaga-Abiko, 2010).

For trust to be established in the supervisory relationship, discussions around values, thoughts, feelings, and beliefs need to occur. Priester (2004) investigated the impact of transparency on the supervisory relationship. Two scenarios with the same supervisor and supervisee were taped, with the dyad discussing multicultural issues as they relate to supervision and the therapy the supervisee is providing. In one scenario, when asked the question of having ever laughed at a racial joke, the supervisor adamantly denies ever having laughed at a racial joke, saying, "No, no, I never have nor would I," and the supervision session resumes. In the other scenario, the supervisor responds, "Yes I have. I am embarrassed and ashamed to admit it, and I wish that I had not done so. I wish that I would have told the joke teller that I thought the joke was offensive and inappropriate. I made it a goal to do so from that point on."

The vast majority of people who viewed the two scenarios responded that they felt that the supervisor who admitted that he had indeed laughed at a racial joke was far more honest and felt they could develop a trusting relationship with this supervisor versus the supervisor who adamantly denied ever having done so. Although uncomfortable, this honesty can help open the door for our supervisees to be vulnerable as well. Supervisors who accept that prejudiced feelings are inevitable, given our cultural heritage and cognitive tendencies, might open up genuine exploration into which feelings can be challenged and changed (Hawkins and Shohet, 2000).

Researchers (e.g., Cook, 1994; Sue & Sue, 2007) have discussed the idea that the power differential inherent in supervision might influence or shape the racial attitudes of the supervisee, which then can be passed on to clients, since the supervisor has the power in the relationship to sway the discussion and the subsequent development of the diversity identity attitudes held by the supervisee. How the supervisor handles the discussion and responses to questions about culture and diversity will ultimately influence the supervisee's willingness to explore these issues openly and honestly. If the supervisor is short or evasive responding to topics of diversity, the supervisee will quickly learn that these are issues to be avoided; whereas, if the supervisor is open and accepting, more discussion and hence, more growth, is likely to occur.

Cook (1994) writes that the "price of ignoring race in supervision may be greatest for those with the least power" (p. 135). If supervisors do not address race or cultural issues in supervision, supervisees might feel that they cannot address race or cultural issues in therapy with their patients. A simple question asked during a supervisory session like, "What role does race or culture play in your patient's presenting issue?" or "How does the patient's race or culture affect your work with the patient?" can greatly help to open up the conversation about these important issues. "Microaggressions" (e.g., Sue et al., 2007), which are subtle, everyday expressions of derision targeted at disenfranchised groups, can be especially beneficial to specifically address in supervision because they are subtle (and therefore easily overlooked) yet impactful.

Pitner and Sakamoto suggest that advising the supervisee as clinician to act as an ethnographer—engaging in a narrative process to help understand how their clients construct their own realities and cultural worldviews— can be a simple technique to help supervisees infuse their clinical approach with diversity awareness. By listening to the client's story from a narrative approach and focusing on how the client has reacted effectively to problems versus being controlled by them, the clinician becomes a collaborator with the client as the client engages in the process of rewriting the living story from a factually based but more empowering perspective (Pitner and Sakamoto, 2005, pp. 688–691).

Diversity Competence

The history of multicultural or diversity competencies is fairly recent, formally only dating back to the 1980s and early 1990s. In 1991, the Association for Multicultural Counseling and Development (AMCD) approved a paper outlining the need and rationale for including a multicultural perspective in counseling, and subsequently competencies were proposed in the three broad categories of: (1) counselor awareness of the counselor's own cultural values and beliefs, (2) counselor awareness of clients' worldviews, and (3) counselor learning of appropriate intervention strategies. This framework is sometimes stated as Awareness, Knowledge, and Skills, emphasizing that competence in all three areas is essential for effective clinical work with a diverse clientele.

Although this three-part model is theoretical and research indicates that multicultural competence may be a single-factor construct (Ponterotto, Rieger, Barrett, & Sparks, 1994), the conceptualization provide a useful organizing model both for conceptualizing diversity competency and for training purposes. The American Psychological Association (APA) adheres to the Guidelines on Multicultural Education, Training, Research, Practice, and Organizational Change for Psychologists (2003), and other disciplines, including social work, psychiatry, professional counseling, and speech language pathology, also have their own set of multicultural guidelines. Ponterott et al. (1994) developed the Multicultural Counselor Awareness Scale-Revised (Form B, MCAS) self-assessment instrument that can be used to measure the three realms of awareness, knowledge, and skills. This instrument can be a useful, exploratory tool to use in supervision and also as a way to start the important conversations on the topic of diversity. The next three subsections will address the three competencies of self-awareness, knowledge, and skills.

Self-Awareness

It is easy to focus on self-awareness at an intellectual level rather than examining assumptions, values, and biases from an emotional or core beliefs point of view. While it can be difficult to acknowledge weaknesses or areas for growth, for diversity awareness, it is paramount for us to understand who we are, where we come from, what is important to us, what is important to our families, and how these factors influence the work we do with our clients and our supervisees. The following are two exercises that can be used to help increase multicultural and diversity self-awareness.

"Who I Am" Exercise

We need to be able to understand ourselves and our own worldview before serving as a bridge to close gaps in a therapeutic relationship. The "Who I Am" exercise can be used to guide supervisees to better self-understanding and awareness. This exercise can also be conceptualized as a poem, and some people get very creative when responding to these prompts. The simple exercise consists of rejoinders to the prompt "I Am." For example, I (Janice Jones) could say: I am a daughter, I am a sister, I am a mother, I am a psychologist, I am a professor, and so on. The "I Am" prompt often helps respondents to reflect on their values and beliefs (e.g., "I am a person who values the gifts that each day brings" or "I am a person who strives to be the voice for the underserved").

The goal of this exercise is to help supervisees recognize the complexity of their own identities and therefore enhance understanding of the need to try to understand the complexity of the identities and influences of the clients they serve. This can help beginning therapists resist the tendency to equate clients with their diagnosis or with only the readily apparent aspects of their identity. Focusing on this from a strengths perspective, the supervisor can work through each statement in the exercise or poem, focusing on strengths and allowing the supervisee to articulate what exactly that statement means to the supervisee. Extrapolating further, a discussion of the meaning of the statements can lead to discussing how these meanings will influence the work the supervisee will be doing with clients.

Circle of Identities Exercise

Participants are instructed to write all of the ways they identify themselves on a sheet of paper, circling each descriptor with a circle of varying sizes to indicate the importance or saliency each identity holds in their life. For example, a Mexican American female graduate student might write 8 to 10 terms, such as: female, Latina, daughter, oldest sister, caregiver, graduate student, ballet lover, loyal dog owner, Catholic, and so on. Participants are then asked to discuss their identities. This exercise, especially when done in a group format, often helps to illuminate that our assumptions of saliency do not always match the importance of specific areas of identity experienced by the other, and also helps to expand the perspective of the other beyond easily identifiable identities or differences (adapted from Metzger, Nadkarni, & Cornish, 2010).

"In-the-Box/Out-of-the-Box" Exercise

In this exercise, which is well suited for group supervision, two boxes are drawn on the board, one for male, one for female. Participants brainstorm the accepted traits, characteristics, and attitudes associated with each gender by society, which are labeled the "in-the-box" behaviors. Participants are also instructed to discuss the consequences for "out-of-the-box" behaviors for men and women, as well as behaviors and attitudes that could be shared by both genders ("common-box" behaviors; Zimmerman and Haddock, 2001).

"Use of Metaphor" Exercise

The use of metaphor to examine the therapeutic relationship is often helpful to the supervisee. The therapeutic relationship can be described as a dance; invite the supervisee to reflect on such questions as who is leading the dance and the differences in styles between the two dancers. Another metaphor is that of skating with a partner on a frozen pond. Describing the "thin ice" at the center and the "safe ice" close to the edge of the pond can often be eye-opening to the supervisee (Cashwell, Looby, and Housley, 1997).

Understanding the Worldview

It is essential that clinicians and supervisors can "understand and can share" (Sue and Sue, 2003, p. 18) the worldview of their clients and supervisees. It would be unreasonable to think that I (Janice Jones) as a Caucasian suburbanite could feel and think like a Latino(a) person; however, it is essential that I understand the other's background, hopes, fears, goals, and what the other person's daily living experience is really like. In an effort to better understand the worldview that the supervisee holds and how that affects the supervisee's perceptual and experiential world, the following exercises might prove helpful.

Worldview Worksheet Exercise

Supervisees are asked to list several aspects of their culture and identity and then to list their ideas about their worldview. Although this exercise appears simple, the thoughts and reflection that might be prompted can be difficult and emotionally provoking for the supervisee. If the supervisee has difficulty generating material, the supervisor can use this as a starting point for gentle exploration or to even assign homework for the supervisee to find information about the supervisee's culture. Clients can also benefit from the exercise, which can generate meaningful dialogue on how diversity impacts them.

Intercultural Sensitizer Exercise

This exercise can help provide supervisees with culturally relevant knowledge about specific groups, either from the literature or clinicians' experience. Supervisees are presented with critical incidents that focus on specific cultural differences and difficulties of the specific group. Each incident involves a brief narrative, followed by several possible explanations that the supervision group discusses, and from the possibilities, chooses the best option. All explanations are discussed, and then the correct explanation, based on the values of the target group (Leong & Kim, 1991). They provide examples of critical incidents in the article "Going Beyond Cultural Sensitivity on the Road to Multiculturalism: Using the Intercultural Sensitizer as a Counselor Training Tool."

"First Person" Exercise

In group supervision, supervisees select or are assigned roles (e.g., client, counselor, significant other in the client's life) and instructed to provide feedback from the perspective of their adopted role as a section of video-recording from a session is watched. Feedback is given in the first person, helping to broaden both their intellectual and experiential perspective (Borders, 1991).

Developing Appropriate Interventions

Although self-awareness and understanding of the worldview of the other is important, to be an effective clinician the supervisee must also be able to implement therapy approaches appropriate to the diverse clientele being served. Sue and Sue (2003) enumerate several specific important cultural skills to be developed:

1. Generate a wide variety of verbal and nonverbal responses.

2. Send and receive verbal and nonverbal messages accurately and appropriately.

3. Exercise agency or institutional intervention skills on behalf of your client when appropriate.

4. Be aware of the client's helping style, recognize the limitations the client possesses, and anticipate the impact on a culturally different client.

5. Be able to play helping roles characterized by an active systemic focus, which leads to environmental interventions. Such a mental health professional is not trapped into the conventional counselor or therapist mode of operation. (Sue & Sue, 2003, pp. 22–23)

Although the APA Multicultural Guidelines (2003) consist of the three factors of self-awareness, cultural or worldview awareness, and implementing culturally or diversity-appropriate interventions, Constantine and Ladany (2001) extended the multicultural–diversity competency construct to a six-dimensional model. Each of these six factors are important to consider when training supervisees in multicultural and diversity competence:

- Self-awareness—understanding how one's own multiple cultural identities, biases, perspectives, and socialization affects attitudes and values

- General knowledge of multicultural issues—including social and social justice issues, discrimination, and prejudicial attitudes

- Multicultural counseling self-efficacy—confidence in one's ability to perform successfully, based on skills, not simply self-perception of competence

- Understanding of unique client variables—understanding how personal attributes, situational variables, context, and other factors affect the client's behavior

- Formation of an effective working alliance—includes addressing issues of diversity within the relationship

- Multicultural counseling skills—having the skills to approach diversity issues effectively in therapy or supervision. (pp. 482–498)

It appears that life experience with diversity combined with formal education and training is the best combination for truly increasing multicultural and diversity competency. Ladany, Inman, Constantine, and Hofheinz (1997) found no relationship between having taken a graduate level course on multicultural issues or experience with multiethnic clients and multicultural case conceptualization skills, suggesting that formal education and training alone may have little value or at the very least is insufficient. Ponterotto, Fuertes, and Chen (2000) suggest that personal experience combined with formal training experience results in higher competency scores.

Conclusion: Final Thoughts on Creating Higher Ground, Not Just Common Ground

The field of psychology and mental health includes a history of some egregious errors and acts, often but not always committed with benevolent intent, which have caused grave harm to groups and individuals because of cultural biases and lack of understanding of other aspects of diversity. Failure to incorporate culture and diversity sensitivity and understanding has resulted in Native American children being removed from their families as recently as the 1970s, standardized testing being used to limit people's options and constrict their futures, and a general but very understandable reluctance for nonmajority groups to use mental health services. The foundation of the ethical service provision among all professions is, "First, do no harm." Although there is certainly more work to be done, the mental health community appears to be making very notable strides in better addressing issues of multiculturalism and diversity in clinical service provision, supervision, research, and training.

However, although not doing harm is a laudable goal, especially given the sometimes tragic results that have occurred because multicultural and diversity issues were not considered or handled poorly, the value added to the entire clinical process by embracing a true appreciation of individual and cultural diversity in clinical work and supervision is often overlooked. We challenge supervisors to adopt a diversity–worldview perspective, which has a much higher goal than simply not providing poor therapy or supervision because of lack of cultural or diversity competence. Focusing on the other half of the story, namely, the many riches to be had through continuously developing diversity and cultural competency, enables clinicians and supervisors to conduct better therapy with all clients as assumptions are explored and not simply accepted, as learning diverse cultural perspectives help foster creativity and enhanced flexibility, and as the proverbial "clinician's toolbox" swells with additional insights and models. Understanding and appreciating the other's worldview and perspective is not only the cornerstone of effective therapy and supervision, it is truly the road to riches in the clinical setting. This enables us not only to achieve the bare minimum goal of making sure we are both "on the same page" and operate from common ground, it enables us to reach richer possibilities and achieve higher ground.

Questions to Consider

- What is my worldview? What worldview does my supervisee hold? How much of my supervisee's worldview do I really know? How could I learn more?

- What cultural values impact my therapeutic work?

- What cultural values impact my supervisory work?

- What cultural values does my supervisee hold, and how do these seem to impact the clinical work? How do they influence our supervisory interactions?

- How am I helping my supervisee increase cultural awareness?

- How am I helping my supervisee develop cultural competence? Am I inadvertently holding back the process in any way? If so, what can I do to further promote my supervisee's growth?

- What clinic structures are in place to support professional development in cultural and diversity competence, and how is the supervisee taking advantage of those?

- How are multicultural and diversity-affirming values being modeled by senior staff and supervisors?

Recommended Readings

Books

Bronstein, P., & Quina, K. (2003). *Teaching gender and multicultural awareness.* Washington, DC: American Psychological Association.

Olkin, R. (1999). *What psychotherapists should know about disability.* New York: Guilford.

Ponterotto, J. G., Casas, J. M., Suzuki, L. A., & Alexander, C. M. (2009). *Handbook of multicultural counseling* (3rd ed.). Thousand Oaks, CA: Sage.

Pope-Davis, D., Coleman, H. L. K., Liu, W. M., & Toporek, R. L. (2003). *Handbook of multicultural competencies in counseling and psychology.* Thousand Oaks, CA: Sage.

Sue D. W., & Sue D. (2012). *Counseling the culturally diverse: Theory and practice* (6th ed.). New York: John Wiley & Sons.

Journal Articles and Book Chapters

American Psychological Association. (2003). Guidelines on multicultural education, training, research, practice, and organizational change for psychologists. *American Psychologist, 58,* 377–402.

Cashwell, C. S., Looby, J., & Housley, W. (1997). Appreciating cultural diversity through clinical supervision. *The Clinical Supervisor, 15,* 75–86.

Gonzalez, R. C. (1997). Postmodern supervision: A multicultural perspective. In D. B. Pope-Davis & H. L. K. Coleman (Eds.), *Multicultural counseling competencies: Assessment, education and training, and supervision* (pp. 350–386). Thousand Oaks, CA: Sage.

Leong, F. T., & Wagner, N. S. (1994). Cross-cultural counseling supervision: What do we know? What we need to know? *Counselor Education & Supervision, 34* (2), 117–132.

Pitner, R. O., & Sakamoto, I. (2005). The role of critical consciousness in multicultural practice: Examining how its strength becomes limitations. *American Journal of Orthopsychiatry, 4,* 684–694.

Trevino, Y. (2012). Reconciling the blessings and challenges of diversity through ancestral spiritual values. In K. Schaaf, K. Lindahl, K. S. Hurty, & G. Cheen (Eds.), *Women, spirituality, and transformative leadership* (pp. 36–39). Woodstock, VT: Skylight Paths Publishing.

References

Abreau, J. M. (2001). Theory and research on stereotypes and perceptual bias: A didactic resource for multicultural trainers. *The Counseling Psychologist, 29,* 487–512.

Ancis, J. R., & Ladany, N. (2001). A multicultural framework for counselor supervision. In L. J. Bradley & N. Ladany (Eds.), *Counselor supervision: Principles, process and practice* (3rd ed) (pp. 53–94). New York: Brunner-Routledge.

Anderson, J., & Carter, R. (2003). *Diversity perspectives for social work practice.* Boston, MA: Allyn & Bacon.

American Psychological Association. (2003). Guidelines on multicultural education, training, research, practice and organizational change for psychologists. *American Psychologist, 58,* 377–402.

Arnett, J. J. (2008). The neglected 95%: Why American psychology needs to become less American. *American Psychologist, 63,* 602.

Baruth, L. G., & Manning, M. L. (2003). *Multicultural counseling and psychotherapy: A lifespan perspective* (3rd ed.). Upper Saddle River, NJ: Merrill Prentice Hall.

Bernard, J. M., & Goodyear, R. K. (1992). *Fundamentals of clinical supervision.* Boston, MA: Allyn and Bacon.

Borders, L. D. (1991). A systematic approach to peer group supervision. *Journal of Counseling and Development, 69,* 248–251.

Butler, S. K. (2003). Multicultural sensitivity and competence in the clinical supervision of school counselors and school psychologists: A context for providing competent services in a multicultural society. *The Clinical Supervisor, 22,* 125–141.

Cashwell, C. S., Looby, J., & Housley, W. (1997). Appreciating cultural diversity through clinical supervision. *The Clinical Supervisor, 15,* 75–86.

Chamberlain, I. F. (2007). *Abdu'l-Baha on divine philosophy.* Boston, MA: Tudor Press.

Chang, E. C. (1996). Cultural differences in optimism, pessimism, and coping: Predictors of subsequent adjustment in Asian American and Caucasian American college students. *Journal of Counseling Psychology, 43,* 113–123.

Chang, E.C., & Banks, K.H. (2007). The color and texture of hope: Some preliminary findings and implications for hope theory and counseling among diverse racial/ethnic groups. *Cultural Diversity and Ethnic Minority Psychology, 13,* 94–103.

Coleman, H. L. K. (1998). General and multicultural counseling competency: Apples and oranges? *Journal of Multicultural Counseling and Development, 26,* 147–156.

Constantine, M. G. (2002). Predictors of satisfaction with counseling: Racial and ethnic minority clients' attitudes toward counseling and ratings of their counselors' general and multicultural counseling competence. *Journal of Counseling Psychology, 49,* 255–263.

Constantine, M. G., & Ladany, N. (2001). New visions for defining and assessing multicultural counseling competence. In J. G. Ponterotto, J. M. Casas, L. A. Suzuki, & C. M. Alexander (Eds.), *Handbook of multicultural counseling* 2nd ed, (pp. 482–498). Thousand Oaks, CA: Sage.

Cook, D. A. (1994). Racial identity in supervision. *Counselor Education and Supervision, 34,* 132-141.

D'Andrea, M., & Daniels, J. (2001). Expanding our thinking about white racism. In J. G. Ponterotto, J. M. Casas, L. A. Suzuki, & C. M. Alexander (Eds.), *Handbook of multicultural counseling.* (pp. 289–319) Thousand Oaks, CA: Sage.

Das, A. K. (1995). Rethinking multicultural counseling: Implications for counselor education. *Journal of Counseling and Development, 74,* 45–52.

DiSalvo, D. (2011). *What makes your brain happy and why you should do the opposite.* Amherst, NY: Prometheus Books.

Dweck, C.S. (2006). *Mindset: The new psychology of success.* New York: Random House, Inc.

Falender, C. A., & Shafranske, E. P. (2004*). Clinical supervision: A competency-based approach.* Washington, DC: APA.

Fiske, S., & Taylor, S. (1991). *Social cognition.* New York: McGraw-Hill.

Gladwell, M. (2008). *Outliers: The story of success.* New York: Little, Brown and Company.

Gonzalez, R., Biever, J. L., & Gardner, G. T. (1994). The multicultural perspective in therapy: A social constructivist approach. *Psychotherapy, 31,* 515–524.

Gonzalez, R. C. (1997). Postmodern supervision: A multicultural perspective. In D. B. Pope-Davis & H. L. K. Coleman (Eds.), *Multicultural counseling competencies: Assessment, education and training, and supervision* (pp. 350–386). Thousand Oaks, CA: Sage.

Hawkins, P., & Shohet, R. (2000). *Supervision in the helping professions* (2nd ed.). Buckingham, UK: Open University Press.

Heine, S. J. (2012). *Cultural psychology* (2nd ed.). New York: WW Norton.

Henrich, J., Heine, S. J., & Norenzayan, A. (2010). Beyond WEIRD: Towards a broad-based behavioral science. *Behavioral and Brain Sciences, 33,* 111–135.

Jones-Smith, E. (2012). *Theories of counseling and psychotherapy: An integrative* approach. Los Angeles, CA: Sage.

Ladany, N., Inman, A. G., Constantine, M. G., & Hofheinz, E. W. (1997). Supervisee multicultural case conceptualization ability and self-reported multicultural competence as functions of supervisee racial identity and supervisor focus. *Journal of Counseling Psychology, 44,* 284–293.

Leong, F. T., & Wagner, N. S. (1994). Cross-cultural counseling supervision: What do we know? What do we need to know? *Counselor Education & Supervision, 34*(2), 117–132.

Leong, F. T. L., & Kim, H. H. W. (1991). Going beyond cultural sensitivity on the road to multiculturalism: Using the Intercultural Sensitizer as a counselor training tool. *Journal of Counseling and Development, 70,* 112–118.

Levoy, G. (1997). *Callings: Finding and following an authentic life.* New York: Harmony Books.

Metzger L. H., Nadkarni, L. I., & Cornish, J. A. E. (2010). An overview of multicultural counseling competencies. In J. A. E. Cornish, B. A. Schreier, L. I. Nadkarni, L. H. Metzger, & E. R. Rodolfa (Eds.), *Handbook of multicultural counseling competencies.* Hoboken, NJ: Wiley.

Ong, A. D., & Edwards, L. M. (2008). Positive affect and adjustment to perceived racism. *Journal of Social and Clinical Psychology, 27,* 105-126.

Pedersen, P. (2000). *Hidden messages in culture-centered counseling: A triad training model.* Thousand Oaks, CA: Sage.

Pitner, R. O., & Sakamoto, I. (2005). The role of critical consciousness in multicultural practice: Examining how its strength becomes limitations. *American Journal of Orthopsychiatry, 4,* 684–694.

Ponterotto, J. G., Fuertes, J. N., & Chen, E. C. (2000). *Models of multicultural counseling.* Hoboken, NJ: John Wiley & Sons Inc.

Ponterotto, J. G., Rieger, B. P., Barrett, A., & Sparks, R. (1994). Assessing multicultural counseling competence: A review of instrumentation. *Journal of Counseling and Development, 72,* 316–322.

Priester, P. E. (2004, August). What about you . . . Have you ever laughed at a racial joke? Credibility tests in cross-racial psychotherapy. Poster presented at American Psychological Association conference, Honolulu, HI.

Reynaga-Abiko, G. (2010). Opportunity amidst challenge: Reflections of a Latina supervisor. *Training and Education in Professional Psychology, 4,* 19–25.

Sue, D. W., Ivey, A. E., & Pederson, P. B. (1996) *A theory of multicultural counseling and therapy.* Pacific Grove, CA: Brooks/Cole.

Sue, D. W., & Sue, D. (1990). *Counseling the culturally different: Theory and practice* (2nd ed.). New York: Wiley.

Sue, D. W., & Sue, D. (2003). *Counseling the culturally diverse: Theory and practice* (4th ed.). New York: Wiley.

Sue, D. W., & Sue, D. (2007). *Counseling the culturally diverse: Theory and practice* (5th ed.). New York: Wiley.

Suzuki, L. A., McRae, M. B., & Short, E. L. (2001). The facets of cultural competence: Searching outside the box. *The Counseling Psychologist, 29,* 842–849.

Torres J. B., Solberg, V. S., & Carlstrom, A. H. (2002). The myth of sameness among Latino men and their machismo. *American Journal of Orthopsychiatry, 72*(2), 163–181.

Torrey, E. F. (1986). *Witchdoctors and psychiatrist: The common roots of psychotherapy and its future.* New York: Harper & Row.

Trevino, Y. (2012). Reconciling the blessings and challenges of diversity through ancestral spiritual values. In K. Schaaf, K. Lindahl, K. S. Hurty, & G. Cheen (Eds.), *Women, spirituality, and transformative leadership* (pp. 36–39). Woodstock, VT: Skylight Paths Publishing.

Yamagishi, T., Hashimoto, H., & Schug, J. (2008). Preferences versus strategies as explanations for culture-specific behavior. *Psychological Science, 19*(6), 579-584.

Zimmerman, T. S., & Haddock, S. A. (2001). The weave of gender and culture in the tapestry of a family therapy training program: Promoting social justice in the practice of family therapy. *Journal of Feminist Family Therapy, 12,* 1–31.

7

Addressing Problems and Framing Solutions

"A problem well-stated is a problem half-solved."

—Charles F. Kettering

"Life is not about waiting for the storms to pass, but learning to dance in the rain."

—Anonymous

"An expert is a person who has made all the mistakes that can be made."

—Neils Bohr

For about a year while I (John Wade) was in graduate school, I worked part-time in customer service for a large bank. Although I would never want to go back to customer service, it was the perfect training ground for gaining perspective on dealing with problems. After all, customer service is mostly about fixing problems. Contrary to common perception, the vast majority of callers were actually quite reasonable and friendly. Of course, you got the occasional phone call that started with the ominous "You people. . ." but that was the exception. After thousands of phone calls from customers with various problems, I was struck by the fact that the bank's most loyal customers, those who talked about us with pride, were not the customers for whom we had never made a mistake. The customers who sang our praises were typically those who had had a problem, often caused by the bank, but the problem had been handled well and corrected. Partnering with the customer to address a problem typically caused the relationship to deepen. In a very real way, problems truly led to opportunity. This is not to say that either party would have chosen for the problem to exist, and I'm certainly not advocating intentionally creating problems as a strategy to increase customer loyalty. But it would be equally remiss to overlook the real potential contained within these often frustrating experiences. Analogously, surprises and mistakes in clinical supervision can also provide opportunities to strengthen the

147

working alliance, especially if the supervisor is nurturing and does not shame the therapist for committing "errors" and welcomes the ambiguity and missteps that occur as part of the learning process (Whiting, 2007, p. 148).

Although we have all undoubtedly heard that opportunities are contained within problems, in everyday life, especially when the stress level is turned up, it is easy to overly focus on the problem and feel "stuck," unable to imagine any possibility of the situation getting better. In customer service at the bank, most problems were easily resolved within a few minutes. Obviously, this is not the rule in clinical supervision. Our perspective and frame of reference plays a huge role in how we perceive problems and envision potential solutions, and it is human nature to become overly fixated on the problem. Research (e.g., Ohman, 2000) on stress suggests that we develop "tunnel vision" when we feel threatened, which can be adaptive in short-term situations when fighting or fleeing are good options. However, having flexibility and the ability to shift perspective are essential to effectively coping with problems and "stuckness" in supervision. This principle is illustrated by the classic picture commonly used in high school math and introductory psychology classes that contains both a beautiful woman or an old hag, depending upon where we focus our attention. Neither perspective is more "right" or "true" than the other. The key, especially in therapy or supervision, is not to try to necessarily find the "truth," which often leads to pressure, defensiveness, and rigidity, but to be able to shift perspective as necessary (Lopez, Snyder, & Rasmussen, 2003).

Supervision can be an anxiety-provoking process for both the supervisor and supervisee. By definition, learning will include some trial and error, and at times the realization that the current path is not working (Peterson and Seligman, 2004, p. 166). The story of when my wife and I (John Wade) bought a new kitchen sink seems to fit in well here (I know what you're thinking, that now they're even trying to throw in the kitchen sink. . .). Several years ago, we had a beautiful, new, shiny, stainless steel kitchen sink installed. However, within a few days, our prized new sink had gotten several minor scratches. It was no longer perfect, and those scratches stood out like a sore thumb. We realized that we had two choices. Actually, the one choice of treating the new sink with kid gloves to avoid any scratches had already passed. The other option was simply to allow more time to pass, and the few minor scratches that were painfully apparent in the unblemished newness would be transformed into a rich patina as more scratches gradually collected, which is what we have today. Of course, both with the kitchen sink and applying this metaphor to supervision, while minor scratches and imperfections add richness and character, deep gouges do real and sometimes permanent damage and are to be carefully avoided.

One of my (John Wade) pet peeves is reading clinical books where every technique or approach presented works as if by magic, and the clients always quickly and effortlessly improve. I remember even reading one book in which the therapist typically did not need a full session for his "cures," even with seemingly difficult issues like schizophrenia. But as we all know, real problems do occur, and sometimes things don't go as planned. A positive psychology approach to problems does not mean minimizing them or trying to put a nice spin on the situation, but rather to appreciate problems as problems and tackle them with a well-equipped tool kit.

This chapter presents several models for approaching the problems that can occur during supervision and offers practical suggestions to help your challenging situations lead to supervisee growth and a stronger supervisee-supervisory relationship. Problems are inevitable, but unlike customer service at a bank, there is not an outside department charged with solving them; however, successfully resolving problems can lead to more growth and development than a smooth journey ever could.

Thinking Outside the Box

The construction of the world-famous Florence Cathedral, which to this day still dominates and defines the Florence landscape, faced seemingly insurmountable challenges that almost doomed its completion (Gelb, 2002). Construction had begun in 1296, but over a hundred years later, the Cathedral had still not been finished. Talk about a problem in need of a solution! The octagonal walls of the cathedral were 180 feet wide and the opening between them was almost 140 feet, making traditional building methods at that time unworkable. Even the original designers of the cathedral had been unable to conceive of how to complete the dome, and had simply expressed faith that at some point in the future God would provide a solution. To try to solve this problem, in 1418 a competition was held inviting the leading architects and engineers to create a design for the dome of the cathedral. Many entries for the competition were received, mostly consisting of the traditional technique of using a central internal scaffolding and support system. However, Italian architect Filippo Brunelleschi proposed a radically different plan, eliminating the central support system and instead using a double shell of herringbone brickwork to raise the dome.

Of course, as stories like this usually go, the architects who reviewed his entry initially scoffed at the idea. But he persevered and insisted on calling another meeting with the judges. This time, he challenged the other architects to stand an egg upright on a flat marble floor and asserted that the person who could do so would be intelligent enough to build the dome. Everyone tried but was unsuccessful until Brunelleschi simply cracked the bottom of the egg on the marble and stood it up. The other architects complained that they could have done this, too, to which he retorted that they could also build his dome if they understood his plans. His plans were subsequently approved by the judges, and he was awarded the contract to build the famous dome. The Duomo, as the Florence Cathedral is typically referred to, remained the largest dome in the world for nearly 500 years, only surpassed when 20th-century building materials like steel and concrete became available.

Gelb (2002), who writes about famous historical figures and noteworthy achievements to illuminate exceptional thinking and perspective, described the lessons that can be learned from Brunelleschi's achievement. He noted that the word "problem" comes from the Latin root *pro*, meaning "forward," and the Latin word *ballein*, meaning "throw." The words "solution" and "solving" come from the Latin root word *solver*, meaning "to loosen up." So, "problem solving" is "the art of moving things forward by loosening up." In other words, Brunelleschi was able to expand his perspective by embracing the problem. When asked to describe how he could think of a solution that no one else could, he explained that when he began a project, he started with a visualization of its successful completion. Equally as important to the ultimate outcome, he did not let the setback of being initially rejected stop him and was able to keep his priorities in focus even when under stress. The rest of this chapter will offer different approaches for "thinking outside the box" and moving things forward when problems and challenges occur in supervision.

Appreciative Inquiry: Not Getting Stuck in the Mud

Most of us have had the experience of getting a car stuck in the mud, and the harder we tried to get it out, the more stuck we got. Even with the best of intentions, this can easily occur in supervision. As supervisors—especially mindful that you are legally and ethically responsible for your supervisee's actions—supervisee mistakes and missteps can be uncomfortable. Quite understandably, clinical supervision can often fall into the well-intentioned trap of being problem focused instead of solution oriented. Cohen (1999) reflected that given the parallel process that exists between supervision and practice, a problem-centered supervision orientation can easily undermine the supervision process by creating resistance in supervision or confusion in clinical work (p. 462).

The appreciative inquiry (AI) model of change (e.g., Ludema, Whitney, Mohr, & Griffin, 2003) is premised on the assumption that what we focus on becomes larger. Consequently, even though well intentioned, the traditional problem-solving approach of addressing difficulties through greater understanding of the problem (i.e., identifying the key problem, analyzing the root causes of failure, searching for possible solutions, and developing an action plan) often serves to further entrench the "stuckness." In contrast, the AI model entails a fundamental perspective shift from trying to avoid what we want less of, to trying to create what more of what is already working and more of what we do want. Intentionally focusing and amplifying the supervisees' strengths and progress will likely increase their sense of agency as therapists, which Bandura (1994) notes is associated with seeking more challenges, persisting with difficult tasks longer, and viewing oneself as capable and successful, even when failure is experienced.

Appreciative inquiry, as the name suggests, is grounded in appreciating the strengths and talents already present in the individual and using questions to illuminate and expand what one wants more of (e.g., Cooperrider and Srivastva, 1987; Cooperrider and Whitney, 1999). The act of *pivoting* embodies this principle, which is the intentional act of turning attention away from what the person does not want to what the person does want (Orem, Binkert, & Clancy, 2007), such as not dwelling on a failed intervention attempt in a session but rather envisioning what a successful intervention would look like. The supervisory stance of affirming and appreciating our supervisees can help lessen the tendency toward self-oriented preoccupation, which can easily happen when supervisees are anxious or beginning training, and also serves to enlarge their focus (Cooperrider, 1990). An effective starting point is simply "being-with," acknowledging the difficulty of the situation, not rejecting or minimizing it, but also not giving it greater focus (Orem, Binkert, & Clancey, 2007, p. 165). Reframing can also be a useful technique, especially with supervisee–supervisory conflicts. A conflict between the supervisee and the supervisor might be more easily resolved if it is strongly connected to the goals and expectations of the supervision, as well as if the emotional processes involved are also addressed (Allen, Szollos, & Williams, 1986, p. 90).

AI questions are meant to express curiosity and not judgment, invite multiple answers rather than the "right" one, and to serve as thought starters (Orem et al., 2007). This concept was foreshadowed in *Letters to a Young Poet,* in which Rainer Marie Rilke (1987) recommended that we embrace questions that engage us to think about our best selves without trying to figure out too quickly what the answers might be. This attitude of unpressured reflection can help facilitate critical thinking, especially when framed as "a form of mental processing with a purpose or anticipated outcome that is applied to relatively complex or unstructured ideas for which there is not an obvious solution" (Moon, 1999, p.23), as is the case with many issues in clinical supervision.

AI notes that the "common sense," problem-solving approach of trying to understand the problem fully in order to "fix" it often keeps us mired in stuckness. Our supervisees focus on problems with the best of intentions, that is, in order to better understand them or keep them from happening again. However, similar to driving, we tend to steer in the direction we are looking, and an overfocus on what we are trying to avoid tends to doom us to getting exactly what we don't want—more of the problem. AI addresses this dilemma by using a "solution-focused" approach, intentionally framing questions from a positive perspective and inquiring about what the solution would look like.

A couple of years ago, I (John Wade) had the privilege of attending two graduation-recognition ceremonies in one day: one for my sixth-grader graduating from elementary school, and another for my ninth-grader graduating from junior high. I was very impressed by the poise and public-speaking ability displayed by the 11- to 12- and 14- to 15-year-olds chosen to represent their schools. But from a positive psychology perspective, what struck me even more was how all of their speeches seemed to naturally gravitate to a strengths perspective of honoring accomplishments, identifying strengths, and acknowledging but moving on from difficult experiences. At first blush, it was a little difficult not to internally roll my eyes hearing a 15-year-old talk about the "wisdom" developed dealing with life struggles and the changes made in life based on learning. But on deeper reflection—that is terrific! Sure, the 15-year-old has more to learn and isn't finished making mistakes, but the same holds true for the 35-year-old, 55-year-old, and 75-year-old, as well as for the seasoned supervisor and the novice clinician. The process of honoring the struggle, acknowledging mistakes made, and openness to change and growth is exactly what we want from not only sixth- and ninth-graders, but also from graduate psychology students, medical residents, speech pathology students, and social work supervisees.

An African proverb asserts that smooth seas do not make good sailors. Difficulties and problems are inevitable and an intrinsic part of the learning process, but how failures and setbacks are perceived by both the supervisor and the supervisee are critical to the learning process of supervision. Supervisees who view setbacks and failures as an expected part of the training process increase their likelihood of recovering more quickly from missteps, as well as their ability to constructively approach future challenges (Seligman, 1990). It is critical for the supervisor to transmit the message that failure is perceived as part of the learning process, because people tend to "persevere only if they perceive falling down as *learning* rather than *failing*" (Heath & Heath, 2010, p. 169). Supervisees typically begin supervision feeling very anxious, and explicitly framing supervision and the learning process from a growth mind-set can help to quiet the anxiety. It can also be useful to address any possible unrealistic or inaccurate expectations that the supervisee might have (Juhnke, 1996).

Strength-based supervision acknowledges both strengths and weaknesses but intentionally focuses on and uses the supervisee's natural abilities to further develop areas of strength, which, in turn, can be used to tackle weaknesses and problems. Wetchler (1990) notes that focusing solely on mistakes or problems in supervision makes it difficult for the supervisee to develop a solid conceptual and practical foundation, which can lead to confusion and ineffectiveness, whereas a solution focused supervision model is designed to create a greater sense of efficacy as a therapist and facilitate the development of an organized clinical schema (p. 131). Put simply, "The knowledge of what supervisees do correctly in therapy is more important to the overall development of personal competency and the well-being of their clients than is a continual focus on clinical mistakes" (Wetchler, 1990, p. 130).

Perspectives from Narrative Supervision

Narrative therapy (e.g., White & Epston, 1990) posits that our identities and behavior are shaped by the accounts of our lives as filtered through our stories or narratives. Narrative therapy helps clients to reauthor or "re-story" their lives to be more in line with their values and hopes instead of constrained by their problems. Michael White (e.g., 1984, 1986), widely regarded as the founder of narrative therapy, when working with children who had encopresis, discovered that progress improved when he talked about the problem as if it were distinct and separate from the child (Tomm, 1989, p. 1). He began using the term "Sneaky Poo" (White, 1984) to talk about the encopresis in a separate and more "hearable" way with his young clients and would ask them about the devious ways "Sneaky Poo" catches children off guard and tricks them, causing unhappiness, frustration, and embarrassment. To ask these questions directly would have resulted in defensiveness and shame, but "externalizing" the problem seemed to offer his clients the emotional distance to examine and talk about difficult issues more openly. He also invited the children to notice and talk about the times they had effectively beaten the problem, helping to bolster their confidence and further "externalize" the problem.

Typically, our identity is at least somewhat fused with our problems, which is even reflected in the everyday language we use (e.g., "I'm depressed" or "she's an alcoholic"). This fusing of problems with identity often makes it very difficult to change, creating defensiveness and ambivalence, as if the idea of change requires letting go of a part of one's identity. As a problem becomes incorporated into the personal identity of a supervisee, it becomes increasingly difficult to escape (Tomm, 1989, p. 2).

Narrative therapy is grounded in the essential assumption that the person is not the problem; the problem is the problem. Typically, this involves naming the problem and then talking about the problem as an entity separate from the person. For instance, with a supervisee who frequently mentions feeling ineffective in session, the supervisor might ask, "What does Ineffectiveness cause you to believe about your abilities? What are instances when Ineffectiveness seems to have the upper hand?" The technique of externalization entails a linguistic separation of the problem from personal identity, which opens "conceptual space" to allow the lessening of the influence of the problem in one's life (Tomm, 1989, p. 1). "Because blame tends to restrain and guilt tends to constrain, reducing their prevalence is liberating. It opens space to explore new efforts in problem solving . . . as a result, the therapeutic process proceeds more smoothly and quickly" (Tomm, 1989, p. 2). The narrative approach has been generalized for use with a wide range of problems and populations, and seems well suited to address problems of supervision, especially given that supervisees are typically unsure about their competence and anxious regarding how they appear to both their supervisor and their clients.

Once the problem has been "externalized," the supervisee can be invited to escape the "oppression" of labeling and focus on creating a "preferred outcome" (Tomm, 1989, p. 3). A core narrative therapy intervention, based on the careful use of language, is to offer an embedded suggestion inviting supervisees to *envision the competent therapist they are becoming* (e.g., "What are two or three possible ways that the competent therapist you are becoming could imagine addressing this issue?"). Progress that is already occurring is made explicit (e.g., "In what ways have you stood up for yourself and not let 'unassertiveness' push you around in session?" [p. 3]).

These types of questions help to create and legitimize the belief that the supervisee has choices (and therefore control) and is an active agent in the course of supervision and the supervisee's clinical work. Pressure is not put on the supervisee to take any particular course of action (with the exception of the possibility of clinical harm), but the available alternatives are emphasized. From the narrative perspective, if the supervisee still feels stuck and does not explore or attempt other possibilities, it is assumed that there are other aspects of the problem that are restraining the supervisee and that additional externalization is required. For example, the supervisee might be under the influence of "fear of failure" or "perfectionism"(p. 3). When viewing a recording of the session, the supervisor and supervisee could watch for instances of the supervisee "accepting invitations" from the externalized problem, and discuss possible courses of action to take to rebuff the problem instead of being pushed around by it in the future (Sekelman & Todd, 1995, p. 27). For instance, the supervisor could ask, "What can you do the next time perfectionism causes you to self-focus and lose connection with your client?"

The narrative perspective emphasizes asking the supervisee to envision different possible narratives and future directions. This dovetails with the Eastern perspective that hope is always contained in difficulty, that we are only looking at one side of the coin at the moment, but the flipside is also contained in the situation, even if it is not visible to us. Hope is the flipside of difficulty. The key to getting unstuck is not to try to find the single "right" answer, but to be able to shift perspective in order to begin forward movement again.

Operating from the yin/yang framework can help illuminate the dark path out of "stuckness" when problems occur in supervision. From an Eastern perspective, operating from a dialectical, yin/yang framework, the question would be, "What is being left out?" when a supervisee is experiencing problems (e.g., Linehan and Dexter-Mazza, 2007). For example, asking this question of the supervisee who is frustrated with a client who tends to ramble and dart from topic to topic will likely prompt the supervisee to explore alternate, possible actions in session, such as interrupting from time to time to encourage deeper conversation, or perhaps using a more directive approach, such as acknowledging the topic jumping and asking the client if this is how the client wants to use the time.

Simply being able to imagine change, even if the details are not yet clear, can help to break the vise of stuckness. It can also be useful (and very validating) to explore the supervisee's intentions when things have gone badly. Intentions are almost always good, even if misguided or poorly executed, and it is a "face-saving" way to open the door to productive exploration of alternative routes or techniques (Edwards & Chen, 1999, p. 354).

Social Constructivist Approaches

Narrative supervision is grounded in social constructionism, which emphasizes the postmodern tenets of collaboration, nondirectiveness, and multiple perspectives (Whiting, 2007). Social constructionism posits that meaning and beliefs are created through social interaction and dialogue. Our reality is influenced and created by the conversations we have and the language we use, therefore, careful attention to language is critical in both therapy and supervision. Since supervision occurs within a context influenced by personal differences and differences of race, gender, culture, and power, it is not surprising from a social constructionism perspective that supervision is not always clear and that problems can arise (Whiting, 2007, p. 140). The social constructionist emphasis on patience, multiple perspectives, and curiosity can be helpful to supervision, where the complexity of the process can easily result in misunderstandings and "misreadings" that require time and openness to disentangle (p. 141).

The tone and patterns set in supervision are of critical importance not only because they impact the effectiveness of supervision but also because they are likely to transfer to the therapist–client relationship (Whiting, 2007, p. 142). A supervisee might present a particularly challenging case as hopeless and the client as intractably stuck. It would be easy for the supervisor to simply accept this version and collude with a narrow range of options. However, operating from a narrative or social constructionist framework, the supervisor would resist the hopelessness of the despair-laden presentation and seek to expand the story and explore other possibilities with the therapist. The supervisor's attitude of discovery and possibility is likely to ripple through and encourage the supervisee to re-story the version of the client (p. 142).

A social constructionist perspective involves approaching therapy and supervision collaboratively; however, this does not mean the supervisor can't challenge the supervisee. The emphasis on collaboration and assuming a non-expert position as the supervisor does not mean that the supervisor does not share experience and knowledge, which are regarded as critical to the supervision process. However, the supervisor does so from a stance of not "preknow-ing" or drawing conclusions. Although the narrative therapy perspective for psychotherapy is grounded in the assumption that clients are the experts on their lives, the same assumption is not made with supervision. Supervisees are not regarded as experts on how to do therapy, although it is believed that they have some natural skills, abilities, and talents that can be focused and enhanced by the supervision process (Bobele, Gardner, & Biever, 1995, p. 18). The social constructionist approach does not preclude the supervisor being directive or focusing on practical discussions; however, it does require thoughtfulness about choices that are made (Whiting, 2007, p. 143). One way this can be accomplished is through a *curious* stance rather than a *pronouncing* stance, which tends to prompt insecurity and defensiveness. Whiting notes that Parry and Doan (1994) suggest that it is helpful to offer supervisory comments with a question mark instead of a period.

Supervisees are assumed to possess strengths and competencies from a Social Constructionist perspective, but often are not aware of them or are not using fully using them, and their assets and resources can be hidden from both themselves and others (Greene, Lee, & Hoffpauir, 2005, p. 268). From the social constructionist perspective, a primary goal when problems occur is that of empowerment, helping the supervisee expand the ability to cope with the challenges and to use them as a stimulus for growth. The supervision process involves the supervisor asking questions to enable the supervisee to identify and amplify existing but often forgotten strengths, competencies, assets, and resources (p. 269). With the focus on collaboration instead of simply needing help, the supervisor can use empowering language to begin supervision sessions with questions such as, "What are you wanting for yourself today in supervision?" or "What concerns of yours do you want to address today?" Questions such as these help foster a sense of personal agency (p. 271), which is vital to effective coping and problem solving.

The Language of Possibilities

From a narrative or social constructionist perspective, the supervisor can broaden the possibilities for the supervisee and increase options by reframing difficulties, offering the supervisee a plausible, alternative interpretation for something defined as negative and undesirable or unchangeable (Greene et al., 2005, p. 272). Our perception of reality and frame of reference greatly influence how problems are perceived and the range of solutions that seem available. People who are unable to change their perception or frame of reference (people who are stuck) tend to see themselves as having few options and thus have little flexibility in dealing with problematic situations (p. 272). "The language of solutions never attempts to deny the existence of problems; rather, it emphasizes the fact that people have strengths, competencies, resources, potentials, and creativity which they or others are ignoring, forgetting, or underutilizing. By focusing the therapeutic dialogue on solutions and strengths, the power of language can facilitate the client and clinician in coconstructing a view of reality that contains an expanded definition of self that includes competence, skills, power, and personal agency" (pp. 272–273).

Role playing is one technique that can be used to help the supervisee view the problem from other perspectives, such as asking the supervisee to role play "as if" the supervisee were the client in different contexts and situations. This is designed to encourage the supervisee to become flexible in generating alternate but viable understandings. For instance, the supervisor could ask the supervisee to role play as the client commenting on the supervision session, "If you were the client, what would you say about our discussion of the problem and the ideas we have generated today in supervision?" (Bobele et al., 1995, pp. 18–19). Or, "From the perspective of the client, what seemed to spark energy or emotion and what seemed to dampen the process in the session?"

Supervision, from a social construction perspective, is understood as the entertainment of multiple, and at times contradictory, ideas at the same time (Bobele et al., 1995, p. 19). As with clients, when stuckness has occurred, the main goal of supervision is to prompt movement and striving for multiple ideas or understandings versus the pressure of having to come up with the one correct answer, and it can be quite liberating. The effective supervisor operates from a perspective of curiosity, which models openness and receptivity for the supervisee, and supervisees are encouraged to generate as many ideas as possible.

However, this is not meant to be relativism run amok. Some ideas and interventions are more helpful than others, and some can, in fact, be harmful to clients (Bobele et al., 1995, p. 20). As supervisors, we have a responsibility not only to the development and training of the supervisee but also the critical responsibility of ensuring the welfare of the clients being served. However, within the range of those that are reasonable and helpful, ideas and suggestions are more likely to be acted upon if the supervisee feels a sense of ownership and comfort with them (Bobele et al., 1995, p. 20). Questions that compel the supervisee to expand perspective can be useful, such as:

- "What do you think the client's understanding is?"

- "What understandings do you have?"

- "What possible understandings might be useful?"

- "What other questions could have been asked that you didn't ask?" (Bobele et al., 1995, p. 20)

Narrative or constructionist supervisors can then expand and refine the supervisee's thinking, adding to or extending the ideas being generated by the supervisee (Bobele et al., 1995, p. 22).

Perspectives from Solution-Focused Supervision

Solution-focused therapy shares many common assumptions with narrative therapy, focusing on strengths, possibilities, and solutions with the goal of guiding the supervisee to identify and build on successes and strengths and to ultimately create solutions. Borrowing from the social work strengths perspective (e.g., Saleebey, 1992), the emphasis of solution-focused therapy is to explore ways to create solutions when the situation seems impossible. Problems are not to be minimized, but ". . . it is as wrong to deny the possible as it is to deny the problem" (Saleebey, 1996, p. 297).

Focusing solely on mistakes or problems can leave supervisees without a solid conceptual and practical foundation, leading to confusion and ineffectiveness (Wetchler, 1990). A problem-oriented perspective in supervision reinforces supervisees' feelings of inadequacy, whereas focusing on solutions or on what supervisees are already doing correctly can help supervisees form a core sense of identity as therapists and a practical framework for clinical application. The solution-focused supervision model is designed to help supervisees recognize the positive aspects of their clinical work, develop an organized clinical schema, and create a sense of self-confidence (Wetchler, 1990, p. 131). It also fosters an expectation of successful resolutions to presenting concerns and the supervisees' potential to bring about change (Juhnke, 1996) by having supervisees identify and articulate those aspects of their clinical work that are effective and encouraging them to repeat these behaviors in similar situations. In other words: Note success and do more of the same.

Supervisees can be assigned the task of identifying what they have done well within a clinical session and reporting it to the supervisor in supervision. The focus is never placed on the correct solution but on what seems to be working for a supervisee with a particular case. Many training difficulties are the result of a lack of knowledge, and the skillful supervisor must determine whether a problem can best be addressed through a solution-focused perspective or simply through education and information (Wetchler, 1990, p. 134). Combining a developmental approach with a solution-focused approach, recognizing that beginning supervisees might need or desire a more education-oriented emphasis (Marek Sandifer, Beach, Coward, and Protinskey, 1994) can lessen supervisee feelings of incompetence or inadequacy when problems are framed as an issue of needing more information.

Solution-focused supervisors encourage supervisees to assume responsibility, generate multiple possible solutions, and initiate new behaviors linked to identified supervision goals. Helpful questions can include:

- "What might you begin doing within your sessions to make progress on this goal?"

- "What would you need to do to accomplish more of the same?

- "How might you do things differently to be even more helpful next time?"

- "How can you continue these positive interventions next week?"

- "How have you noticed your counseling skills improving since our last meeting?"

- "What will you be doing between the end of this session and the beginning of our next session to increase your counseling skills?" (Juhnke,1996)

Thomas (1994) draws upon solution-focused therapy, combined with narrative, competency-based, and possibility therapy models to focus on eliciting the life experience, education, and training of the supervisee to bear on problems. He notes that supervisees are typically hard enough on themselves already, and borrowing from the language of narrative therapy, many therapists have "problem-saturated views" of themselves doing therapy. Referencing de Shazer (1984) assertion that there is no such thing as resistance, the supervisor's task is to develop "fit" and find ways to cooperate with the learning experience and style of the supervisee through curiosity and a genuine desire to know the supervisee's opinions and perspectives (Thomas, 1994, pp. 13–15). Helping to illuminate glimmers of hope in seemingly intractable situations can also go a long way to lowering supervisee resistance.

The following are practical questions that a supervisor might use to facilitate movement and growth (Thomas, 1994, pp. 15–17):

Saliency

- "What is the most important thing I need know about your therapy at this time?"

- "What would be the most helpful for us to focus on?"

Maintaining a solution focus

- "How has your therapy changed or improved since our last supervision?"

- "When things are better, what are you doing differently?"

Setting goals

- "How will you know when things have improved for you?"

- "What is a small step that you could make in this direction (of the goal)?"

- "What is the smallest change you could make that would likely make a difference?"

- "What will be the first thing I (or another person) will notice about your therapy when it improves?"

Identifying exceptions to problems

- "When is the problem just a little different?"

- "When are you doing some of what you want to do in relation to this problem?"

Making exceptions meaningful

- "How did you decide to do that?"

- "What did your clients notice about you when you had an influence on this problem?"

- "How have your (mistakes, errors, etc.) made you a better therapist?"

- "So it isn't much better—what have you been doing to keep it from getting worse?"

- "How have you managed to decrease _____ since our last session?"

Future orientation and keeping the changes going

- "What specifically do you need to focus on doing this week to keep the problem from returning?"

Prompting supervisees with questions that invite them to assume responsibility for their growth and development and to reflect thoughtfully on the learning process helps supervisees make progress toward the ultimate goal of learning to become their own supervisors.

Sekelman and Todd (1995) also applied de Shazer solution-focused model (1985, 1988, 1991) to supervision, emphasizing an exception-oriented perspective based on identifying positive and productive therapist behavior patterns with clients and guiding supervisees to understand what helped to produce these beneficial outcomes. Through this exception-oriented focus, supervisees can make distinctions between productive and nonproductive behaviors and explore conditions under which the positive events occurred, leading to new discoveries about performance in specific goal and skill areas (Sekelman and Todd, 1995, p. 23).

One application of this approach is to ask the supervisee to locate two places on the session video recording that the supervisee felt had gone well and two places where the supervisee felt stuck. The supervision session would begin with watching the segments the supervisee identified as going well. The supervisor would intentionally highlight the successes with agency questions (e.g., "How did you do that?" and amplification questions, e.g., "What will you have to do to get that to happen more often with this client?"). Focusing on the successes first permits a natural transition to examining how to apply components of these successes to the instances of difficulty and also can bolster the supervisee's feelings of efficacy (Sekelman & Todd, 1995, p. 23).

The simple, but often overlooked strategy of just doing something different if things aren't working is encouraged, especially if the supervisee appears frustrated or stuck (Sekelman and Todd, 1995, p. 23). The supervisor might ask the supervisee to do something different in session with the client next time, no matter how "off the wall" it might seem (p. 26). Of course, judgment must be used before using such a directive, and comfort with the supervisee's level of clinical judgment and ethical decision making needs to be firmly established; however, giving permission to think outside of the box can be very liberating.

Sekelman and Todd (1995) note that the use of presuppositional language (e.g., words like *when* and *will)* has been found to be correlated with positive treatment outcomes (Gingerich, de Shazer, and Weiner-Davis, 1988). The expectancy for change often directly influences the supervisee's behavior (Sekelman & Todd, 1995, p. 25). For example, a supervisee who is having trouble being assertive in sessions could be asked to imagine the video recording two sessions later, when the supervisee is taking charge appropriately in session (Sekelman & Todd, 1995, p. 25). The use of de Shazer's (1985, 1988, 1991) ubiquitous miracle questions can also be effective when the supervisee is at an impasse: "Suppose that, prior to your next session, a miracle happened, and your impasse with the client is solved. How will you be able to tell that the miracle really happened? What will you be doing differently with the client in session? How did you get that to happen? What will you have to continue to do to make that happen more often?" Such questions can help unlock the supervisee's creativity and expertise in finding alternatives with their stuck cases (Sekelman and Todd, 1995, pp. 25–26).

Handling Conflict in Supervision

A problem of particular difficulty and discomfort to most supervisors is dealing with conflict in the supervisee–supervisory relationship. Although this is only one of an unlimited array of potential difficulties that can arise in supervision, we will focus on this issue more in depth because it can be particularly problematic and challenging. Nelson, Barnes, Evans, and Triggiano (2008) interviewed supervisors identified as "wise" by their professional peers about their experiences and strategies for handling conflict in clinical supervision. This research provides useful insights to an often confounding problem, and the methodology of studying best practices and learning from the experts embodies the essence of positive psychology research.

Potential Causes of Conflict

The supervisory situation, in which the supervisee is expected to be receptive to feedback, take risks, and be vulnerable, can be rife with the potential for conflict (Nelson et al., 2008, p. 172). Several factors were identified by the "wise" supervisors as frequently contributing when conflict occurred, including lack of direction for supervisors within the agency, prioritizing of service demands over training, and supervisor expectations that are too high and not consistent with the supervisee's level of development (Nelson et al., 2008, p. 178). The most frequently stated lesson from past conflict experiences is the importance of communicating clear expectations at the beginning of supervision and providing more feedback early. Preparing supervisees to receive supervision was recommended by several supervisors, including providing explicit suggestions for how to best use the supervision process. Upon recognizing a particularly challenging supervision conflict, many supervisors voiced regret about not having consulted with a colleague earlier in the process. Supervisors viewed both their own and supervisee anxiety as contributing to and accompanying the development of conflicts; however, supervisors stated that this anxiety can also be harnessed to promote supervisee development, notably by talking openly with their supervisees about their anxieties and concerns, particularly from a here-and-now perspective (Nelson et al., 2008, p. 180). Along these lines, Marek et al. (1994) note that when supervisees' goals are at odds with the supervisors' goals for them, it likely reflects their developmental needs at their particular stage of experience and training, and should be interpreted as potentially help-ful information and a good place to start a discussion of what the supervisee needs from supervision.

Opportunities Contained Within Conflict

Although often uncomfortable, conflict can create heightened opportunities for growth. If the supervisor handles the differences well, the supervisee is provided an opportunity to learn critical lessons about how to manage conflict situations with clients in a therapeutic and potentially transformative manner. Openness to con-flict was identified as a core competency held by the "wise" supervisors, with all of the supervisors expressing their commitment to approaching and working through conflicted situations with supervisees. "The capacity of therapeutic relationships to recover from therapeutic breaches is thought to enhance client trust that relation-ships can survive misunderstandings and disagreements as well as client confidence that he or she can successfully resolve them. A skillful therapist can guide a client through the process of accepting the therapist's inevitable fallibility, thus enhancing client capacity to accept his or her own; a skillful supervisor can guide the develop-ing therapist through a similar process" (Nelson et al., 2008, p. 172).

Strategies for Approaching Conflict

The "wise" supervisors expressed the belief that many difficulties in supervi-sion can be mitigated through the establishment of a strong working relation-ship, and that they intentionally nurtured trust in the working alliance to enable supervisees to approach conflict with courage. One supervisor stated that he wanted to model "an open door and put out the welcome mat for talking about the supervisory relationship very openly" (Nelson et al., 2008, p. 177). Humility was another key factor noted among "wise" supervisors, having both awareness and acceptance of their shortcomings as supervisors.

Not surprisingly, many supervisors expressed great enjoyment from doing supervision and excitement about learning from their supervisees (Nelson et al., 2008, p. 177). This attitude likely is contagious and helps to soften the edges of conflict. Although "wise" supervisors are able to handle conflict effec-tively, it doesn't mean that they like it. Most of the expert supervisors stated that they believed conflict was natural and useful, but personally found it extremely stressful to address (p. 179). However, most felt that it can be highly productive and were committed to addressing it when necessary, and used the process to become more self-aware of cognitive and behavioral changes they could make to improve their supervision (p. 181).

Not surprisingly, self-reflection also appears to be important. Wise supervisors appear to have thoroughly examined their part and the roles they play in conflicts and have worked to identify necessary personal changes to make to keep growing (Nelson et al., 2008, p. 179). Supervisors also described mentally talking themselves through conflicts (self-coaching) during difficult or conflicted situations.

The following were also identified by the expert supervisors as important to effectively managing conflicted situations in supervision:

- Openness to conflict and interpersonal processing

- Identifying interpersonal and contextual factors contributing to disagreements and misunderstandings

- Working to empathize with the supervisee

- Identifying and appreciating supervisee strengths rather than simply focusing on difficulties

- Seeking out professional consultation from colleagues; professional support and consultation were deemed critical to their ability to process, understand, and strategize about how to approach conflicts in supervision

- Becoming more active with supervisees when appropriate, such as using skills and theory training, assisting with problem solving, modeling desired behaviors, and using more direct observation to increase understanding of supervisee skills and interpersonal style

- Exercising patience

- Clarifying supervisee developmental needs

- Framing problems developmentally and identifying supervisee needs that, if met, might lead to conflict resolution

- Willingness to learn from mistakes

- Humility and transparency (Nelson et al., 2008, pp. 179–181)

Kottler and Hazler (1997) offer practical advice to supervisees experiencing difficulty with their supervision, encouraging them to ask for practical examples to help clarify verbal descriptions and theory, and even to request demonstrations to help move the supervision session from theory to practice. Such a request can be communicated as a genuine compliment of the supervisor's abilities. Kottler and Hazler acknowledge the power differential in supervision, and advise supervisees to express inquisitiveness—a highly desirable supervisee quality—but not doubts about the supervisor's suggestions or judgment, noting that "expressing your concerns as personal curiosity rather than supervisor-focused doubts is a good starting place for getting difficult issues into the conversation" (p. 214).

Facilitating Change

In the book *Switch: How to Change Things When Change Is Hard* by Chip and Dan Heath (2010), the authors poignantly describe the inherent human difficulties and obstacles involved in creating positive change and suggest a framework for dealing with problems and difficult situations that seems very applicable to clinical supervision. Their model is based upon the conceptualization of the self formulated by Jonathan Haidt in *The Happiness Hypothesis* (2006), as consisting of the two components of the *rider* (our logic and reason) and the *elephant* (everything else—our emotions, genetics, past history, fear, hopes, habits, learning, etc.). We tend to overly identify with the rider and believe that if we simply operate with the right information, change should naturally occur and be easy. But as anyone who has ever tried to change a behavior knows, information alone does not go very far. The key, according to Haidt, is to have both the elephant and rider work together. Neglecting or underestimating the power of the elephant (the observation of the relative size of the elephant to the rider indicates the strength of each) is usually met with frustration. Heath and Heath (2010) use the elephant and rider conceptualization as the unifying metaphor in their framework for dealing with problems and creating change. They assert that to create change in the face of problems, it is essential to "direct the rider, motivate the elephant, and shape the path" (p. 259). Each of these steps will be described in some detail.

Directing the Rider

At times, problems can seem too complex or daunting to tackle, and we can feel discouraged because it seems like big problems will invariably require big solutions. Heath and Heath (2010) referred to the striking example to counteract this common perception when Save the Children was invited by the Vietnam government in 1990 to fight malnutrition that was plaguing the country. Jerry Sternin, the leader of the effort, was given six months to complete the project. If ever there were a problem that seemed large and intractable—persistent hunger in a third-world, war-ravaged country was it! He realized that analyzing the causes of malnutrition would not likely yield useful information and instead focused on finding the "bright spots," the pockets of good nutrition that were already naturally occurring even though the overall picture was bleak. The team quickly discovered that although most villagers had roughly the same amount of food to work with, some mothers had noticeably healthier children. These "bright spot" mothers were doing a couple of small but important things differently. They were feeding their children four times a day instead of the usual two, allowing for better absorption of the food nutrients, and were also adding tiny shrimp and crabs and sweet potato greens to the rice, which were readily available in the local rice paddies. These simple steps yielded very significant results, illustrating that relatively small changes can sometimes have a big impact on big problems.

When presented with problems, our logic and reason (the rider) tend to remain stuck in contemplation and analysis, and the analysis is most typically directed at problems, not the bright spots, often creating "analysis paralysis" and inaction. Heath and Heath asserted that what looks like resistance is often the lack of clarity (2010, p. 15). In the Vietnamese nutrition example, the mothers certainly had the motivation to feed their children well, but the correct path wasn't clear. Having knowledge of the simple yet essential factors of good nutrition, which the practicing mothers began to share with other local mothers, made clear the steps for the mothers to take and became the springboard for hope.

This effort to fight malnutrition worked when many other efforts have failed in part because the critical steps were clear. Making decisions requires careful thought and self-control, which tends to exhaust the rider (e.g., Vohs et al., 2008). Routine behavior feels comfortable because it does not require choices, but when change is needed to respond to a problem, being on autopilot doesn't work. Uncertainty tends to make us emotionally uncomfortable (it makes the elephant anxious), typically resulting in defaulting to the most familiar path even if it is not effective or appropriate for the situation. Although you can't script every move—that would be like trying to foresee the 17th move in a chess game—it is critical to provide clear direction for the essential steps (Heath and Heath, 2010, p. 56).

For instance, using again the example of a supervisee who has trouble being assertive in session, it is essential for the supervisor to discuss with the supervisee a small number of useful clues—such as when the client is story telling—that can serve as indicators of when to become more active in session. Many supervisees, especially early in their development, have difficulty "going deeper" in session. Having practical, concrete suggestions of questions to ask to elucidate affect and markers regarding when to encourage clients to stay with their feelings can go a long way toward helping supervisees put this goal into practice.

Motivating the Elephant

To effectively work with our supervisees during times of difficulty, we not only need to provide direction but also to engage the supervisee's elephant for the supervisee to be willing to make desired changes. Although supervisees generally (although not always) are motivated to learn and grow, roadblocks frequently occur in subtle ways. When trying to change behavior, often our first instinct as supervisors is to teach; however, by doing so, we are often speaking to the rider when we should be speaking to the elephant (Heath & Heath, 2010, p. 113).

I'm sure we have all had the experience of possessing more than sufficient information to make a desired change, but of still struggling to do so (e.g., losing weight, quitting smoking, or staying more current with our clinical notes). A sense of progress with any learning or change attempt is critical because the elephant is easily demoralized. Thus, as supervisors, it is helpful to plan for early success. It is much easier to take a step if it feels like the next step rather than the first step. It is essential as supervisors that we communicate that the goal of supervision is not expertise but increasing competence. Planning for early success creates hope, which is critical to the change effort (p. 141). When even only small progress is occurring, "the Elephant feels less scared and less reluctant, because things are working. With each step, the Elephant starts *feeling* the change. A journey that started with dread is evolving, slowly, toward a feeling of confidence and pride. And at the same time the change is shrinking, the Elephant is *growing*" (p. 148).

Effectively engaging the elephant also requires continued motivation in spite of failure. Lack of success is to be expected at times with clinical training. Continuing with the language of the elephant and the rider, the elephant hates to fail, which typically triggers a flight reaction to escape from what feels aversive and uncomfortable. To effectively manage this as a supervisor, you have to create the expectation of failure along the way to longer-term success: "We will struggle, we will fail, we will be knocked down—but throughout, we'll get better, and we'll succeed in the end"(Heath & Heath, 2010, p. 169). Supervisors can also lessen anxiety by giving the message that, just as for clients, change and growth will likely not be a straightforward process, but often come in fits and starts.

Shaping the Path

The final component is to "shape the path" by removing obstacles in the way of change or learning when possible. The situation and the context often exerts powerful influence on our behavior, and it is easy to be guilty of the fundamental attribution error with our supervisees and confuse situational difficulties with problem characteristics of the supervisee. Heath and Heath (2010) refer to Wansink's (2006) research on eating to illustrate this concept, in which moviegoers were given free popcorn. After the movie, the remaining amount in the popcorn tubs was carefully weighed, and as expected, some people ate more than others. If that was all the information you had, it would be easy to make assumptions about the participants' eating behaviors, assuming that those who ate more had less willpower, were less health conscious, and so on. However, a key detail of the experiment was that participants were given either a small or large container of popcorn, and those with the larger tubs consistently ate more. The marathon runner with a large tub of popcorn was likely to eat more than the person who never exercises but was given a smaller container. What appeared to be a "people problem" for those who ate more was actually a situation problem. When the situation changes, behavior tends to change.

One of the first students I (John Wade) ever supervised had a rather narcissistic first client who liked to frequently pop up out of his chair during the session and perform monologues directly into the recording microphone hanging down from the ceiling. As you might imagine, the therapy was not going smoothly, and the supervisee did not look very effective or feel very competent. However, after a couple of frustrating sessions, my cosupervisor had the presence of mind to change the situation by discontinuing taping the sessions, having the supervisee tell his client that he was no longer being recorded. Although we did not have the tape to see this, the supervisee reported that the dynamics in session changed dramatically, and subsequent tapes with other clients showed a competent, developing therapist, in contrast to the sessions with his first client who would have challenged even seasoned therapists to be effective.

Embracing the Shadow

As we have tried to stress throughout the book so far, a strength-based supervision approach does not mean blindly focusing only on strengths and successes. As with most things, balance is the key. Jungian psychology posits that the archetype of the "shadow" tends to be fueled when either consciously or unconsciously material perceived or judged not to be acceptable is regulated and censored to the realm of the shadow instead of conscious awareness (Fitzgerald & Oliver, 2006). If positivity and solution-focused norms become excessive, self-censoring is likely to occur with material and experiences that are believed to fall outside of these norm, relegating them to the shadow through cognitive and emotional censoring (Fitzgerald, Oliver, & Hoxsey, 2010).

More simply put: our supervisees are not likely to share experiences with us as supervisors, and are even likely to push information away from their own self-awareness, that they believe is unacceptable and not consistent with prevailing norms. There is the danger that if a strengths focus is erroneously equated with merely focusing on successes, important experiences to be learned from will be ignored and repressed. Although much can be gained by focusing and building on instances of success, much can also be gained from examining experiences of struggle, and too much emphasis on only the positive can create the unintended consequence of empowering the "shadow."

Canoeing provides a useful metaphor for working with the shadow in supervision (Wade, 2012). Experienced white-water navigators know that it is important to be constantly aware of where the rocks are, and that we are in fact safer by using a strategy of intentionally getting close to the large rocks or boulders; if we are pushed into the rocks or spilled out of the canoe, we are much less likely to get hurt if we are close to the potential danger because less force is built up. Sometimes, we can even use the rocks to help us maneuver. Often, difficulties in clinical practice and in supervision occur not just because the client is difficult but because uncomfortable aspects of the self emerge. When this happens, similar to white-water canoeing, the most useful strategy is to create a safe and nonjudgmental atmosphere that invites the supervisee to approach the difficulties with eyes wide open and encouragement to get close to and embrace rather than avoid the problems (pp. 37–38).

One component of embracing and therefore effectively managing the shadow is modeling reflective thinking and encouraging it from our supervisees. Supervision involves providing a holding environment and the message of acceptance for the inherent discomfort of the process of awareness and examination of the shadow (Wade, 2012, p. 38). "Reflective supervision" focuses on promoting wholeness through inviting supervisees to embrace the more distressing aspects of themselves as clinicians in training. Shamoon-Shanock (1991) aptly describes this process as valuing strengths and partnering around vulnerabilities. Reflection within the supervision process is most likely to be effective and promote a wholeness perspective if conducted with an unpressured attitude (Moon, 1999, p. 23).

This is supported by a perspective of authenticity and genuine interest by the supervisor, which encourages the supervisee to share strengths and also allow vulnerabilities to be seen, helping to widen the supervisee's perspective (Shahmoon-Shanok, 1991, pp. 8–9). Shamoon-Shanok (2006) describes this process of supervision as "supervision," which like a superhero, enables the supervisee to see deeper, wider, and further, and to bring the "invisible" into focus. "Paradoxically, we can only become 'super-visors' by creating trusting and nurturing supervision relationships that encourage our supervisees to have the willingness to acknowledge bruised shins and fear of flying as they attempt to leap over tall buildings" (Wade, 2012, p. 39).

As supervisors, it is important to be mindful and try to avoid actions that prompt defensiveness and censoring, such as judging, discounting, neglecting, simplistically imposing positive reframes, or overly idealizing our supervisees, which reduces the space for them to acknowledge and explore difficulties (Oliver et al., 2011). The following are some practical suggestions for ways to set the stage for the Shadow to be more easily acknowledged and embraced:

- Acknowledge the potential discomfort of growing as a clinician without either rejecting or minimizing these feelings or giving them greater focus (Orem et al., 2007). Normalizing difficulty and failure creates space for the Shadow to be accepted instead of distanced.

- Reframe typical supervisee reactions to reduce the dichotomy between "unacceptable" and "acceptable," and set the stage for more effortless and natural incorporation of the Shadow. For example, supervisors can send a powerful message of normalization and acceptance by telling new supervisees that anxiety about the process of clinical development is normal, and, in fact, indicates the highly desirable quality of concern and investment in doing the job right.

• Encourage and model reflective thinking, resisting when appropriate the reflex to impart information to our supervisees and allowing them to grapple with dilemmas and distress, instead using these as teaching moments to critically reflect on the decision-making process. By doing so, we metaphorically teach our supervisees "how to fish" versus "giving them a fish for a day" (Wade, 2012, p. 38).

Conclusion

Problems, if successfully navigated, help to define us and strengthen our resourcefulness and adaptability. Haidt (2006) observed that difficult situations such as trauma and loss tend to result in growth only if three conditions are met: (1) the individual has strong social support, (2) the crisis is used as an opportunity to reevaluate priorities, and (3) the individual realizes the possession of greater strength than previously realized through being tested and surviving. We have revised this framework slightly to adapt it to supervision. It seems that the inevitable problems and difficulties inherent in the supervision and training process will lead ultimately to growth and positive outcomes if the following occur:

1. The supervisor creates a respectful, safe, nonjudgmental atmosphere in supervision to explore both the situation and the personal factors involved in the difficulty. (Successful navigation of this process can strengthen the supervision relationship.)

2. The supervisee conducts self-examination and also examines the situation openly, honestly, and with as much perspective as possible.

3. Through the process of supervision, the supervisee recognizes what needs to be changed and commits to working on it.

People are complex and supervision can be messy. The goal-attainment process is rarely a simple, linear endeavor, and it usually requires managing and overcoming obstacles and challenges that can become barriers to growth and change (Peterson, 2006). Problems in supervision, both with the supervisee's clinical work and also with the supervisory working alliance, are to be expected. However, if the supervision process can be approached with a general spirit of enjoyment and love of learning, many "quarters" will be deposited in the supervisory alliance "bank account," making the path easier when the inevitable obstacles and "withdrawals" do occur. "Wise" supervisors seem to embody this concept, and express great enjoyment from doing supervision and excitement about learning from their supervisees (Nelson et al., 2008, p. 177). This perspective of enjoying and welcoming the process is contagious (Doherty, 1997) and can help supervisees cope with problems and adverse circumstances more effectively and lead to the creation of positive spirals. Positive emotions not only equate to feeling good and feeling able to do more, but to actually having more cognitive resources to do so (e.g., Fredrickson, 2003). In the workplace, highly satisfied employees are more likely to take on new responsibilities or bigger challenges (Judge & Ilies, 2004), and difficulties are more likely to be embraced as manageable rather than feared. Supervisors who are able to work effectively with supervisees as they stumble in their developmental path are able to nurture their sense of self-efficacy, which in turn enables them to take on more serious challenges, persist with difficulties, and see themselves as capable and successful even when they experience failure (Bandura, 1994).

Questions to Consider

- What are my beliefs about working through or overcoming problems? Are there ways that my beliefs may be limiting myself or my supervisees?

- Who are my role models for effectively managing problems? What characteristics of these people do I admire? What is one small way I can "act into" one of these qualities?

- Consider a current situation that one of your supervisees is struggling with. Reframe this issue into what I would like to see more of, not less of.

- What problems have I successfully navigated in my professional development?

- What am I doing to convey the message that problems are to be expected and to normalize the struggle for my supervisees?

- Identify a current or recent problem or conflict with a supervisee. What insight would my "wise self" have for the situation?

Recommended Readings

Books

de Shazer S. (1988). *Clues: Investigating solutions in brief therapy.* New York: W.W. Norton.

Gelb M. J. (2002). *Discover your genius: How to think like history's ten most revolutionary minds.* New York: HarperCollins Publishers Inc.

Heath, C., & Heath, D. (2010). *Switch: How to change things when change is hard.* Broadway Books: New York.

Ludema, J. D., Whitney, D., Mohr, B.J ., & Griffin, T. J. (2003). *The appreciative inquiry summit.* San Francisco, CA: Barrett-Koehler Publishers, Inc.

Seligman, M. E. P. (1990). *Learned optimism.* New York: Knopf.

Articles

Bobele, M., Gardner, G., & Biever, J. (1995). Supervision as social construction. *Journal of Systematic Therapies, 14,* 15–25.

Juhnke, G. A. (1996). Solution-focused supervision: Promoting supervisee skills and confidence through successful solutions. *Counselor Education and Supervision, 36,* 48–58.

Nelson, M. L., Barnes, K. L., Evans, A. L., & Triggiano, P. J. (2008). Working with conflict in supervision: Wise supervisors' perspectives. *Journal of Counseling Psychology, 55,* 172–184.

Sekelman, M. D., & Todd, T. C. (1995). Co-creating a context for change in the supervisory system: The solution-focused supervision model. *Journal of Systematic Therapies, 14,* 21–33.

Tomm, K. (1989). Externalizing the problem and internalizing personal agency. *Journal of Strategic and Systematic Therapies, 8,* 1–5.

References

Allen, G. J., Szollos, S. J., & Williams, B. E. (1986). Doctoral students' comparative evaluations of best and worst psychotherapy supervision. *Professional Psychology, 17,* 91–99.

Bandura, A. (1994). Self-efficacy. In V. S. Ramachaudran (Ed.), *Encyclopedia of human behavior* (Vol. 4, pp. 71–81). New York: Academic Press.

Bobele, M., Gardner, G., & Biever, J. (1995). Supervision as social construction. *Journal of Systematic Therapies, 14,* 15–25.

Cohen, B. (1999). Intervention and supervision in strengths-based social work practice. *Families in Society, 80,* 460–466.

Cooperrider, D. L. (1990). Positive image, positive action: The affirmative basis for organizing. In S. Srivastva & D. L. Cooperrider (Eds.), *Appreciative management and leadership: The power of positive thought and action in organizations* (pp. 91–125). San Francisco, CA: Jossey-Bass

Cooperrider, D. L., & Srivastva, S. (1987). Appreciative inquiry in organizational change. In R. W. Woodman & E. Pasmore (Eds.), *Research in organizational change and development: An annual series featuring advances in theory* (pp. 129–169). San Francisco, CA: Berrett-Koehler.

Cooperrider, D. L., & Whitney, D. (1999). Appreciative inquiry: A positive revolution in change. In P. Holman & T. Devane (Eds.), *The change handbook: Group methods for shaping the future* (pp. 245–261). San Francisco: CA: Berrett-Koehler.

de Shazer (1984). The death of resistance. *Family Process, 23,* 11–17.

de Shazer (1985). *Keys to solution in brief therapy.* New York: W.W. Norton.

de Shazer (1988). *Clues: Investigating solutions in brief therapy.* New York: W.W. Norton.

de Shazer (1991). *Putting difference to work.* New York: W.W. Norton.

Doherty, D. R. (1997). The emotional contagion scale: A measure of individual differences. *Journal of Nonverbal Behavior. 21*(2), 131–154.

Edwards, J. K., & Chen, M. (1999). Strength-based supervision: Frameworks, current practice, and future directions: A *Wu-wei* method. *The Family Journal: Counseling and Therapy for Couples and Families, 7,* 349–357.

Fitzgerald, S. P., & Oliver, C. (2006, October). *Walking the dark side of positive organizational behavior: Appreciating the role of the shadow.* Clearwater, FL: Proceedings of the annual meeting of the Southern Academy of Management.

Fitzgerald, S. P., Oliver, C., & Hoxsety, J. (2010). Appreciative inquiry as a shadow process. *Journal of Management Inquiry, 19,* 220–233.

Fredrickson, B. L. (2003). Positive emotions and upward spirals in organizations. In K. S. Cameron, J. E. Dutton, & R. E. Quinn (Eds.), *Positive organizational scholarship: Foundations of a new discipline* (pp. 163–175). San Francisco, CA: Berrett-Koehler.

Gelb, M. J. (2002). *Discover your genius: How to think like history's ten most revolutionary minds.* New York: HarperCollins Publishers Inc.

Gingerich, W., deShazer, S., & Weiner-Davis, M. (1988). Constructing change: A research view of interviewing. In E. Lipcheck (Ed.), *Interviewing* (pp. 21–32). Rockville, MD: Aspen Press.

Greene, G. J., Lee, M. Y., & Hoffpauir, S. (2005). The languages of empowerment and strengths in clinical social work: A constructivist perspective. *Families in Society, 86,* 267–277.

Haidt, J. (2006). *The happiness hypothesis: Finding modern truth in ancient wisdom.* New York: Basic Books.

Heath, C., & Heath, D. (2010). *Switch: How to change things when change is hard.* New York: Broadway Books.

Judge, T. A., Piccolo, R. F., & Ilies, R. (2004). The forgotten ones? The validity of consideration and initiating structure in leadership research. *Journal of applied psychology, 89,* 36–51.

Juhnke, G. A. (1996). Solution-focused supervision: Promoting supervisee skills and confidence through successful solutions. *Counselor Education and Supervision, 36,* 48–58.

Kottler, J. A., & Hazler, R. J. (1997). *What you never learned in graduate school: A survival guide for therapists.* New York: W.W. Norton.

Linehan, M. M., & Dexter-Mazza, E. T. (2007). Dialectical behavioral therapy for borderline personality disorders. In D. H. Barlow (Ed.), *Clinical handbook for psychological disorders* (4th ed.). New York: Guilford Press.

Lopez, S. J., Snyder, C. R., & Rasmussen, H. N. (2003). Striking a vital balance: Developing a complimentary focus on human weaknesses and strength through positive psychological assessment. In S. J. Lopez & C. R. Snyder (Eds.), *Positive psychological assessment: A handbook of models and measures.* Washington, DC: American Psychological Association.

Ludema, J. D., Whitney, D., Mohr, B. J., & Griffin, T. J. (2003). *The appreciative inquiry summit.* San Francisco, CA: Barrett-Koehler Publishers, Inc.

Marek, L. I., Sandifer, D. M., Beach, A., Coward, R. L., & Protinskey, H. O. (1994). Supervision without the problem: A model of solution-focused supervision. *Journal of Family Psychotherapy, 5,* 57–64.

Moon, J. (1999). *A handbook of reflective and experiential learning.* London: RoutledgeFalmer.

Nelson, M. L., Barnes, K. L., Evans, A. L., & Triggiano, P. J. (2008). Working with conflict in supervision: Wise supervisors' perspectives. *Journal of Counseling Psychology, 55,* 172–184.

Ohman, A. (2000). Fear and anxiety: Evolutionary, cognitive, and clinical perspectives. In M. Lewis & J. M. Haviland-Jones (Eds.), *Handbook of emotions* (2nd ed., pp. 573–593). New York: Guilford Press.

Oliver, C., Fitzgerald, S. P., & Hoxsey, J. C. (2011). Critical appreciation of appreciative inquiry: Reflexive choices for shadow dancing. *Review of Business Research, 11,* 45–59.

Orem, S. L., Binkert, J., & Clancy, A.L. (2007). *Appreciative coaching: A positive process for change.* San Francisco, CA: Jossey-Bass.

Parry, A., & Doan, R. E. (1994*). Story re-visions: Narrative therapy in the postmodern world.* New York: Guilford.

Peterson, C., & Seligman, M. E. P. (2004). *Character strengths and virtues: A handbook and classification.* New York: Oxford University Press

Peterson, D. B. (2006). People are complex and the world is messy: A behavior-based approach to executive coaching. In D. R. Stober & A. M. Grant (Eds.), *Evidence-based coaching handbook: Putting best practices to work for your clients* (pp. 51–76). Hoboken, NJ: John Wiley & Sons

Rilke, R. M. (1987). *Letters to a young poet.* New York: Vintage Books.

Saleebey, D. (1992). *The strengths perspective in social work practice.* White Plains, NY: Longman.

Saleebey, D. (1996). The strengths perspective in social work practice: Extensions and cautions. *Social Work, 41,* 296–305.

Sekelman, M. D., & Todd, T. C. (1995). Co-creating a context for change in the supervisory system: The solution-focused supervision model. *Journal of Systematic Therapies, 14,* 21–33.

Seligman, M. E. P. (1990). *Learned optimism.* New York: Knopf.

Shamoon-Shanok, R. (1991). The supervisory relationship: Integrator, resource, and guide. *Zero to Three, 12,* 16–19.

Shamoon-Shanok, R. (2006). Reflective supervision for an integrated model: What, why and how? In G. M. Foley & J. D. Hochman (Eds.), *Mental health in early intervention: Achieving unity in principles and practice* (pp. 343–381). Baltimore, MD: Brookes Publishing.

Thomas, F. N. (1994) Solution-oriented supervision: The coaxing of expertise. *The Family Journal: Counseling and Therapy for Couples and Families, 2,* 11–18.

Tomm, K. (1989). Externalizing the problem and internalizing personal agency. *Journal of Strategic and Systematic Therapies, 8,* 1–5.

Vohs, K. D., Baumeiser, R. F., Schmeichel, B. J., Twenge, J. M., Nelson, N. M., & Tice, D. M. (2008). Making choices impairs subsequent self-control: A limited resource account of decision-making, self-regulation, and active initiative. *Journal of Personality and Social Psychology, 94,* 883–898.

Wade, J. C. (2012). Appreciatively embracing the shadow in training and supervision. *AI Practitioner, 14,* 37–39.

Wansink, B., Just, D. R., & Payne, C. R. (2009). Mindless eating and healthy heuristics for the irrational. *The American Economic Review,* 165-169.

Wetchler, J. L. (1990). Solution-focused supervision. *Family Therapy, 17,* 129–138.

Whiting, J. B. (2007). Authors, artists, and social constructionism: A case study of narrative supervision. *The American Journal of Family Therapy, 35,* 139–150.

White, M. (1984). Pseudoencopresis: From avalance to victory, from vicious to virtuous cycle. *Family Systems Medicine, 2,* 150–160.

White, M. (1986). Negative explanation, restraint, and double description: A template for family therapy. *Family Process, 25,* 169–184.

White, M., & Epston, D. (1990). *Narrative means to therapeutic ends.* New York: W.W. Norton.

Beyond Competency:
Expertise and Lifelong Learning

"It is not that I'm so smart. But I stay with the questions much longer."
—Albert Einstein

"We are what we repeatedly do. Excellence then, is not an act, but a habit."
—Aristotle

"You live and learn. At any rate, you live."
—Douglas Adams, *Mostly Harmless*, 2000

Not as Easy as It Seems

Practice makes perfect, or so we've been told. Unfortunately, research from a wide range of fields indicates that once a level of basic competence has been reached, people typically don't continue to become better with increased years of experience. The amount of clinical experience has been found to have negligible impact on psychologists' ability to assess personality disorders. Surgeons are no better at predicting hospital stays after surgery than residents are. Experienced stockbrokers do not make their clients more money than novice stockbrokers. The same lack of benefit from experience has also been found with psychiatrists, college admissions officers, court judges, personnel selectors, and intelligence analysts (Shanteau, 1992). Growth and improvement is typically highly valued in the workplace in the early stages of development, but tends not to be rewarded as much once basic proficiency has been achieved. This tendency for learning to peak at competency has been coined the "experience trap" (Colvin, 2008), and in some instances, people actually get worse with experience. For instance, more experienced doctors typically score lower on tests of medical knowledge than less experienced doctors (Caamerer & Johnson, 1991).

175

Although the thought of sending mental health students out to practice on unsuspecting clients with no training or supervision would seem unconscionable, not to mention unethical, the research seems to be mixed whether supervision and experience actually have any impact on clinical effectiveness. In fact, researchers have investigated whether clinical training serves any purpose, and several reviews of the literature have concluded that professionally trained therapists do not perform any better than paraprofessionals (e.g., Berman & Norton, 1985; Christensen & Jacobson, 1994; Durlak, 1979). One study actually found that clients receiving services from paraprofessionals were more likely to benefit than clients receiving treatment from professionals, a finding that would cast serious doubt about the effectiveness of clinical training (Hattie, Sharpley, & Rogers, 1984). Berman and Norton (1985) identified methodological problems with the Hattie et al. study and reanalyzed the data, and the new results indicated that professional clinicians were equally as effective as paraprofessionals. Although there is probably some consolation that formally trained therapists were not found to be worse than untrained therapists, it is disquieting that training and supervision do not seem to lead to better treatment outcomes. Interestingly, novice medical students were found to have more limited "schematic structures" and experts' schemata were more precisely and richly detailed, but in spite of these differences, novices and experts reasoned in much the same manner (Johnson et al., 1981). Garb (2005) observed that the literature on clinical assessment suggests that experienced clinicians are no more accurate making diagnoses than are less experienced clinicians, and that practicing clinicians do not make more valid judgments than graduate students in mental health fields. However, although diagnostic accuracy does not increase with experience, confidence in clinical judgment does (Garb, 1989). Clinicians aren't getting better with experience but they think they are—not a good combination. Based on the lack of research demonstrating a correlation between training or experience with improved clinical outcomes, the American Psychological Association (1982) was forced to conclude that there is no evidence that either professional training or expertise is related to professional competence.

If the story were to stop here, it would be pretty demoralizing. No one enters the mental health field to become merely competent and stop improving, and certainly no one wants to invest in supervision and training, either as a supervisor or supervisee, for it not to matter. The goal of training and supervision is for it to lead to increased clinical proficiency and more sophisticated decision making, and it is hoped that greater experience will lead to continued and deepening growth. The dubious research findings certainly present a cautionary tale that training and experience do not automatically lead to greater competence. However, like most broad-brush caricatures, much important information is contained in the details and in the exceptions, which are examined throughout the rest of the chapter.

More recent research suggests that supervision and training do matter and contribute to better clinical outcomes. Callahan, Almstrom, Swift, Borja, and Heath (2009) report significantly higher premature termination rates in training clinics compared to other outpatient settings (over 75% versus between 40–60%), and that client improvements occur more slowly with fewer successful outcomes among therapists in training, with supervisors accounting for 16% of the variance in outcome. The researchers assert that supervision may be the most important mechanism for developing competencies, especially with "client-focused" supervision compared to supervision that focused on administrative case management. Improved client outcomes appear to be especially strong among supervisees if a strong positive emotional response to the supervisor is present (Dodenhoff, 1981).

The focus of this chapter is to discuss the learning process in detail and to provide suggestions about how to set the stage for continued learning and growth, starting during the supervision process and hopefully extending throughout one's professional career. The troubling findings on the lack of evidence connecting supervision to clinical growth have had the impact of prompting a competency movement within clinical training, attempting to more directly connect training to objectively measurable outcomes. This chapter, however, attempts to go beyond competency and also examines how both excellence and lifelong learning can be achieved.

Cognitive Processes

Although the research is mixed regarding the effects of supervision and experience on clinical outcomes, there are striking differences in the cognitive processes between novices and experts. It appears that learning and skill acquisition is a developmental process in which supervisees in the early stages of learning memorize many pieces of relevant information but have difficulty synthesizing the parts into a larger gestalt. However, with increasing experience, they can more easily connect new knowledge and information to their existing knowledge base and develop more flexible models to deal with the novelty and complexity that characterize adaptive expertise (Holyoak, 1991). The greater the fund of knowledge, the more easily new information can find a place to stick and be meaningfully incorporated. I (John Wade) distinctly remember being aware of this as a beginning master's student struggling to make sense of the clinical classes I was taking before I had yet to see a client, realizing that I would be able to make much better use of all of the useful and relevant textbook information I was learning once I had actual clinical experience to serve as a framework to structure the new information.

Experience appears to fundamentally change the cognitive processing and therefore positively affect clinicians' judgments and ability to gather and use information (Lichtenberg, 1997, pp. 228–229). A review of selected literature (Lichtenberg, 1997, p. 234) indicates that in contrast to novices, experts tend to

- Spend a greater amount of time understanding or analyzing problems before attempting solutions
- Have a larger knowledge base from which to work
- Have a better organized or structured knowledge base
- Have the ability to perceive large, meaningful patterns in their domain
- Have greater proceduralization (automatic processing) of knowledge (characterized by speed, lack of effort, and lack of control)
- Have superior long- and short-term memories
- Have the ability to see and represent problems in their domain at a deeper (more meaningful) level
- Have stronger self-monitoring skills

Ironically, Frensch and Sternberg (1989) suggest that although a large, well-organized and "automated" knowledge base is good in most situations, expert performance is likely to be poorer than that of nonexpert in "ill-structured situations," such as those frequently encountered in clinical situations when existing information has to be incorporated with new, incompatible information, or when existing information has to be consciously selected, or new knowledge has to be created. Johnson et al. (1981) found that although novice medical students had more limited schematic structures than those of experts, whose schemata were more precisely and richly detailed, experts and novices reasoned in much the same manner. However, Lichtenberg (1997) suggests that based on research in other problem-solving domains (e.g., Voss & Post, 1988), experts should be better than novices in very meaningful ways, including decomposing and transforming ill-structured clinical problems into a set of well-structured (or better structured, solvable) sub-problems and to identify (or impose) "parameters" (i.e., procedures, tasks, and goals) on those subproblems; and they have more and better-organized clinical "tools" (frameworks, interventions, and assessment strategies) to select from and use in the service of reaching a meaningful solution to the problem (p. 233).

Shortcuts and Stumbling Blocks

Although experience helps us to develop more efficient cognitive processes and to create more automatic pathways that enable us to more deeply and fully understand clinical situations, our humanness is never far away. Just as

10 eyewitnesses can recount the exact same incident 10 different ways, our perception and thought processes are subject to biases, blind spots, and limitations. Tracey (2011) describes some of the more common traps of misperception and heuristics (mental shortcuts that allow us to solve problems and make judgments more efficiently) that clinicians tend to fall prey to:

- Confirmatory bias—the tendency to seek out information that is supportive of our prior beliefs or assumptions about the client, which in turn, erroneously leads to increased confidence in our appraisal. The term *illusion of validity* captures the unjustified sense of confidence that often comes with clinical judgment (Kahnheman & Klein, 2009, p. 517).

- Representativeness heuristic—the extent to which something matches relevant categories, for example, diagnostic categories or personality labels. We are prone to viewing individuals through the lens of the category that the individual appears to fit.

- Anchoring heuristic—the tendency to let initial information and impressions determine subsequent decision making, for example, how the client seems during the first session greatly influences the lens through which the client is viewed in subsequent sessions. People tend to form their initial judgments on the basis of some salient information and then make insufficient adjustments away from the initial judgment as additional information is presented.

- Availability heuristic—the tendency to make judgments concerning the likelihood of an event occurring based on the ease that examples can be brought to mind. This is influenced by factors such as exposure, mood, the vividness of the example, and the perceived plausibility (regardless of the probability). This phenomenon seems to be evidenced by the observation that certain diagnoses seem to go in "fads" and are overutilized.

Add to all of these mental traps the tendency of humans not to be very inquisitive. Perkins, Farady, and Bushey (1991) explain that generally we quickly take a position, look for evidence that supports it, and stop exploring alternative possibilities once we find just enough evidence so that our position makes sense and therefore seems "confirmed." Perkins et al. labeled the tendency not to invest much energy seeking alternative possibilities as the "makes sense" stopping rule. Unless we are intentional about overriding our natural proclivities, our mental inquisitiveness tends to cease once we find a reason that "makes sense," even if better explanations may exist or we have only a modest grasp of the information. Even when we try to be open-minded, it is inherently difficult, and if we add the additional factor of perceiving pressure or a reason to want to defend our position (such as being observed during supervision), our ability to seek or recognize contradictory evidence deteriorates even further. Little wonder we have so much trouble learning from experience. We are much more likely to interpret a moderately successful experience with a client using interpersonal therapy (if that is our preferred method) as evidence that the interpersonal approach worked, versus trying to consider whether another approach may have been better suited to the client's needs or presenting concerns and could have potentially been more effective.

The use of heuristics often comes with a price. Research shows that even highly intelligent people have great difficulty judging probabilities, making predictions, and coping with uncertainty, often as a direct result of the use of these mental shortcuts (Slovic, Fischhoff, & Lichtenstein, 1985). It is commonly assumed that those with considerable experience would use all relevant information to make decisions, but the underuse of available information has been reported for experts in many fields, including clinical psychologists (Goldberg, 1970).

Reason for Hope

Although reliance upon heuristics allows for the efficient processing of information and can assist in the expediency of problem solving and decision making (Anderson, 1981), these "efficiency aids" fundamentally are biases, and like all biases, self-awareness and the ability to relinquish them when appropriate are critical. Garb (2005) asserts that clinicians have trouble learning from experience because their judgment strategies are not always accurate and suggests that clinicians need to be more willing to revise initial impressions of clients and to entertain alternative hypotheses. Probabilistic thinking needs to be embraced, and clinicians shouldn't feel that they have to be able to explain all of their clients' behaviors. Cognitive flexibility—the ability to entertain alternative perspectives and to seek and incorporate new information—is not only the hallmark of good mental health, it should also be an intentional goal to be fostered in clinical supervisees through supervision. Excessive rigidity is equated with mental and emotional dysfunction, and the same holds true for conducting psychotherapy as well. Providing a supportive, embracing environment increases the ability to broaden one's perspective and cultivates flexibility and open-mindedness. As a supervisor, creating a nurturing environment in which the supervisee feels the freedom to admit and explore mistakes and uncertainty seems critical to identifying limitations and errors of perception, broadening perspective, and encouraging cognitive flexibility.

As we probably suggest to our clients in their efforts to improve, self-awareness and self-monitoring are the keys to change and growth. Self-monitoring and self-regulating our decision-making and judgment strategies are essential to using heuristics constructively, and not letting heuristics become biases that trap us into limited perception and blinded judgment, resulting in sub-par clinical treatment and potentially harm to our clients. The good news is that even though experts are not immune to the cognitive illusions that affect other people (Kahneman, 1991), studies within cognitive psychology have shown expert superiority over novices in nearly every aspect of cognitive functioning, from memory and learning to problem solving and reasoning (Anderson, 1981).

Seligman (2011) notes that intelligence is largely equated with mental-processing speed. The more quickly we can run through certain cognitive tasks, the more it frees our attention and mental energy to focus on other matters. Using heuristics to take mental shortcuts is at times very necessary, otherwise we would be overwhelmed with all of the information to sort through. However, speed is only part of the equation. Clinical effectiveness also greatly depends on knowing when to slow down, when to operate slowly and reflectively. Good training encourages this of supervisees, and builds in time for unhurried reflection and conversation and the thorough contemplation of possibilities.

The origins of the "heuristics and biases" understanding of judgment and decision making can be traced to Paul Meehl (1954). He reviewed the literature of studies that compared the accuracy of forecasts made by human judges (mostly clinical psychologists) and those predicted by simple statistical models and found that statistical predictions proved to be more accurate than human predictions in almost every case. Kahneman and Klein (2009) observed that research focusing on the flawed judgment of clinicians is primarily associated with the heuristics and biases model, whereas the naturalistic decision making (NDM) model focuses more on successes of expert intuition. The NDM model grew out of the research on master chess players (e.g., Chase and Simon, 1973; deGroot, 1978), which found that chess grand masters could identify promising moves rapidly, while mediocre players did not even consider the best moves. Chess experts also differed from weaker players in their ability to appreciate the dynamics of complex positions and quickly judge potential moves as promising or pointless. Intuition was regarded as simply the recognition of patterns stored in memory, with greater memory leading to increased efficacy (Kahneman & Klein, 2009, pp. 515–516). Research on the decision making of another group, fire ground commanders, found that they were able to evaluate options by mentally simulating them to see if they would work in the situation they were facing, enabling them to effectively use their tacit knowledge.

Although experts seem to do no better than novices in some fields, there are domains in which experts do consistently perform better (livestock judges, astronomers, test pilots, chess masters, mathematicians, accountants, grain inspectors, photo interpreters, and insurance analysts). This is in contrast to those professions in which experts tend to do poorly compared to novices (e.g., stockbrokers, clinical psychologists, psychiatrists, college admissions officers, court judges, personnel selectors, and intelligence analysts.) Shanteau (1992) observed notable differences in the task characteristics associated with good and poor performance in experts. Good performance in experts tends to be associated with: making decisions about things versus behavior;

static versus changeable stimuli; predictable versus unpredictable problems; repetitive versus unique tasks; the presence of readily available feedback and objective analysis; the expectation of some errors; and the breaking down of problems into smaller, component parts. Obviously, the factors correlated with increased performance with experience are difficult to come by in clinical situations. (This would probably be a much easier chapter to write for livestock judges.)

Dawes (1994) asserted that because counselors do not experience feedback about the effects of their responses on either an immediate or a continuous basis, their actions cannot be "shaped" automatically by their consequences as they are in motor skills. Less predictable behavioral domains provide fewer chances to learn, for example, less repetition and opportunity to receive feedback (Shanteau, 1992). The situation has a profound impact on learning opportunities, leading Kahneman and Klein to assert that if an environment provides valid cues and good feedback, skill and expert intuition will eventually develop in individuals with sufficient talent (2009, p. 524).

Shanteau (1992) proposed the "theory of expert competence" to help explain the discrepancy between the research on judgment and decision making—which indicates that experts make flawed decisions in part due to the biasing effects of judgmental heuristics—and cognitive science research—which indicates that experts are more competent and different from novices in every other aspect of cognitive functioning. According to Shanteau, the following five factors facilitate the emergence of skills and abilities:

1. Domain knowledge—not only textbook knowledge, but insights gained from experience in working on real problems. Domain knowledge is necessary but not sufficient for expertise.

2. Psychological traits—strong self-confidence, excellent communication skills, the ability to adapt to new responsibilities, and a clear sense of responsibility.

3. Cognitive skills—highly developed attention abilities, a sense of what is relevant, the ability to identify exceptions to the rules, and the capability to work effectively under stress.

4. Decision strategies—making use of dynamic feedback, relying on decision aids, decomposing complex decision problems, and prethinking solutions to tough situations.

5. Task characteristics—even with the appropriate knowledge, skills, and strategies, the competence observed in an expert depends on the task.

Although the task characteristics of the situation are usually determined by circumstances, the other four factors can serve as useful guideposts for areas to intentionally target for supervisee growth and development.

Learning to Learn

Deliberate Practice

The various challenges and obstacles to learning are numerous, and it is clear that refining therapeutic skills and developing keen clinical judgment are more than the process of simply accumulating more client hours. One of the hallmarks of positive psychology is the attempt to understand the pathways to success through the intentional study of high achievers and excellent performance. Anders Ericsson could be called the "high achiever" of high achievement research. He has devoted much of his professional career to learning about excellence by studying people who exemplify outstanding accomplishment in their respective fields. Ericsson and Charness (1994) trace the roots of understanding exemplary performance to the humanistic goal of understanding how people might improve their lives by gaining insight from the lives of people who exemplify excellence. Quoting Maslow (1971) note that "if we want to know how fast a human being can run, then it is no use to average out the speed of a 'good sample' of the population; it is far better to collect Olympic gold medal winners and see how well they can do it" (p. 7).

Ericsson and Charness (1994) observed that exceptional performance has often been thought to result from incremental increases in knowledge and skill due to the extended effects of experience. Talent also is often identified as the cause of excellence. However, as sports fans have astutely attested, if innate talent was the sum of the equation, Michael Jordan would not have been cut from his high school basketball team. Expert performance is not the automatic consequence of more experience with an activity, but rather the result of structured learning and effortful adaptation. One of the ways practice and more practice appear to be helpful are through the creation of mental maps of necessary information. Experts appear to be able to form an internal representation of relevant information that increases their ability to reason, plan, and evaluate consequences of possible actions.

To attain exceptional levels of performance, people must undergo a very long period of active learning during which they refine and improve their skills, ideally under the supervision of a teacher or a coach (Ericsson and Charness, 1994). In many of the fields studied, expert performance appears to take at least 10 years of intense practice and study, and in fact, the 10-year or "10,000-hour rule" has become so widely accepted that it has started to enter the common vernacular. Winning international competitions in sports, arts, and science appears to require at least 10 years of preparation and typically longer. Malcolm Gladwell (2008) discusses this concept in a very entertaining fashion in *Outliers: The Story of Success*, in which he describes noteworthy examples of outstanding achievement. He uses the example that Bill Gates "practiced" computer programming for years during high school by sneaking out of his house every night and staying at the University of Washington computing lab until dawn, gaining the "magic" 10,000 hours of programming experience by his early 20s. Gladwell also told the story of the Beatles practicing at a seedy strip club in Hamburg, Germany, for years before emerging on the popular music scene. The venue was important, because they played 8-hour sets 6 days a week, giving them more than sufficient playing time to attain "expert"-level knowledge and skill, and enabling them to reach the 10,000 hours milestone in just 6 years (and perhaps also causing Ringo Starr to scream "I've got blisters on my fingers" at the end of the song "Helter Skelter.") The significance of these examples is not to imply that a monumental number of clinical hours needs to be obtained (it certainly can often be difficult enough merely to complete the number of hours required in training programs), but that passion, love of learning, curiosity, and persistent practice are important to the development of expertise.

Mere practice is not enough. Casual tennis players know that just hitting a few balls every Saturday morning, or even playing a full match five days a week, is unlikely to translate to making the professional circuit. Ericsson and Charness (1994) explain that to truly improve, individuals have to monitor their training with full and effortful concentration to get the benefit of the feedback contained in experience (p. 738).

Easier said than done. One difficulty especially relevant to the practice of psychotherapy is that clinicians do not encounter the same situations on a frequent or predictable basis. For example, a tennis player wanting to improve the backhand lob might only hit two to three backhand lobs during an entire game, hardly enough practice on that particular skill to produce improvement. This situation is magnified many times over in counseling, in which every client and every problem is unique. In tennis, for the player to be expected to improve the backhand lob, the coach would have the player practice many repetitions focused on an identified target to hit, giving the player hundreds of opportunities to practice the specific stroke, and deliberately tailoring the practice to address to specific skill to be improved. The fact that this is usually not the case in clinical training might provide some insight as to why the effects of training are so unclear. Conducting psychotherapy and assessment are obviously much more complex than playing tennis or the piano, but focusing on mastering the individual components of the process seems likely to also yield improved understanding and proficiency with the entire process.

Colvin (2008) further expands on the concept of "deliberate practice." He notes that the teacher (or supervisor or coach) has the advantage of being able to view the supervisee with a clear, unbiased perspective, and consequently is in a good position to design well-suited training and practice activities. Simply put, the supervisor can see the supervisee in ways the supervisee cannot. This is one reason why even the best performers (e.g., pianists, golf players) still use teachers and coaches even when their skill far supersedes that of their teachers. Without supervision or coaching, we typically do just what we've done before, even if intentionally practicing, whereas supervision is designed to stretch us beyond our current capabilities. In fact, some elite athletes change coaches or use a supplemental coach in order to help with specific issues that have developed and to stay at a peak level of performance.

Deliberate practice consists of several key ingredients:

- Identifying sharply defined elements of performance to be improved and working intently on them

- High repetition of the specific skill or technique (which often does not occur with the specific activities we need to improve in real-life situations)

- Practice in the "learning zone," where the skills and abilities are just out of reach, not in the "comfort zone," where we are not being challenged, or the "panic zone," where we are overwhelmed

- Full and focused concentration

It is essential to be intentional about learning and not let the activities become automatic, which can easily occur after much practice. Colvin notes that "great performers never allow themselves to reach the automatic, arrested-development stage in their chosen field. That is the effect of continual, deliberate practice—avoiding automaticity" (Colvin, 2008, p. 83)

Colvin (2008, pp. 105–108) uses Benjamin Franklin's efforts to become a better writer as an example of deliberate practice. As a teenager, Ben's father found an exchange of letters between Ben and a friend. He gave his son feedback on his writing, starting with the positive qualities, but then pointing out certain elements that could be improved. Ben began practicing by reading passages from the *Spectator*, an English periodical of the time, making brief notes about the meaning of each sentence, and then a few days later he would try to express the meaning of each sentence in his own words. He then compared his essay to the original and identified the faults, such as poor vocabulary and poor organization, and would make corrections. He practiced writing his essays in verse to intentionally expand his vocabulary, and to work on his organization, he would mix up his note cards and weeks later after he had forgotten them, try to put them in the correct order. This example perfectly illustrates the principles of deliberate practice, namely, identifying specific goals to work on, practicing regularly and intentionally, and comparing the results with the target.

Several components are critical to implementing deliberate practice:

- Identify the immediate next steps to practice. Supervisors have the valuable role of recommending the skills and abilities that need to be further developed and providing feedback on performance.

- Set goals on specific tasks. Keep in mind that collaborative goal setting typically leads to higher supervisee investment and commitment.

- Mindfully self-regulate during practice. Goals themselves serve an attention-focusing function, but intentional self-coaching throughout the process is important for enhanced learning.

- Self-observe, including observing your own thinking. Be reflective throughout, and ask yourself questions such as, "How is it working?" "Can I try using another skill here?"

- Reflect carefully after the practice—judge yourself against the standard you were trying to achieve. Be specific, not vague and general.

Consider how different the deliberate practice model is from the typical training or supervision scenario in which the supervisor asks the supervisee to watch tape of a session, discusses strengths and weaknesses, perhaps considers new strategies or approaches, and the supervisee then "practices" with clients for another week. Although this sounds very reasonable and certainly has utility, it would be like a football team never practicing or scrimmaging and only playing real games and briefly reviewing film clips of the game afterward. The thought of trying to improve without practicing between games seems farfetched in sports but tends to be the norm in mental health training, especially after the initial focus on "microskills" in the early stages of training, when role playing and direct practicing are more commonplace.

Extensive, deliberate practice appears to give us more than just better-developed technical ability but also helps to develop "deep domain expertise" in which experts are able to separate important from trivial information and know what to focus on (Colvin, 2008, pp. 93–98). Great performers all possess large, highly developed, intricate mental models of their domains, which contribute to the development of expertise in three major ways (pp. 122–124):

- Form the framework on which to incorporate the growing knowledge of the domain

- Help to distinguish relevant from irrelevant information—this is very helpful when novel situations are encountered because it frees mental resources to focus on what is really important. A study of top performing pilots compared to apprentices indicated that the apprentices recalled more "filler" words from air traffic control radio communications but expert pilots recalled more of the important concept words because they had a rich mental model to enable them to focus their mental energy on what really mattered.

- Help to identify the next steps more easily

Although the impact of experience on clinician effectiveness might be mixed, research clearly indicates that some therapists are significantly more effective than others. Wampold and Brown (2005) studied licensed mental health providers and found that the clients of the most effective therapists improved at a rate approximately 50% higher and dropped out at a rate approximately 50% lower than the least effective clinicians. Miller, Hubble, and Duncan (2007) examined highly effective therapists and applied Ericsson's deliberate practice paradigm to the practice of psychotherapy, condensing deliberate practice into these three critical steps: (1) thinking (in advance), (2) acting, and (3) reflecting. Exemplary therapists are found to be much more consciously mindful than less effective therapists and place more emphasis on the value of feedback, taking steps to solicit feedback both directly from the client and also through reflecting on the session shortly afterward. During the reflection phase, top therapists tend to review the details of their performance, identify specific actions and alternative strategies for reaching their goals, and take responsibility (e.g., not blaming poor outcomes on the client or having a bad day).

Creating Good Habits

The foundation of positive behavioral change is setting realistic and meaningful goals and taking practical steps to make progress toward achieving those goals. Most goals can usually be attained in many different ways. This flexibility can be helpful because it provides options, which are especially important when one path becomes unavailable or is not proving to be effective. However, flexibility in pursuing goals can also become a source of stress and inaction because we have to decide how to implement our goals. Heath and Heath (2010) provide a very articulate description of how "unclear pathways" can lead to paralysis in *Switch: How to Change When Change Is Hard*, and Schwartz (2004) compellingly details the correlations between the expanding choices of modern life and increased stress in his book *The Paradox of Choice: Why More Is Less*. We are generally much less effective trying to develop strategies and problem solve when we are immersed in the situation. Action initiation or "goal pursuit" can be greatly facilitated when plans are made in advance for the strategies to be used (Gollwitzer, 1999). "Anticipatory decisions" are less restrictive because they allow us to more easily identify the array of possible opportunities for instrumental behavior. Good opportunities often present themselves only for a short time, but when goal pursuit is planned, goal-directed behaviors can be initiated immediately once a relevant situation is encountered (p. 494). Because effortful deliberation during the situation is no longer required, action initiation should be more efficient in the sense of demanding fewer cognitive resources, and might at times even occur without conscious intent (p. 494).

Setting "implementation intentions"—specifying how, where, and when a goal (or smaller steps toward achieving a larger goal) will be implemented— is strongly associated with actual goal attainment (Gollwitzer & Brandstatter, 1997). A simple study helps to illustrate this concept. College students were given the opportunity to receive extra credit by writing a report on how they spent Christmas Eve, to be completed no more than 48 hours after the event. Half of the participants were instructed to form implementation intentions by indicating on a questionnaire exactly when and where they intended to write the report during the 48-hour period. The other half were not requested to choose a specific time and place. Three-fourths of the implementation-intention participants had written the reports in the requested time period, whereas only one-third of the control participants did so. The simple act of pairing intention with specific plans appeared to yield very significant results. Goal attainment is also more likely to occur when intentions are framed as learning goals (to learn how to perform a given task) rather than as performance goals (to find out through a task how capable one is; Dweck, 1996).

Anticipatory planning, in the form of implementation intentions, helps to link desired "goal-directed behavior" to anticipated situations, for example, when my client begins to talk about symptoms, I will ask my client to use scaling; when a client starts to express ambivalence, I will "honor the resistance" by exploring the concerns about talking about the topic. Implementation intentions link the initiation of goal-directed responses to situational cues, which makes it easier to implement the right action at the right time because it eliminates in-the-moment decision making (Gollwitzer, 1999). The more our behavior can be linked to situational cues, the more likely we are to take action and to feel confident in the appropriateness of our responses because they have been considered in advance.

The use of implementation intentions enables us to be more highly attuned to potential good situations for the use of a particular behavior, that is, more alert to good opportunities (Gollwitzer, p. 495). The implication is that stronger links and greater benefit will be generated from mental rehearsal. Translated to supervision and learning, this means that identifying a behavior to emphasize (e.g., practice using deepening prompts when the client expresses emotion) is best achieved when paired with implementation intentions specifying how and when these behaviors will be used (e.g., use deepening prompts when the client states a feeling and appears well contained, but not if the client is decomposing). The use of implementation intentions also helps to automatize action initiation, freeing more cognitive resources for activity other than deciding when and how to initiate action (p. 498).

This is similar to the development of habits. Supervision can be regarded to have gone well if the supervisee has developed good habits; if the supevisee's "default" tendencies reflect sound clinical judgment and behavior. Through the use of implementation intentions, the automatic action initiation stems from the mental act of pairing a desired goal-directed behavior with the appropriate situation, whereas the development of habits requires behavioral practice (repetition and consistency). A benefit of using implementation intentions, in addition to the freeing of mental resources as new habits are developed, is that the new habits are created much more quickly. Implementation intentions are "as effective in automatizing action initiation as the repeated and consistent practice implied in habits. Apparently, implementation intentions create instant habits" (Gollwitzer, p. 499).

Reflection

Active learning—in which new knowledge and understanding is integrated with existing knowledge—is critical to improving and growing from experience. *Reflection* is the cornerstone of active learning, emphasizing the purposeful, critical analysis of knowledge and experience in order to achieve deeper meaning and understanding and greater conceptual flexibility. Reflection appears to fulfill several functions, including helping to make sense of complex situations and enabling learning from experience; however, it does not automatically flow from all experiences. Reflection tends to occur most naturally when we anticipate novel or challenging situations, but reflection is important during all stages of development to learn effectively from one's experience (Mann, Gordon, & MacLeod, 2009, p. 596).

Not only do increased awareness and reflective self-assessment seem to be the cornerstone of all major psychotherapies, they also appear to be activities that have been valued throughout time by noteworthy thinkers and historical figures. Michael Gelb (2002) examined the thinking patterns and approaches to life learning of ten extraordinary figures of history in the book *Discover Your Genius: How* to *Think Like History's Ten Most Revolutionary Minds*. Biographical sketches in the book included varied and seminal figures such as Plato, Columbus, Shakespeare, Jefferson, and Einstein. Each of these history-shaping individuals engaged in some form of ongoing self-reflection, often in the form of regular journaling. Interestingly, most also regularly took long walks, which seem likely to have served as an avenue to promote self-reflection. Creating mechanisms and taking the time to foster self-reflection and heightened self-awareness seems critical to the development of judgment and expertise and should be routinely incorporated into clinical training across all stages of development. After all, if Jefferson could find time to do so while running the country, and Einstein while discovering the theory of relativity, so can we both as supervisors and as practicing clinicians.

Reflection can be intentionally used to revisit clinical experiences to learn from them. Schon (1983) introduced the concept of the "reflective practitioner," asserting that the process of reflection produces new understanding and potentially can lead to new responses and behavior. This is especially helpful when the clinician feels stuck, and the usual actions or responses are not effective. Unfortunately, the reflective practice tends to diminish with increased years of experience and in settings where the scientific basis of clinical practice is not reinforced (Mamede & Schmidt, 2005). This makes it all the more important for both individual supervisors and agency settings as a whole to create the culture of valuing and promoting lifelong growth and development and to design structured situations where that is likely to occur, for example, case conceptualization meetings, regular professional development opportunities, in discussions of recent articles and books, watching webinars as a staff, sharing information learned from recent conferences, and so on.

Mameade and Schmidt (2005) suggest a framework used in medicine as a basis for applying reflective practice to clinical practice:

- Deliberate induction—taking time to reflect on unfamiliar problems

- Deliberate deduction—logically deducing the consequences of various possible hypotheses or courses of action

- Testing—evaluating predictions against the problem being explored

- Openness to reflection—engaging in constructive activity when faced with an unfamiliar situation

- Metareasoning—thinking critically about one's own thinking process

A survey of physician teachers found that half of the teachers investigated believed that reflecting on failures was as or more important than reflecting on successes (Pinsky & Irby, 1997). Distinguished clinical teachers in medicine identified three basic phases of reflection:

- Anticipatory reflection—using past experience for planning teaching activities

- Reflection-in-action—maintaining flexibility during teaching

- Reflection-on-action—thoughtful analysis of the experience afterward

In fact, successful teaching has been defined as an intentional process of observing, reflecting, and experimenting (Pinsky, Monson, & Irby, 1998).

Contextual factors can significantly help or hinder the development of reflection and reflective capability. Across diverse settings and methods, it appears that the most influential elements in enabling the development of reflection practice are a supportive environment, both intellectually and emotionally, an authentic context, accommodation for individual differences in learning style, mentoring, group discussion, support, and the free expression of opinions. Additional enabling factors are the perception of the relevance of reflection, an organizational climate that includes respect between professionals, and time for reflection. Time pressure in a busy environment has been found to act as a barrier to reflection (Mamede & Schmidt, 2005). Given proper environmental support, complex problems can stimulate reflective thinking, especially in practice settings where the scientific basis of clinical practice is continuously revisited. The learning environment, especially with the modeling of mentors and supervisors, can have an encouraging or inhibiting effect on reflective thinking.

High achievers (a category that would include most graduate students or practicing professionals) face unique challenges (Argyris, 1991). Although this was not our personal experience, Argyris asserts that many professionals and high achievers have rarely experienced failure and consequently have not learned how to learn from failure. He uses the analogy of a thermostat to illustrate reflective learning. A single-loop thermostat simply maintains the heat at the temperature it is set, clicking on or off if the temperature gets too cold or too hot. However, a hypothetical double-loop thermostat would add the additional step of asking, "Why am I set at 68 degrees?" and then explore whether another temperature might be more economical (p.4). If "learning how to learn" has not been mastered, people tend to rely on single-loop strategies, and when these go wrong, frequently become defensive. Potential embarrassment can be even greater for those accustomed to success, which inhibits learning. True learning also involves the often uncomfortable process of observing or realizing the discrepancies between our intentions and execution, between the way we think we are acting and the way we really are (p. 7). Although potentially uncomfortable, this opens the door for us to examine the thought processes and decision-making processes we used and to identify and consider alternatives that can be tried in future situations. To use the thermostat model again, noting discrepancies between intentions and outcomes can prompt us to "click on" reflective thinking and take steps to reduce the discrepancy.

Discovery and insight can also be facilitated by the use of the Socratic method, an age-old technique based on using questions intended to stimulate the supervisee's creative and critical thought processes (Overholser, 1991). Questions prompting supervisees to more fully examine their decisions and courses of action can assist in anticipating the potential risks and probable benefits of various approaches and interventions. The Socratic technique can also promote autonomy by providing the foundation for rational self-awareness and self-initiated discovery (p. 71).

Self-monitoring and self-regulation are essential to growth as a clinician. In fact, Moffett (2009) asserts that ". . . one of the ultimate goals of supervision is for the supervisee to learn how to supervise oneself, for example, to anticipate one's readiness for a particular clinical task, to reflect on one's work routinely, to consider the impact of one's interventions, to recognize and use one's emotional responses to a patient for the benefit of the patient, and to generate alternative potential interventions if indicated" (p. 79). Self-reflection can help the therapist prepare for work with an unfamiliar patient population, modality, or setting. Supervisors can prompt guided self-reflection by generating a list of questions that address issues known to be problematic, and having the supervisee reflect and write answers as a means of priming the supervisee for potential challenges and further discussion. "The expectation is that, once so primed, the supervisee, when encountering personal difficulties in their clinical work, will be better prepared to recognize and manage these challenges effectively or at least more readily bring them up for discussion in supervision sessions" (p. 78).

This format asks supervisees to predict their concrete actions in hypothetical situations, for example, "In what situations would you interrupt a session to consult with your supervisor?" "What would you think, feel, and do when working with a client who has values that are antithetical to yours?" or "What could you do if an intervention is obviously going badly?" Moffett suggests that the importance of preparation and routine self-reflection is implicitly emphasized through this approach, and the development of an effective supervisory relationship is accelerated by making it clear that supervisees are expected to experience some challenges in supervision and that virtually any topic is welcome for discussion.

Conclusion: Final Thoughts on Excellence and Learning

Regardless of approach, the ultimate goal of psychotherapy is for clients to learn to become their own therapists. This involves learning to internalize the "voice" of the therapist, developing greater perspective, flexibility, and coping skills, and above all, being able to consistently operate with self-awareness, self-monitoring, and self-regulation. Much of the same can be said for supervision—ultimately, the goal of supervision goes beyond learning technical skills, clinical judgment, and conceptualization ability to developing the most important ability of all, learning to learn, and in essence, becoming one's own supervisor.

The process of learning during graduate school or professional training is usually very structured and well identified, typically involving both peer and institutional support. The path for growth is clear (and mandatory). Unfortunately, this is usually not the case following licensure. Although the steps to take to advance one's career at times may be at least somewhat clear, the steps to make progress toward clinical excellence are seldom even considered. Goals can't be reached that aren't set. The process of supervision isn't complete until supervisees complete the formal training program, having considered how they want to be more proficient in 1 year, 3 years, 5 years, 10 years, and so on, and the steps they need to make growth happen. Excellence can only be achieved when learning is viewed as a lifelong process.

Questions to Consider

For the supervisor:

- How am I helping my supervisee to internalize the supervisory process? Am I making the learning process transparent to the supervisee?

- Are there steps I can take to lower barriers for my supervisee to learn?

- What values do I think my supervisee would say I most value?

- How much time is being spent in supervision sessions practicing skills to be learned?

- How am I helping my supervisee become aware of cognitive biases? Am I doing so in such a way that will help increase awareness when my supervisee is not in my presence?

For the agency or training program:

- Are the expectations clear?

- How is the value of on-going learning and professional growth being modeled by the senior staff?

- How is time for reflection built into the schedule?

- Is excellence valued over mere competence? If so, how is this demonstrated?

- What structures are in place to promote continued professional growth and development through a variety of methods?

Recommended Readings

Books

Anderson, J. R. (1981). *Cognitive skills and their acquisition.* Hillsdale, NJ: Erlbaum.

Colvin, G. (2008). *Talent is overrated: what really separates world-class performers from everybody else.* New York: Penguin.

Ericsson, K. A. (1996). *The road to excellence: The acquisition of expert performance in the arts and sciences, sports, and games.* Hillsdale, NJ: Lawrence Erlbaum Associates, Inc.

Articles

Ericsson, K. A., & Charness, N. (1994). Expert performance: Its structure and acquisition. *American Psychologist, 49,* 725–747.

Lichtenberg, J. W. (1997). Expertise on counseling psychology: A concept in search of support. *Educational Psychology Review, 9,* 221–238.

Miller, S., Hubble, M., & Duncan, B. (2007, November/December). Supershrinks. *Psychotherapy Networker* 27–56.

References

Adams, D. (2000). *Mostly harmless.* New York: Ballantine Books.

American Psychological Association. (1982). *Report of the task force on the evaluation of education, training, and service in psychology.* Washington, DC: Author.

Anderson, J. R. (1981). *Cognitive skills and their acquisition.* Hillsdale, NJ: Erlbaum.

Argyris, C. (1991). Teaching smart people how to learn. *Harvard Business Review Reflections, 4*, 5–15.

Berman, J. S., & Norton, N. C. (1985). Does professional training make a therapist more effective? *Psychological Bulletin, 98*, 401–407.

Caamerer, C. F., & Johnson, E. J. (1991). The process-performance paradox in expert judgment: How can experts know so much and predict so badly? In K. Anders Ericsson & J. Smith (Eds.), *Toward a general theory of expertise: Prospects and Limits* (pp. 195–217). New York: Cambridge University Press.

Callahan, J. L., Almstrom, C. M., Swift, J. K., Borja, S. E., & Heath, C. J. (2009). Exploring the contribution of supervisors to intervention outcomes. *Training and Education in Professional Psychology, 3*, 72–77.

Chase, W. G., & Simon, H. A. (1973). The mind's eye in chess. In W. G. Chase (Ed.), *Visual information processing* (pp. 215–281). New York: Academic Press.

Christensen, A., & Jacobson, N. S. (1994). Who (or what) can do psychotherapy: The status and challenge of nonprofessional therapies. *Psychological Science, 5*, 8–14.

Colvin, G. (2008). *Talent is overrated: what really separates world-class performers from everybody else.* New York: Penguin.

Dawes, R. R. (1994). *House of cards: Psychology and psychotherapy built on myth.* New York: Free Press.

deGroot, A. D. (1978). *Thought and choice in chess.* The Hague: Mouton. (Original work published 1946).

Dodenhoff, J. T. (1981). Interpersonal attraction and direct-indirect supervisor influence as predictors of counselor trainee effectiveness. *Journal of Counseling Psychology, 28*, 47–52.

Durlak, J. (1979). Comparative effectiveness of paraprofessional helpers. *Psychological Bulletin, 86*, 80–92.

Dweck, C. S. (1996) Implicit theories as organizers of goals and behavior. In P. M. Gollwitzer, & J. A. Bargh (Eds.), *The psychology of action: Linking cognition and motivation to action* (pp. 69–90). New York: Guilford.

Ericsson, K. A., & Charness, N. (1994). Expert performance: Its structure and acquisition. *American Psychologist, 49*, 725–747.

Frensch, R. A., & Sternberg, R. J. (1989). Expertise and intelligent thinking: When is it worse to know better? In R. J. Sternberg (Ed.), *Advances in the psychology of human intelligence* (Vol. 5, pp. 157–188). Hillsdale, NJ: Erlbaum.

Garb, H. N. (2005). Clinical judgment and decision making. *Clinical Psychology, 1*, 67–89.

Gelb, M. J. (2002). *Discover your genius: How to think like history's ten most revolutionary minds.* New York: HarperCollins Publishers, Inc.

Gladwell, M. (2008) *Outliers: The story of success.* New York: Little, Brown and Company.

Goldberg, L. R. (1970). Man vs. model of man: A rationale, plus some evidence, for a method of improving clinical inferences. *Psychological Bulletin, 73*, 422–432.

Gollwizter, P. M. (1999). Implementation intentions. *American Psychologist, 54,* 503–493.

Gollwitzer, P. M., & Brandstatter, V. (1997). Implementation intentions and effective goal pursuit. *Journal of Personality and Social Psychology, 73,* 186–199.

Hattie, J. A., Sharpley, C. F., & Rogers, H. J. (1984). Comparative effectiveness of professional and paraprofessional helpers. *Psychological Bulletin, 95,* 534–541.

Heath, C. & Heath, D. (2010). *Switch: How to change things when change is hard.* Broadway Books: New York.

Holyoak, K. J. (1991). Symbolic connectionism: Toward third generation theories. In K. A. Ericsson & J. Smith (Eds.), *Toward a general theory of expertise: Prospects and limits* (pp. 301–336). New York: Cambridge University Press.

Johnson, P. E., Duran, A. S., Hassebrock, F., Moller, J., Prietula, M., Feltovich, P. J., & Swanson, D. B. (1981). Expertise and Error in Diagnostic Reasoning*. *Cognitive science, 5,* 235–283.

Kahneman, D. (1991). Judgment and decision making: A personal view. *Psychological Science, 2,* 142–145.

Kahneman, D., & Klein, G. (2009). Conditions for intuitive expertise. *American Psychologist, 64,* 515–526. doi: 10.1037/a0016755

Lichtenberg, J. W. (1997). Expertise on counseling psychology: A concept in search of support. *Educational Psychology Review, 9,* 221–238.

Mamede, S., & Schmidt, H. (2005). The structure of reflective practice in medicine. *Advances in Health Sciences Education, Theory and Practice, 10,* 327–337.

Mann, K., Gordon, K., & MacLeod, A. (2009). Reflection and reflective practice in health professions education: A systemic review. *Advances in Health Science Education, 14,* 595–621.

Maslow, A. H.(1971). *The farther reaches of human nature.* New York: The Viking Press.

Meehl, P. E. (1954). *Clinical vs. statistical prediction: A theoretical analysis and review of the evidence.* Minneapolis, MN: University of Minnesota Press.

Miller, S., Hubble, M., & Duncan, B. (2007, November/December). Supershrinks. *Psychotherapy Networker, 27–56.*

Moffett, L. A. (2009). Directed self-reflection protocols in supervision. *Training and Education in Professional Psychology, 3*(2), 78–83.

Overholser, J. C. (1991). The Socratic method as a technique in psychotherapy supervision. *Professional Psychology: Research and Practice, 22,* 68–74.

Perkins, D. N., Farady, M., & Bushey, B. (1991). Everyday reasoning and the roots of intelligence. In J. F. Voss, D. N. Perkins, & J. W. Segal (Eds.), *Informal reasoning and education* (pp. 83–105). Hillsdale, NJ: Erlbaum.

Pinsky, L., & Irby, D. (1997). If at first you don't succeed: Using failure to improve teaching. *Academic Medicine, 72*(11), 973–976.

Pinsky, L., Monson, D., & Irby, D. (1998). How excellent teachers are made: Reflecting on success to improve teaching. *Advances in Health Sciences Education, 3,* 207–215.

Schon, D. (1983). *The reflective practitioner.* San Francisco, CA: Jossey-Bass.

Schwartz, B. (2004). *Paradox of choice: Why more is less.* New York: Harper Collins Publishers.

Seligman, M.E.P. (2011). *Flourishing: A visionary new understanding of happiness and well-being.* New York: Free Press.

Shanteau, J. (1992). Competence in experts: The role of task characteristics. *Organizational Behavior and Human Decision Processes, 53,* 252–266.

Slovic, P., Fischhoff, B., & Lichtenstein, S. (1985). Regulation of risk: A psychological perspective. In R. Noll (Ed.), *Social science and regulatory policy.* Berkeley, CA: University of California Press.

Tracey, T. J. (2011). Why is there so little expertise in psychotherapy? Presented as part of the symposium, *Expertise in Psychotherapy—Following the Yellow Brick Road?* (B. Wampold, Chair). Annual meeting of the American Psychological Association, August 2011, Washington, DC.

Voss, J. F., & Post, T. A. (1988). On the solving of ill-structured problems. In M. T. H. Chi, R. Glaser, & M. J. Farr, (Eds.), *The nature of expertise* (pp. 261–285). Hillsdale, NJ: Erlbaum.

Wampold, B. E., & Brown, J. B. (2005). Estimating variability in outcomes attributable to therapists: A naturalistic study of outcomes in managed care. *Journal of Consulting and Clinical Psychology, 73,* 914–923.

9

Fostering Ethical Behavior

"Educating the mind without educating the heart is no education at all."
—Aristotle

"True education does not consist merely in the acquiring of a few facts of science, history, literature, or art, but in the development of character."
—David O. McKay

It is probably safe to say that very few clinicians start their day plotting how to be unethical with their clients or supervisees, and it is almost unthinkable to imagine that they would put in the years of education, training, and sacrifice to obtain entry into a helping profession merely to be able to violate the trust of their clients or supervisees. But yet, ethical infractions obviously do occur. The names of the offenders that are routinely printed in the pages of professional association newsletters provide witness to this disturbing fact. Behind the printed names are stories of pain, betrayal, and violation. And the damage often extends not only to clients and supervisees but to clinicians and supervisors as well, resulting in the loss of reputation, and at times, in the loss of career and livelihood, even though these individuals brought the consequences upon themselves.

Most people who enter helping professions do so with noble intentions (if it's for the money, Janice Jones and I are still waiting. . .), and it's easy to think that legal and ethical violations are only perpetrated by nameless, faceless others who have somehow lost, or perhaps never had, a moral compass. But before we begin exploring the topics of ethics and ethics training, we invite you to consider your own driving patterns as a glimpse into the complexity that lies just beneath the surface of simply knowing and following the rules. Have you ever driven above the speed limit? If so (I'm betting that almost everyone who is reading this has gone faster than the posted speed limit upon occasion), what were you telling yourself at the time? "I'm only going 62 in a 55 mph zone, so I'm not really speeding. . . . Everyone else is speeding, and I would in fact be driving unsafely not to go with the flow of traffic. . . . I'm a really safe driver, I can go a few miles above the limit and still be safe. . . . I'm driving a lot slower than I would be on the Autobahn. . . . I know I'm going 80 in a 55 mph zone, but I'm a really good driver and I'm being very careful. . . . I'm running behind, and my child is at day care, and I don't want to have to pay a dollar per minute for being late. . . . or, I'm speeding!? You can't be serious—I'm driving a Prius!"

We presumably know the traffic regulations and know that the posted speed limit is designed to keep us safe, but in spite of the fact of knowing the law and the dangers of speeding, we almost all do it. (Of course, as Dave Barry (1999) insightfully observed, we are all better-than-average drivers, so it's okay.) The purpose of being asked to self-examine your driving habits is not to try to impose a puritanical, rule-bound guilt trip, but rather to illustrate the complexity of even ordinary, everyday legal and ethical issues, and most importantly, how easy it is for all of us to be vulnerable to committing legal or ethical violations.

Most books or chapters on ethics focus primarily on providing information on proper legal and ethical conduct and perhaps also detail the potential consequences of failing to do so. Although providing a thorough working knowledge to our supervisees of their professional legal and ethical responsibilities is imperative, it is also insufficient. Providing a comprehensive coverage of the legal and ethical requirements for various mental health disciplines is beyond the scope of this chapter and is usually addressed through other venues, such as ethics courses and professional workshops. The focus of this chapter instead is primarily on the often overlooked parts of the ethical equation, that of translating information and knowledge into action. This chapter addresses both the vulnerabilities we are all prone to and also examines ways to facilitate ethical "resiliency" to help us and our supervisees more effectively address the human tendencies that can land even the most well-intended supervisee or clinician into ethical quicksand.

A Positive Approach to Ethics

Tjeltveit and Gottlieb (2010) note that many ethics-training experiences appear to intentionally raise anxiety. Given the seriousness of the topic and the weight of responsibility that mental health professionals have both to supervisees and to clients, this is certainly understandable. However, this violates the well-established principle that too much anxiety disrupts cognition and might foster confusion instead of clarity (p. 100). They suggest that a positive approach, focused on ethical "ceilings" rather than "floors," is best, and that if clinicians are encouraged to do their best, they will be less likely to fall below the standard of care (p. 100). Handelsman, Knapp, and Gottlieb (2002) echo the sentiment that professional ethics focuses too heavily on avoiding or punishing misconduct rather than promoting the highest ethical conduct, and that similar to the pathology perspective within clinical psychology, the prevailing models of ethics are often too rule-bound and defensive.

My (John Wade) personal experience as a licensed psychologist who regularly attends continuing education trainings on ethics is that it is easy to leave ethics workshops trembling with fear and feeling like the next client who walks into your office might sue you and attempt to destroy your life and your career. Clients are transformed from people who are struggling and need your help to the enemy from whom you must vigilantly protect yourself. Even though the letters CYA are never specifically mentioned, they tend to keep running through your mind for days after ethics trainings. Although it is obviously important to practice risk management, it is hard to imagine that an adversarial mindset can be helpful to the therapeutic relationship. No matter how intuitively appealing, fear is generally not a good training technique. Wilson (2011) made this point very dramatically by noting that the popular crime-prevention program, *Scared Straight*, designed to prevent at-risk youth from starting on a life of crime by taking them into federal penitentiaries to see the horrors of prison life firsthand, actually increased criminal activity by an average of 13% compared to equally at-risk, nonparticipants who did not participate in the program.

Knapp and VandeCreek (2012) offer a detailed "positive" and "active" approach to ethics, explaining that just as positive psychology has shifted the goals of psychology from an almost exclusive focus on pathology to a science that focuses on positive traits and civic virtues, the goal of positive ethics is to shift the emphasis away from an almost exclusive focus on wrongdoing and disciplinary actions toward "an articulated vision of high ethical standards" (p. 11). The "floor" approach, focused on meeting the minimum legal and ethical standards adopted by mental health professions, is regarded as an incomplete view of ethics. Bersoff (1994) stated that the *American Psychological Association (APA) Ethics Code* ". . . at best, builds an ethical floor but hardly urges us to reach for the ceiling" (p. 385). Handelsman et al. (2005) observe that the 1992 *APA Ethics Code* was divided into two sections, the aspirational ethical principles and the enforceable standards of conduct. However, as a practical matter, psychologists equate the ethics code with standards of conduct and ignore the aspirational principles (p. 733).

Although clinical ethics is grounded in the principle of "first, do no harm," clinicians invariably want to do more than just avoid being punished; they also want to have a positive impact on the lives of their clients (Knapp & VandeCreek, 2012, p. 4). Effective treatment depends upon this. Many of us have probably heard that most clients desire to go beyond the "dead-man cure," in which they would be "cured" of their symptoms if they simply died. Obviously, clients want more than just the mere absence of symptoms; they also want positive factors to exist in their lives. Similarly, the goal of positive ethics is to go beyond the "dead clinician" standard, in which no harm would be done to the client if the clinician were dead (but obviously, no help either).

The "floor" approach toward ethics minimizes the spirit and underlying philosophy behind the guidelines and fails to consider the ways ethics can uplift clinical practice. Ethics can also be viewed not only as a way to avoid problematic behavior and punishment but also as a way to help clinicians fulfill their highest potential (Knapp & VandeCreek, 2012, pp. 9–10). Ethics should not only focus on how not to harm clients but on how to be better at helping them. Positive or active ethics are similar to the General (aspirational) Principles found in the *APA Ethics Code* in that positive ethics encourages psychologists to live up to their highest ethical standards (p. 10). The disciplinary and aspirational aims of ethics can be interactive. Mental health professionals can better fulfill their professional responsibilities if they understand and can apply the moral principles that underlie the disciplinary codes. Disciplinary codes alone are not sufficient in themselves to guide practitioners in all situations, as ethical quandries often require clinicians to interpret and apply the ethical standards and to rely on their personal code of ethics to guide them (p. 4), especially when two or more ethical principles might be at odds in a given situation. This is not to say that instruction in the legal floor has no place—it is important to know the laws that govern the practice of psychology and to appreciate risk-management principles to identify ways that patients can be harmed (or perceive that they have been harmed). But clinicians who are more aware of the moral principles that underlie their professional ethics codes will likely be more effective at handling the grey areas in which they need to exercise substantial judgment (p. 13). Operating with a heightened sense of legal and ethical knowledge is likely to lead to better judgment and decision making.

Handelsman, et al. (2002) suggest that the hallmark of positive ethics is that clinicians "consider ethics in a multifaceted context, with greater awareness of both internal (e.g., personal and professional values) and external (e.g., societal influences on professional behavior) perspectives" (p. 732). Just as research and clinical activities have traditionally focused on pathology and problems, so, too has the field of ethics tended to focus on "deficiencies in ethical behavior, bad actions, and bad actors" (p. 732). Even armed with detailed working knowledge of the professional ethics code and legal regulations, in the daily life of a supervisor or clinician, numerous gray area situations and dilemmas arise for which good reasons exist to justify two or more mutually exclusive actions. For example, a therapist might have to decide whether to violate confidentiality to warn a possible victim that a patient may attempt harm. In this example, the therapist must weigh the importance of confidentiality and respect for the patient's autonomy against the potential harm that might come to a third party. The ethics codes do little to assist in situations like this when ethical standards and principles are pitted against each other. Codes are limited to specific prohibitions and aspirational principles. Thus, ethical reasoning and careful thinking are imperative (p. 737), which leads directly into the next section, which covers ethical decision-making models.

Decision-Making Models

This section briefly introduces an overview of some of the more commonly included factors of ethical decision making. Obviously, it can be very helpful to have a prediscussed "flow-chart" for when supervisory or clinical situations start to become ethically murky or downright confusing. However, later in the chapter we also discuss that although having a concrete, straightforward ethical decision-making model to follow is important, most current models neglect important and influential variables of real-world, ethical decision making and action.

Supervisees and clinicians might encounter ethical quandries because of lack of familiarity with their professional ethical codes or state or federal laws. However, even with exemplary knowledge, at times situations are encountered in which ethics codes and regulations or laws do not provide explicit direction. Many standards in the *APA* and other professional ethics codes require the use of professional judgment in their implementation. This is often the case when words such as *reasonably, appropriately,* or *potentially* are used. In these situations, it is especially important to have ethical decision-making strategies and skills (Knapp & VandeCreek, 2012, pp. 35–36). At times, professional ethics codes are silent and do not give specific guidance on complicated issues. For example, the 1992 *APA Ethics Code* made no reference to the transmission of information through e-mail or conducting services through electronic means. (It should be noted that although this chapter uses the *APA Ethics Code* as its main reference, other professional organizations in mental health have their own specific ethical guidelines, including the American Counseling Association, the National Association of Social Workers, and the American Association for Marriage and Family Therapy.) More recent commentaries in the professional literature have attempted to provide guidance, but until recently psychologists who used electronic transmission for professional purposes had to decide for themselves whether and how to use them (pp. 36–37). In situations such as these, it is especially important to have well-reasoned judgment and solid decision-making skills. Most ethics textbooks present some type of decision-making model, often including many of the following steps:

- Identifying the problem
- Defining the issues
- Consulting the laws and ethics code
- Seeking consultation
- Identifying legal and ethical obligations
- Generating alternatives
- Listing potential consequences (Knapp & VandeCreek, 2012, p. 38)

Knapp and VandeCreek (2012) present an intentionally simplified decision-making model, recognizing that especially under times of stress that "simple" is more likely to be remembered and followed. Their five-step model consists of the following components:

1. *Identify or scrutinize the problem*—determine which moral or ethical principles might be threatened. This identification can happen on either a cognitive or emotional level, for example, a strain in the relationship or emotional uneasiness is often the first indication of a problem. It is important for supervisees to know the ethics codes and professional standards well so they will be able to easily recognize when ethical standards might be at risk.

2. *Develop alternatives or hypotheses*—that are consistent with general moral principles. This involves the generation of solutions. The ability to reach the best decision usually requires the development of a wide range of useful alternatives. Especially problematic is cognitive rigidity, which is the tendency to fixate on one possible solution without allowing for alternative strategies and explanations. This can be improved by consultation, considering ethics codes and relevant laws, and an awareness of cognitive and emotional influences on decision making. Consultation can help to reduce strong emotions and allow the clinician to process information more clearly. Also, the process of describing the dilemma can help the person to clarify and think through the process more clearly.

3. *Evaluate or analyze options*—the option chosen will depend on striking the optimal balance or ranking of moral and ethical principles. Recognize the ambiguity and tension that are present in many ethically challenging situations, that each possible solution likely has both advantages and disadvantages. This can arise because of lack of information but also emotional interference and cognitive biases. Also, it can be important to recognize that how the options are presented to those involved can often significantly impact the outcome.

4. *Act or perform the best option*—recognizing that at times perfect solutions are not to be found. Recognize that reaching a solution does not necessarily mean that it will be implemented. Bernard and Jara (1986) found that many psychology graduate students who reached the "right" solution to an ethical dilemma did not intend to act on that solution. The reasons aren't clear, but it could be that some of the students did not believe that the ethics code or risk-management guidelines reflected what they believed to be the most moral or ethical response.

5. *Evaluate the results*—judging the extent to which the actions taken fulfilled ethical and moral principles. Also evaluate whether the course of action has

a realistic chance of success, and in the case of competing ethical principles, whether the decision minimized the negative effects of violating the infringed moral principle and was made as impartially as possible without including extraneous information. Especially in training settings, ethical problem solving should always be reviewed and processed as a learning opportunity. (pp. 41–45)

This decision-making model is not presented to imply that it is the best or the only one that should be used. It can be very useful in the supervision process for the supervisor and supervisee to discuss how ethical dilemmas should be approached and to collaboratively create and decide upon an ethical decision-making model. It is, however, certainly preferable to have done this before ethical quandries arise, because it is much easier to simply execute a plan developed under calm and considered circumstances than to try to problem solve under pressure.

Ethical Vulnerabilities

The influence of personal factors can not only affect our daily lives but our professional judgment as well. Danziger, Levav, and Avnaim-Pesso (2011) provide a striking example of this. They reviewed over 1,000 decisions made by parole judges in an Israeli prison system, finding that approximately one-third of the prisoners were granted parole. However, the time of day of the prisoner's hearing made a dramatic difference. Those who appeared before the judge early in the morning when the judge was well rested and well fed received parole about 65% of the time, whereas those who appeared late in the day were granted parole less than 10% of the time. Notable differences also depended on whether the prisoner was seen shortly before lunch (released 20% of the time) versus right after lunch (released 60% of the time). Justice might be blind, but it does get hungry and tired.

Apart from being truly disturbing, these findings raise the question that if judges, whose very job description is to uphold laws and ethical standards, can have their judgment so dramatically influenced by common hunger pangs and fatigue, how can we as mental health professionals expect to be immune to similar everyday influences on our cognitive processing? It seems that the answer certainly can't lie in the ability to be unbiased and impartial, because if that is the only basis of solid ethical decision making and behavior, we are all doomed. Although the primary emphasis of ethics training is usually focused on providing information, it seems imperative that our human nature, consisting of biases, cognitive lapses, and emotional sways be acknowledged, for fear that it impacts our ethical judgment and decision making just as it did with the parole judges. Knowledge of our professional ethical codes as well as state legal codes is imperative, but as all of us involved with behavior change know, knowledge alone does not necessarily translate into practice.

Although anyone who has ever grocery shopped when hungry knows all too well that our physical and emotional states influence our decision making, this too frequently is not given enough acknowledgment in the arena of ethics, often with spectacularly disastrous results. Everyday life is replete with examples that information, even combined with good intention, is insufficient. Failed attempts to quit smoking, lose weight, exercise more regularly, or stop procrastinating all illustrate this principle. Although we seem to intuitively understand this at the personal level, professional circles seem to have been slow to embrace the importance of nonrationale factors. The highly influential Chicago School of Economics forecasting model rests on the assumption of rational expectations, for example, that simple supply and demand works in a linear fashion. The dot. com bubble, the housing bubble, the Great Recession, and chia pets have finally started to bring home the patently obvious conclusion that nonrational factors frequently play a role in people's decisions.

Ethical knowledge does not necessarily result in ethical behavior (e.g., Smith, McGuire, Abbott, & Blau, 1991). Even the best cognitive and rational strategies can be insufficient. Our ethical responses are shaped by various factors, including: being able to recognize that ethical dilemmas are present, social and cultural influences, habits, emotions, identity, virtue and character, multiple or competing motivations, prior decisions, and the executive and organizational skills needed to implement decisions. These factors all have the potential to overpower knowledge of ethics codes and rational decision making (Tjeltveit & Gottlieb, 2010, p. 99)

The bottom line, as with many things in our lives, is that we can know the right thing to do and still not do it. Bernard and Jara (1986) asked a nationwide sample of clinical psychology graduate students to respond to two hypothetical situations involving ethical violations. In one situation, subjects were asked to assume they had firsthand knowledge that a fellow student was sexually involved with a client who was being seen as part of a therapy practicum. In the other, participants were to assume that they were aware of serious errors of judgment on the part of a fellow student that were apparently the result of a drinking problem. Subjects were asked to state what they felt they *should* do and also what they felt they *would* do. Five possible responses were provided that ranged from "nothing" to "report it to the ethics committee." Results indicated that although the great majority of students had no difficulty in recognizing the need for action, approximately half of the sample stated that they *would* do less than they realized they *should* do. In other words, the vast majority of students knew what they should do but only about half believed they would actually do it. The researchers concluded that this appeared to be a function of individual values, not a function of knowledge.

As an extension of the Bernard and Jara (1986) study, Bernard, Murphy and Little (1987) surveyed over 500 professional clinicians regarding similar scenarios (a male clinician who was sexually involved with a client and a problem-drinker, alcoholic clinician who was showing poor clinical judgment).

The numbers were somewhat more encouraging for the professionals than for the students regarding the intention to adhere to ethical guidelines, with 63% of the clinicians responding that they believed they would do what they felt they should do for the sexual violation scenario, and 74% for the problem-drinking, alcoholism scenario. However, although greater numbers of licensed clinicians indicated they would adhere more closely to professional and ethical expectations, approximately one-fourth and one-third, depending on the scenario, still stated they likely would not. It would be interesting for future research to investigate why ethical codes are adhered to more faithfully among practicing professionals than supervisees (which does seem to be an encouraging sign). This difference in perspective between practicing clinicians and supervisees would seem to be an important potential component for ethics training.

The conclusions of these two studies suggest that discussing the values important to the supervisee that will likely guide the supervisee's ethical perspective should be an essential component of supervision. For instance, Wilkins et al. (1990) found that whether clinicians indicated they *would* do what they believed they *should* do varied by situation and by their closeness to the person exhibiting ethically questionable behavior. Fly, van Bark, Weinman, Kitchener, and Lang (1997) reported that 54% of graduate students who had committed an ethical transgression had completed an ethics course and suggested that as a profession we are not thinking broadly enough about how to help students develop ethical behavior (p. 494). Besides information, personal values and cultural, social, and emotional factors can also affect moral behavior and judgment (Haidt, 2001, 2007). Prevention efforts that only focus on rules, regulations, statutes, and procedures are likely too narrowly focused. This is necessary but not sufficient, especially for clinicians who face a myriad of complex issues (Tjetlveit & Gottlieb, 2010, p. 100).

Most ethical decision-making models focus on logic and reason for making ethical judgments but are generally empirically unproven and ignore the fact that many nonrational factors influence ethical thinking and action. Nonrational factors versus well-reasoned principles are often considered risk factors for acting unethically; however, Rogerson, Gottlieb, Handlesman, Knapp, and Younggren (2011) suggest that because nonrational factors are so much a part of the human process that ethics training would likely benefit from including them (p. 620) versus merely instructing supervisees to power on past them. Tjeltveit and Gottlieb (2010) suggest that supervisors can help prevent ethical missteps and boost the protective factors of their supervisees by increasing "ethical resilience" and decreasing vulnerabilities. The most effective supervisors challenge their supervisees to explore their perceptions, intuitions, assumptions, and logic (Knapp and VandeCreek, 2012, p. 42). The next section explores in some detail some of the various ways that supervisees and all mental health professionals are likely to be prone to ethical improprieties and suggests ways that "ethical resilience" can be enhanced.

Individual and General Vulnerabilities

Humanness is the foundation of good therapy and supervision, but it is a double-edged sword, and can be both the friend but also the enemy of ethical behavior. Ethical vulnerabilities can be thought of as those aspects of our professional lives that are not well guarded from an ethical lapse (Tjelvteit and Gottlieb, 2010)—areas in which, even if well intended, we may be more prone to ill-considered thinking and judgment. Vulnerabilities can be both general and idiosyncratic. General vulnerabilities affect everyone; for example, we are all prone to making errors in judgment when fatigued or stressed (p. 101). I remember as a child, when I used to roller-skate every Friday night, that almost all of my falls happened in the last 20 minutes, not during the first 3 hours. Transferring this to supervision, it is much easier to imagine making an ethical misstep when hurried, stressed, or overbooked with clients. Idiosyncratic vulnerabilities are specific to the individual and stem from our character, habits, personalities, and personal histories. Even very competent and ethically minded professionals, when experiencing heightened stressors such as divorce, major medical concerns, family problems, and so on, may become vulnerable in ways they never imagined or experienced before. Consultation at the right time may increase resilience and make all the difference in how the therapist handles an ethically complex case in which there is a great potential for ethical misstep (Tjeltviet and Gottlieb, 2010, p. 102).

Nonrational Processes and Cognitive Biases

Rogerson et al. (2011) examined the research on ethical judgment and compellingly concluded that ethical decision making is plagued by the same cognitive biases that affect everyday human life. Contextual, interpersonal, and intuitive factors all influence the ethical decision-making process in subtle yet powerful ways, and ethics theory and training would benefit from including these unavoidable, nonrational factors (p. 616).

Kahneman (e.g., 2003) has compiled a massive body of evidence, crossing disciplines, which indicates that our attempts at "rational decision making" are often anything but "rational." He explains that we tend to use heuristics or "mental shortcuts" instead of more effortful thinking, which can lead us to be susceptible to prematurely foreclosing the consideration of possible alternatives and simply going with whatever option seems reasonable to end the tension, even if a better option might become apparent with more consideration. This is especially likely to be true regarding ethical dilemmas that are inherently anxiety provoking. For example, the regret of hindsight might tempt people to make decisions that will minimize their anticipated regret for not having chosen a different option. This could lead a clinician to not confront a colleague about a possible ethical lapse because the clinician is more concerned about avoiding the regret of a false alarm than about letting an ethical violation occur (Rogerson et al., 2011, p. 616). Being aware of our tendencies for cognitive biases is especially important because we tend to make decisions that are justified by subjective reasons, and these self-constructed narratives make us especially likely to be overly confident (Baron, 2000).

Person–Situational Variables

Both individual and situational variables, such as the inherent pressure of specific ethical dilemmas or the climate and mores of an organization, influence individuals' ethical decision making. Specifically, Trevino (1986) asserts that cognitions of right or wrong (knowledge of ethical principles and professional regulations) "are not enough to explain or predict ethical decision-making behavior," but rather interact with individual and situational variables to determine how an individual acts in response to an ethical dilemma (p. 602). The individual characteristics of ego strength, field dependence, and locus of control are proposed to act as mediating variables and influence the likelihood that someone will act in accordance with personal cognitions of what is right or wrong. Various situational variables can influence the interpretation and responses to ethically challenging situations. For example, the job context and the broader organizational culture influence decision making through variables such as unwritten rules, expectations, and other pressures (p. 602).

Poor Role Modeling

More than half (51%) of beginning- to intern-level supervisees reported at least one ethical violation by their supervisors (Ladany, Lehrman-Waterman, Molinaro, & Wolgast, 1999). These infractions most commonly involved inadequate performance evaluation, confidentiality issues relevant to supervision, and the inability to work with alternate perspectives. Greater nonadherence to ethical guidelines was significantly related to a weaker supervisory alliance and lower supervisee satisfaction. However, although more than half of the supervisors did not adhere to at least one ethical guideline, most typically involving violations pertaining to the evaluation of supervisees (33%), most of the supervisors adhered to most of the guidelines most of the time (p. 457). Certainly, conflicting messages and confusion can be inadvertently sent through the inconsistent application of ethical principles.

Uncertainty

Healy (2003) conducted a qualitative study that examined social workers' ethical tension as they evaluated the decisional capacity of elderly individuals experiencing varying degrees of cognitive impairment. Their evaluations and reports would have considerable impact both on the treatment process for their clients and future treatment decisions and directions, as well as considerable impact on the lives of the individuals being evaluated. Three areas emerged as being highly relevant to the social workers' ethical decisions: (1) clinical uncertainty—instances when the proper course of action isn't clear; (2) pressure from other professionals; and (3) the combination of pressure from other professionals and clinical uncertainty (p. 293). The authors noted that often ethical decisions, especially when other professionals are involved, are often the result of collaboration and negotiation, rather than merely based on isolated and abstracted information, such as test results or clinical impressions. Although the involvement of other professionals and other parties can serve to broaden perspective and mitigate against errors of judgment or inappropriate judgment, it can also prompt the desire to please and therefore cloud clinical and ethical judgment. Clinical uncertainty, especially the inability to predict outcomes concerning the management of safety risks, adds additional pressure and confusion to the ethical decision-making process (p. 296).

Anxiety, Stress, and Fatigue

We are all prone to making errors in judgment when fatigued or stressed. Especially if we have lost sight of our vulnerabilities, the stressful nature of our work or personal lives can quickly create exposure to ethical risks (Tjeltviet and Gottlieb, 2010, p. 100). For example, high anxiety can cause a practitioner to select the first solution that comes to mind to reduce the tension, even when the "just good enough" solution might not be optimal (Knapp & VandeCreek, 2012, p. 41).

Explaining the biology of "being frazzled," Arnsten (1998) notes that under stress, our thoughts become disorganized and we lose concentration, and when we become distracted and disorganized, habitual responses are left to control our behavior (p. 1711). Basically, we think less and become more reactive. Exposure to even mild to moderate uncontrollable stress impairs prefrontal cortical functioning (p. 1712). Arnsten states what every parent of an adolescent knows, that we need prefrontal cortex regulation to act appropriately (p. 1712) and that stress impairs our ability to think effectively.

In the well-known book *Social Intelligence,* Daniel Goleman (2006) emphasized the importance of creating a supportive and calming workplace. He recounts that the slogan "banish fear" was the admonition of industry-changing quality control expert Richard Deming, who often observed that fear tended to immobilize workers, causing them to be reluctant to speak up, share new ideas, or try to create improvements. Not only does high anxiety shrink the cognitive space available for our attention, it restricts our ability to take in new information and generate fresh ideas or perspective (Goleman, 2006, p. 268), which are all critical to the cognitive flexibility needed to appropriately recognize and respond to ethical dilemmas. Of course, there is an optimal range of stress, as exemplified by an upside-down *U*, with too little stress leading to boredom and the loss of attention at the low end, and too much stress leading to tunnel vision and paralysis at the other end of the continuum (Noteboom, Barnholt, & Enoka, 2001). Bottom line: too nonchalant an attitude, and we do not be pay enough attention to be alert to potential ethical transgressions; but too much stress, and our attention and focus are constricted and our cognitive resources too overwhelmed to be able to think clearly or respond appropriately.

The solution to the ethical vulnerabilities and cognitive biases that we and our supervisees inherently have is not to try to somehow magically exorcise them, but rather to be cognizant of our tendencies and to navigate them effectively with our eyes open. It can take hard work to embrace the rough waters of self-examination. Pope, Sonne, and Green (2006) identify several characteristics that are paramount to practicing ethical prevention: courage, flexibility, emotional honesty, and intellectual honesty combined with a willingness to challenge and talk about one's own vulnerabilities. That can be a tall order. A few of the more common vulnerabilities are listed below:

- The noble desire to help others, which is hopefully shared by everyone in the helping professions, can help supervisees sustain effort even in the face of adversity, but it can also be a vulnerability causing well-meaning therapists to lose sight of appropriate boundaries. Behnke (2008) noted that there is no one thing that has gotten more psychologists in ethical trouble than the desire to be helpful.

- Personal feelings and intuitions can obscure good judgment and interfere with sound decision making because they are primarily emotional, not intellectual or reasoned (Tjeltviet & Gottlieb, 2010, p. 103).

- Problems can also arise when therapists act on their values or adhere to ethical guidelines in rigid, nonreflective ways. For example, a well-meaning therapist might cause harm to the therapeutic relationship by refusing to accept a small gift that a client thoughtfully picked out, trying to strictly adhere to the principle of not accepting gifts from clients (Tjeltviet & Gottlieb, 2010, p. 104). Flexibility in this area is of even greater importance when working with clients from cultures where bestowing gifts is customary and a sign of respect and gratitude.

Vulnerability, if acknowledged and properly managed, can also be the birthplace of ethical resiliency. The next section focuses on ways that ethical resilience, both for our supervisees and hopefully ourselves as well, can be nurtured and enhanced.

Developing Ethical Resilience

Much of the knowledge we have of resiliency comes from research conducted on children, who, despite many challenges such as poverty and neglect, managed to be healthy and successful (e.g., Masten, 2001). Both internal (personal) and external (environmental) resources can be used to help build resiliency. Supervision can be viewed as an external resource that can help supervisees to both identify external resources—such as positive, ethical role models and opportunities for consultation—and also explore their own internal resources and capitalize on them. Protective factors are an important aspect of resilience, and the opportunities for exploration, discussion, and guidance can be important protective factors. The quality of relationships, which enables these factors to more easily occur, is consistently highlighted in any discussion of resilience (Snyder & Lopez, 2007).

The intent of increasing ethical resiliency is to avoid or effectively navigate difficult situations where there are strong temptations to transgress (Tjeltveit & Gottlieb, 2010, p. 100). Despite the best of intentions, mental health practitioners might find themselves engaging in ethically problematic behavior that could have been prevented.

All mental health professionals have vulnerabilities that might increase the likelihood of committing ethical infractions, but similar to the yin-and-yang metaphor of two sides of the same coin, the same factors that create vulnerability often can, if properly identified and addressed, help lead to the development of greater resilience (Tjeltveit & Gottlieb, 2010, p. 98).

Certainly having a good working knowledge of professional ethics codes, state laws, and risk-management principles is a very important resource to have in the ethical resilience tool kit. However, other factors are essential in being able to put learned information into action. Tjeltviet and Gottlieb (2010) assert that "in our view, the profession has focused too much on logical and quasi-legal reasoning to analyze the development of such transgressions and too little on personal resilience and the ability to address vulnerabilities that form the antecedents of sound preventive ethical practice" (p. 107).

The following are some suggestions for increasing ethical resilience through supervision:

- Supervisors will ideally develop and employ strategies that encourage students, not simply to meet the minimum standards of care, but to go beyond them and strive for their highest ethical goals (Tjeltviet & Gottlieb, 2010, pp. 107–108).

- Emotional and situational factors exert the same powerful influence on clinicians as they do on people in general. Professionals striving for ethical excellence need to pay particular attention to their emotional states and to societal factors that may influence them (Tjeltviet & Gottlieb, 2010, pp. 107–108).

- Clinicians should regularly engage in self-assessment and reevaluate their vulnerabilities and resilience, especially during periods of intense stress, such as divorce, illness, or major loss. The basic principle is that we are usually much more effective when operating with awareness, but it is difficult to steer ourselves in a good direction with our eyes closed (Tjeltviet & Gottlieb, 2010, pp. 107–108).

- Encourage supervisees, through modeling and creating a tone of nonjudgment, to engage in the "risky willingness" of discussing one's vulnerabilities (Tjeltviet & Gottlieb, 2010, p. 101).

- Engage in ongoing self-examination regarding one's feelings, motivations, and values, ideally well in advance of problematic behavior (Tjeltviet & Gottlieb, 2010, pp. 99–100).

- If supervisees and clinicians are simply reminded or remind themselves of their professional responsibilities, they may be more likely to analyze and more thoroughly consider information and make more prudent decisions (Baron, 2000).

- Simply making supervisees aware of their "blind spot" tendencies seems to eliminate this bias (Pronin & Kugler, 2007).

- Probably most importantly, resilience can be enhanced by our social relationships and support networks, including regular contact and consultation with colleagues (Tjeltviet & Gottlieb, 2010, p. 101). Develop a "moral community" to provide supervisees with consultation and support when faced with tough ethical decisions. This can both help bolster the ego strength necessary to implement a difficult course of action, and faculty can address the real professional consequences of acting unethically for the student and the client (Knapp & VandeCreek, 2012).

- Implementing ethical solutions usually involves considerable tact and sensitivity if done well, which can often greatly increase the impact and outcome, and also the client's receptivity. Reminding supervisees that they also have options regarding how ethical decisions and actions are presented to clients can often greatly increase their feelings of control and ownership during challenging ethical situations. Supervisees can typically benefit from consulting with others regarding how to best implement their desired responses (Knapp & VandeCreek, 2012, p. 45).

- Good self-care is important, referring not merely to avoiding impairment and ethical violations but "also to avoiding ethical mediocrity and moving toward excellence" (Tjeltviet & Gottlieb, 2010, p. 105).

- Just as we would recommend therapy or treatment for anyone experiencing psychological difficulty, we also need to take that advice to heart for ourselves, and seek appropriate help when we are struggling with personal or psychological concerns. Koocher and Keith-Spiegel (1998) informally estimate that about half of the psychologists brought before the APA Ethics Committee appeared to have an emotional disorder related to their ethical improprieties.

- When vulnerabilities increase too much, clinicians need to be open to turning to psychotherapy or supervision (not combining the two) to help them honestly face themselves and their vulnerabilities and rebuild resilience (Tjeltviet & Gottlieb, 2010, pp. 107–108).

Rogerson et al. (2011) advise that ethical decision making improves when mental health professionals work to consider problems carefully and guard against cognitive distortions by employing a self-reflective attitude that incorporates self-monitoring and disconfirming strategies into their daily work habits. This can be done by acknowledging that their initial thoughts could be wrong and resisting the impulse to act on the first seemingly sufficient solution that occurs to them, and instead, actively seeking alternative perspectives and being a devil's advocate for themselves. (If they don't, and things go badly, someone else might gladly fill that role.) The authors also advise against framing ethical dilemmas in black-and-white, all-or-nothing terms. Awareness of the pitfalls and errors of ethical reasoning can be supplemented with positively framed considerations as a matter of professional development (Rogerson et al., 2011, p. 620). For example, a supervisor might work with the concept of loyalty in supervision, illuminating that it can serve very positive functions in the service of client care; however, in certain instances, it can also tempt a therapist to put perceived loyalty to a client ahead of adherence to ethical or professional guidelines. It is also important to recognize that acting ethically does not always feel good, at least not at the time (Rogerson et al., 2011, p. 622).

The bottom line, as all mental health practitioners know, is that the things we are not consciously aware of are the things that typically cause us problems;

> Reason cannot overcome the power of the passions merely by ignoring them. Emotions and values exert their powerful influence through automatic and intuitive processes. Acknowledging and understanding the resulting tendencies and biases represent a promising path to a more realistic, accurate, and helpful conceptualization of decision making, particularly in emotionally charged situations. (Rogerson et al., 2011, p. 622)

It is also imperative that, in addition to recognizing our weaknesses and vulnerabilities, we don't overestimate our ability to simply exert willpower to overcome our weaknesses. Economist George Loewenstein (e.g., Ariely & Loewenstein, 2006) introduced the concept of the "hot-cold empathy gap" to illustrate the inability we often have during cool, rational, peaceful moments to appreciate how we'll behave during the temptation of the heat of the moment. (Anyone who has ever planned a diet while eating a plate of nachos has experienced this.) Consultation, which augments both support and accountability, can be a crucial mechanism to help us resist our well-meaning intentions that in the back of our mind we suspect might get us into ethical quicksand.

Ethical Issues for Clinical Supervision

The following section attempts only to highlight a handful of the issues that might arise in clinical supervision. It is not meant to be complete—entire big, heavy textbooks are written about ethics—but rather to just provide a brief overview of some of the issues to be alert to in supervision. The reader is encouraged to consider how ethical resilience could be applied to these different situations.

Informed Consent

Informed consent essentially means that the recipient of services, whether the client or the supervisee, has all of the necessary information from which to make a fully informed decision. This information usually includes items such as: the qualifications and credentials of the supervisor and supervisee; limits of confidentiality; risks and benefits of treatment; what will be expected from the client; and logistics, such as length of treatment and cost, type of approach or treatment (Bernard & Goodyear, 2004). Clients must be informed as treatment is beginning that their therapist is a trainee and the name of the supervisor and of any recording of sessions that might be done and who will have access to the recordings.

Supervisees also have the right to informed consent and to be aware of what will be involved in the process of supervision and to know how they will be evaluated. Preferably, this information is also given in written form and signed by both the supervisee and supervisor. This seems especially important given the discomfort that many supervisors appear to have giving feedback, especially if it is critical, and the inherent anxiety that can be present in the evaluation process.

Dual Relationships and Boundary Issues

Dual or multiple relationships exist when a therapist or supervisor has more than one role or type of relationship with a client or supervisee. Examples of dual relationships in supervision include providing therapy for a former supervisee or developing an emotional relationship with a current or former supervisee. For both therapy and supervision, sexual involvement between therapist–client and supervisor–supervisee has received the most attention in the literature (Bernard & Goodyear, 2004). It is probably not surprising that sexual attraction develops at times. With my (John Wade) supervisees, I have at times described the not uncommon therapy session—the other person hangs onto your every word, seems to trust you deeply, you feel connected at a meaningful level. . . . Is it a date (a good one) or a therapy session? Of course, attraction does not mean that the feeling will be acted upon or become problematic in any way, but it does seem imperative for supervisees to know that romantic feelings might arise in both therapy and supervision, and like all things ethical, they are much more likely to be managed well if acknowledged and brought under the light of supervision.

Multiple roles are not in and of themselves problematic, for example, a clinical supervisor might also serve as a research advisor to the same supervisee, but care needs to be taken that the inherent power differential in the relationship does not cause harm. The *Ethical Principles of Psychologists and Code of Conduct* (APA, 2002) states:

> 3.05(a) A psychologist refrains from entering into multiple relationships if the multiple relationship would reasonably be expected to impair the psychologist's objectivity, competence, or effectiveness in performing his or her functions as a psychologist, or otherwise risk exploitation or harm to the person with whom the professional relationship exists.

However, multiple relationships that would not reasonably be expected to cause harm are not considered unethical.

Some multiple relationships can be helpful to the supervisee, while others can cause harm. Helpful multiple relationships might include simultaneously being a supervisor and also serving on the dissertation committee for the same student, or serving as both a clinical supervisor and research advisor to your supervisee. The potential for starting down the slippery slope is probably minimized in relationships such as these because the roles are clearly defined and essentially contain "job descriptions" (Gottlieb, Robinson, & Younggren, 2007). Harmful relationships occur when a supervisor begins to move from a professional relationship into a personal relationship. It can often be hard to determine exactly when a relationship begins to transition from being purely professional to personal, since of course, the personal, human element is important to all meaningful relationships. If a supervisor is at a professional meeting with a supervisee and lunch is served, it seems natural that they would eat together. Does it become a more personal relationship if they choose instead to go to eat at a nearby bistro for a more intimate lunch? Does the mere mention of the word intimate make the relationship problematic? Gutheil and Gabbard (1993) term this the "slippery slope," capturing that it is difficult to know when you have crossed the line, and like all slopes, once you are on the downhill side, it is easy to very quickly pick up speed and head for disaster.

Competence

The issue of supervisee competency is certainly one that exemplifies the inherent "grayness" and ambiguity involved in effectively applying ethical principles. Sherry (1991) noted the developmental nature of the supervisory process, that by definition, the supervisee is in training to learn and is not yet competent to independently perform many of the assigned tasks. The supervisor is in the challenging position of having to attend to the best interest of both the client and the supervisee, to provide the supervisee clinical experiences through which to learn, while at the same time protecting clients from harm and providing them the competent treatment they are seeking.

Both supervisors and clinicians have the ethical responsibility to only practice within their scope of competence (for supervisees, this includes with the support and guidance of a supervisor who is competent in the area being practiced). Practicing within their scope of competence can be challenging to supervisors in many different ways. Many practicing supervisors have not had any specific training or classes in supervision, and as with teaching, being an effective clinician does not automatically translate into being an effective supervisor. Moreover, supervision activities frequently are not monitored, aside from supervisee evaluation forms that by nature are not anonymous, making honest feedback difficult to obtain. And as Chapter 8 discussed, once we achieve competence, it is very easy to become complacent and stop challenging ourselves or learning new information, causing our very competence to potentially become shaky over time.

Similar to the importance of therapy clients learning to self-monitor, a fundamental task of supervision is for the supervisor to help the supervisee learn to self-evaluate (Vasquez, 1992). This is imperative given the ethical mandate of only practicing within one's scope of competence. After formal supervision ends, this typically is an internally driven assessment that must be done by the individual clinician. This is especially important because with experience, our confidence as clinicians tends to increase, but not our ability (Garb, 1989), creating a context in which it becomes easy to begin to practice outside of one's scope of competence.

Pope and Vasquez (1998) discuss both intellectual competence (i.e., knowledge of research, theory, conceptualization, and treatment efficacy) and emotional competence (i.e., knowledge of self in all aspects relevant to clinical work) as related to ethics. This mirrors the *2002 APA Ethic Code's* conceptualization of competence as consisting of both "skill-based competence and relational competence" (Campbell, Vasques, Behnke, and Kinscherff, 2010, p. 46). Skill-based competence includes such skills as professional experience, consultation, supervised experience, and continuing education and training, while relational competence consists of interpersonal observation and intrapersonal insight.

Conclusion

Reviewing the literature on clinical ethics, it is apparent that the vast majority of the focus has been on the individual, with ethical responsibility mostly placed with the individual clinician, and not the larger system. This chapter has replicated this focus, again emphasizing the individuals, namely the supervisor and supervisee and the clinician and the client. Certainly, individual supervisees and supervisors have ethical responsibilities and need to be cognizant of their professional roles and obligations. However, perhaps it would be helpful and more accurate to conceptualize ethics as somewhat analogous to workplace safety, in that at the bare minimum, the aim is to avoid accidents and harm, or in this case, ethical infractions resulting in harm. (Of course, as should be well established after reading the chapter, hopefully the true aim is to provide the best and most ethically sensitive treatment at all times.) Within the workplace safety model, business and industry don't treat safety as solely the individual responsibility of the employee not to get injured with the heavy equipment or run over a coworker's foot with a forklift. It is also considered a corporate responsibility to create the optimal work environment so that accidents become less likely and safety is easier to achieve, even when individual employees have a bad day. Factories do not post signs over individual lockers reading, "112 days since Bill had an accident," but post large group signs stating how long since anyone in the company has had an accident, since safety is regarded as a team effort.

This same principle would seem advantageous to apply to ethics in mental health settings as well, if our goal is truly to reduce the likelihood of ethical transgressions and increase ethical resilience. As supervisors, we need to be asking ourselves how we can make it more likely for our supervisees to make good ethical decisions and less likely that they will have errors of judgment or ill-chosen behavior. As administrators, we have an ethical responsibility to structure the workplace according to the same goals. Budget cuts and unreasonable demands can exert powerful pressures and stress on all mental health workers and supervisees. Ethics often operates in the arena of competing demands, and certainly there can be tension between the need to serve more clients who otherwise might not receive services and the need to protect clinicians from operating in a state of chronic stress and feeling frazzled. Many professions, such as pilots and truck drivers, have strict regulations that prevent them from working when overly fatigued, limiting their work hours per day or per week. The same principle, although probably not to be enforced with the same precision, should be considered with the mental health professions. It is not a sound risk-management plan to create conditions for stress and near-burnout to be the norm—as is all too often the case in many settings—and expect the staff to somehow be the exceptions and rise above the negative influences. Each individual certainly has a responsibility to engage in reasonable self-care as part of providing competent service to both clients and supervisees, but agencies must also share in that responsibility by creating the right conditions. Increasing pressures to provide more service with fewer resources is a reality, but it seems prudent to follow the airline guidelines of not letting pilots fly without enough rest (self-care) and keeping planes grounded until they have been regularly inspected (frequent consultation).

In case you are still not convinced of the importance of creating the right conditions for ethical behavior to flourish, recall the classic "Good Samaritan" study (Darley & Batson, 1973). The influence of situational and personality variables on helping behavior was examined by recreating a "Good Samaritan" situation. Princeton University seminary students who were going between two buildings were observed as they encountered a shabbily dressed person slumped by the side of the road, obviously in distress. Students who were in a hurry to reach their destinations were much more likely to pass by without stopping (only 10% stopped to help) versus subjects who were not in a hurry (63% stopped). Interestingly, half of the students were in fact on their way to give a short talk on the parable of the Good Samaritan, whereas the other half were walking to give a talk on a nonrelevant topic. This made no significant difference in the likelihood of their giving the victim help; in fact, some students were observed actually stepping over the man in distress in their hurry to get to their talk on time *on the parable of the Good Samaritan!* Discussions of this well-known study often mention the "fundamental attribution error," that is, the tendency to overestimate the influence of disposition factors such as personality (or qualities of character and knowledge of ethics) and under-estimate the importance of situational factors. If we are in distress, we would much rather be seen by someone with time to spare than someone in a hurry who has rehearsed a talk about helping someone in distress. Although not studied, it is not far fetched to think that clients would also be better served by clinicians in settings that truly support ethical behavior than clinicians very knowledgeable about legal and ethical issues who are in a rush to get to their next clients.

Questions to Consider

- As a supervisor, how will I make sure that my supervisees have a solid working knowledge of important ethical principles and professional regulations?

- Given that I will only be meeting with my supervisees for an hour or two a week at best, how can I ensure that ethics are sufficiently addressed, along with all of the other competing demands of supervision time?

- How am I creating an atmosphere that will encourage supervisees to feel comfortable consulting with me on ethical dilemmas even before problems become painfully obvious?

- If my supervisee became attracted to a client, would my supervisee be likely to bring this to supervision for processing? If not, how can I make it more likely that my supervisee will do so?

- What are some recent examples from everyday life where I have made non-rational decisions?

- When have I been able to recognize ill-considered decisions quickly and not act on them, what enabled me to do this?

- What are at least three ethical vulnerabilities that I am likely prone to?

- As a supervisor, looking at myself from the eyes of my supervisees, would I be happy with the examples I am setting regarding ethical behavior and good self-care?

- How do I typically approach ambiguous situations? How can I increase my comfort being ambiguous so that I can seriously consider multiple perspectives and options before coming to a decision?

- How can I gently remind my supervisees of their "blind-spot tendencies" without being negative or nagging?

- Because we all have three blind spots, what are three of mine?

- What are some situations (e.g., divorce or death of a loved one) when seeking consultation and support would be essential?

- How can I recognize my vulnerabilities—what are the subtle cues or warning signs?

- When have I allowed myself to get too close to "ethical quicksand" in the past? How can I recognize situations like this more quickly in the future?

- What situations have I faced when two ethical principles seemed at odds with each other? How did I resolve these situations?

- Are there ways in which the training or agency setting could be more supportive of developing ethical resiliency?

Recommended Readings

Books

Baron, J. (2000). *Thinking and deciding* (3rd ed.). New York: Cambridge University Press.

Campbell, L., Vasquez, M., Behnke, S., & Kinscherff, R. (2010). *APA Ethics Code commentary and case illustrations.* APA: Washington, DC.

Goleman, D. (2006). *Social intelligence.* New York: Bantam Dell.

Handelsman, M. M., Knapp, S., & Gottlieb, M. C. (2002). Positive ethics. In C. R. Snyder & S. Lopez (Eds.), *Handbook of positive psychology* (pp. 731–744). New York: Oxford University Press.

Knapp, S. J., & VandeCreek, L. D. (2012). *Practical ethics for psychologists: A positive approach* (2nd ed.). Washington, DC: American Psychological Association.

Koocher, G. P., & Keith-Spiegel, P. (1998). *Ethics in psychology: Professional standards and cases* (2nd ed.). New York: Oxford University Press.

Articles

Bersoff, D. (1994). Explicit ambiguity: The 1992 *Ethics Code* as oxymoron. *Professional Psychology: Research and Practice, 25,* 382–387.

Garb, H. N. (2005). Clinical judgment and decision making. *Clinical Psychology, 1,* 67–89.

Haidt, J. (2001). The emotional dog and its rational tail: A social intuitionist approach to moral judgment. *Psychological Review, 108,* 814–834.

Rogerson, M. D., Gottlieb, M. C., Handlesman, M. M., Knapp, S., & Younggren, J. (2011). Nonrational processes in ethical decision making. *American Psychologist, 66,* 614–623.

Tjeltveit, A. C., & Gottlieb, M. C. (2010). Avoiding the road to ethical disaster: Overcoming vulnerabilities and developing resilience. *Psychotherapy Theory, Research, Practice, Training, 47,* 98–110.

References

Ariely, D., & Loewenstein, G. (2006). The heat of the moment: The effect of sexual arousal on sexual decision making. *Journal of Behavioral Decision Making, 19,* 87–98.

Arnsten, A. F. T. (1998). The biology of being frazzled. *Science, 280,* 1711–1712.

Baron, J. (2000). *Thinking and deciding* (3rd ed.). New York: Cambridge University Press.

Barry, D. (1999). *Dave Barry turns 50.* New York: The Ballantine Publishing Group.

Behnke, S. (2008, August). Discussant. In N. S. Rubin (Chair), *International ethics rounds: Dilemmas and guidance for consultants, clinicians, investigators and educators.* Presented at the annual meeting of the American Psychological Association, Boston.

Bernard, J., & Jara, C. (1986). The failure of clinical psychology students to apply understood ethical principles. *Professional Psychology: Research and Practice, 17,* 313–315.

Bernard, J. M., & Goodyear, R. K. (2004). *The fundamentals of clinical supervision* (3rd ed.). Boston, MA: Allyn & Bacon.

Bernard, J. M., Murphy, M., & Little, M. (1987). The failure of clinical psychologists to apply ethical principles. *Professional Psychology: Research and Practice, 18,* 5, 489–491.

Bersoff, D. (1994). Explicit ambiguity: The 1992 Ethics Code as oxymoron. *Professional Psychology: Research and Practice, 25,* 382–387.

Campbell, L., Vasquez, M., Behnke, S., & Kinscherff, R. The APA Code of Ethics: Alive and Applied. Washington, DC: American Psychological Association.

Danziger, S., Levav, J., & Avnaim-Pesso, L. (2011). Breakfast, lunch, and their effect on judicial decisions. *Proceedings of the National Academy of Sciences, 108,* 6889–6892.

Darley, J. M., & Batson, C. D. (1973). "From Jerusalem to Jericho": A study of situational and dispositional variables in helping behavior. *Journal of Personality and Social Psychology, 27*(1), 100.

Fly, B. J., van Bark, W. P., Weinman, L., Kitchener, K. S., & Lang, P. R. (1997). Ethical transgressions of psychology graduate students: Critical incidents with implications for training. *Professional Psychology: Research and Practice, 28,* 492–495.

Garb, H. N. (1989). Clinical judgment, clinical training, and professional experience. *Psychological Bulletin, 105,* 387–396.

Goleman, D. (2006). *Social intelligence.* New York: Bantam Dell.

Gottlieb, M. C., Robinson, K., & Younggren, J. N. (2007). Multiple relations in supervision: Guidance for administrators, supervisors and students. *Professional Psychology: Research and Practice, 38,* 241–247.

Gutheil, T. G., & Gabbard, G. O. (1993). The concept of boundaries in clinical practice: Theoretical and risk management dimensions. *American Journal of Psychiatry, 150,* 188–196.

Haidt, J. (2001). The emotional dog and its rational tail: A social intuitionist approach to moral judgment. *Psychological Review, 108,* 814–834.

Haidt, J. (2007, May 18). The new synthesis in moral psychology. *Science, 216,* 998–1002.

Handelsman, M. M., Knapp, S., & Gottlieb, M. C. (2002). Positive ethics. In C. R. Snyder & S. Lopez (Eds.), *Handbook of positive psychology* (pp. 731–744). New York: Oxford University Press.

Healy, T. C. (2003). Ethical decision making: Pressure and uncertainty as complicating factors. *Health & Social Work, 28,* 293–300.

Kahneman, D. (2003). A perspective on judgment and choice: mapping bounded rationality. *American psychologist, 58,* 697–720.

Knapp, S. J., & VandeCreek, L. D. (2012). *Practical ethics for psychologists: A positive approach* (2nd ed.). Washington, DC: American Psychological Association.

Koocher, G. P., & Keith-Spiegel, P. (1998). *Ethics in psychology: Professional standards and cases* (2nd ed.). New York: Oxford University Press.

Ladany, N., Lehrman-Waterman, D., Molinaro, M., & Wolgast, B. (1999). Psychotherapy supervision ethical practices: Adherence to guidelines, the supervisory working alliance, and supervisor satisfaction. *The Counseling Psychologist, 27,* 443–475.

Masten, A. (2001). Ordinary magic: Resilience processes in development. *American Psychologist, 56*(3), 227–238.

Noteboom, J. T., Barnholt, K. R., & Enoka, R. M. (2001). Activation of the arousal response and impairment of performance increase with anxiety and stressor intensity. *Journal of Applied Physiology, 91*(5), 2093–2101.

Pope, K. S., Sonne, J. L., & Green, B. (2006). *What therapists don't talk about and why: Understanding taboos that hurt us and our clients.* San Francisco, CA: Jossey Bass.

Pope, K. S., & Vasquez, M. J. T. (1998). *Ethics in psychotherapy and counseling* (2nd ed.) San Francisco, CA: Jossey-Bass.

Pronin, E., & Kugler, M. B. (2007). Valuing thoughts, ignoring behavior: The introspection illusion as a source of the bias blind spot. *Journal of Experimental Social Psychology, 43,* 565–578.

Rogerson, M. D., Gottlieb, M. C., Handlesman, M. M., Knapp, S., & Younggren, J. (2011). Nonrational processes in ethical decision making. *American Psychologist, 66,* 614–623.

Sherry, P. (1991). Ethical issues in the conduct of supervision. *The Counseling Psychologist, 19,* 566–584.

Smith, T. S., McGuire, J. M., Abbott, D. W., & Blau, B. I. (1991). Clinical ethical decision making: An investigation of the rationales used to do less than one believes one should. *Professional Psychology: Research and Practice, 22,* 235–239.

Snyder, C. R., Lopez, S. J., & Pedrotti, J.T. (2007). *Positive psychology: The scientific and practical explorations of human strengths* (2nd ed.). Thousand Oaks, CA: Sage.

Tjeltveit, A. C., & Gottlieb, M.C. (2010). Avoiding the road to ethical disaster: Overcoming vulnerabilities and developing resilience. *Psychotherapy Theory, Research, Practice, Training, 47,* 98–110.

Trevino, L. K. (1986). Ethical decision making in organizations: A person-situation interactionist model. *Academy of Management Review, 11,* 601–617.

Vasquez, M. J. T. (1992). Psychologists as clinical supervisor: Promoting ethical practice. *Professional Psychology: Research and Practice, 23,* 196–202.

Wilkins, M. A., McGuire, J. M., Abbott, D. W., & Blau, B. I. (1990). Willingness to apply understood ethical principles. *Journal of Clinical Psychology, 46,* 539–547.

Wilson, T. (2011). *Redirect: The surprising new science of psychological change.* New York: Little, Brown and Company.

10

Final Thoughts: Weeding the Garden

"If your actions inspire others to dream more, learn more, do more and become more, you are a leader."

—John Quincy Adams

Much of the power we have as mental health clinicians and supervisors resides in our ability to ask thoughtful and engaging questions. Certainly, other interventions can be very useful as well, ranging from reflection to offering insight to simple didactic instruction. However, Rich Hanson, author of *Buddha's Brain* (2009), was probably very much on target when he stated that great questions lead to enlightenment. The very act of "enlightenment," or illuminating what was previously unseen, expands one's field of vision and possibilities. Moreover, Senay, Albarracin, and Noguchi (2010) discovered while doing research on "introspective self-talk" that working with questions engages our minds much more deeply than does responding to declarative statements and forces us into a problem-solving mode to consider the steps necessary to achieve our goals.

As with clinical work, the ultimate goal of supervision is to help those we are entrusted with to learn to problem solve and function effectively on their own.

Socrates famously asserted that "the unexamined life is not worth living." While there probably are instances when ignorance is bliss, supervision certainly isn't one of those times. Reflection and examination seem to be the solutions to many of the traps and stumbling blocks of professional development. As we have tried to make clear throughout the book, positive psychology is not about just focusing on the positive, although having an eye toward the bright spots can certainly serve as a powerful pull toward expanding effective behavior. The potential for risk and problems certainly exists, and asking ourselves and our supervisees questions to anticipate and prepare for potential problems can be very helpful. Imagine the different outcome that might have occurred if prior to the Great Recession of 2007–2009, government officials had seriously considered and prepared for the potential problems that could have been foreseen with a housing bubble and banks too big to fail making risky loans. Good questions almost always help us to gain perspective and expand our perceptions, for example:

- Assuming that I have blind spots—as we all do—what possibly are some of mine, as a supervisor?

- How might they currently affect my supervision?

- How might my supervisee be perceiving supervision differently from how I want it to be perceived and valued?

- Assuming that we all make mistakes, what is a current mistake that I might be making with my supervisees? Drawing upon my strengths, how might I change to increase the likelihood of a better outcome?

As we ask ourselves these and other questions, it is important to keep in mind the human tendency to be overly self-critical and view ourselves compassionately, acknowledging our humanness and giving ourselves credit for the willingness to engage in constructive self-examination.

We will quickly and briefly review the main topics of the book with the goal of reflection in mind. Martin Seligman (2011) aptly noted that it can be very tempting to want to overly simplify and to view psychological phenomena from the perspective of "monoism," that is, assuming that one simple psychological theory can explain all of human behavior (pp. 9–10). For example, we witness countless examples of learning principles operating in our lives on a daily basis, from training our pets to raising children to marketers shaping consumer behavior. John Watson (e.g., 1930) was undeniably on to something when he formulated early learning theories. However, when he famously asserted that, "Give me a dozen healthy infants, well formed, and my own specified world to bring them up in, and I'll guarantee to take any one at random and train him to become any type of specialist I might select—doctor, lawyer, artist, merchant-chief, and, yes, even beggar-man and thief, regardless of his talents, penchants, tendencies, abilities, vocations, and race of his ancestors" (1930, p. 82), he most certainly overstated his case and lost credibility. Our strength-based supervision model, grounded in constructs of positive psychology, will hopefully have practical value to supervisors and help shape the understanding of how training and supervision is conceptualized. However, we also understand that all models should be viewed within the context of the wealth of knowledge that already exists, and just as with the blind men viewing the elephant described in Chapter 1, the better goal is not to strive for the "right" understanding, but rather to strive for the most complete understanding to truly get the full picture.

We have tried to provide you with a blend of practical application grounded in empirical research. We have intentionally taken a multidisciplinary approach and complemented the research from mental health disciplines with information and findings from many other associated fields, ranging from nursing to speech pathology. We firmly believe in Abraham Maslow's (1971) axiom that to understand exemplary behavior, one must study exemplars of success, including—to use today's business vernacular—understanding "best practices."

Much of effective supervision depends upon properly setting the stage for good outcomes to be more likely to occur. "Setting the stage" occurs in many different forms, ranging from understanding the attributes of good supervisors and supervisees to having supportive institutional variables in place. Interpersonal variables are the most important factor in increasing the likelihood of effective supervision. No supervisee is an island. We are all subject to the subtle, and sometimes not so subtle, influence of the norms of the work setting and culture we operate in. Martha Beck (2013) noted that even by our mere presence, we influence each other. She explained that in the 1660s, Dutch scientist Christian Huygens observed that if there are several clocks hanging on a wall, over time, the pendulums all start to move in sync. This phenomenon was termed *entrainment*. The principle of entrainment seems to operate with human beings as well, meaning that effective training and supervision is dependent not only upon supervisors providing good supervision at the individual level, but effective agency leaders and administrators setting the tone and creating the norms of a work climate conducive to providing effective mental health services and quality supervision. Obviously, we believe that grounding supervision and training in the principles and constructs of positive psychology can be an effective way to do so. Administrators have a special responsibility to foster an atmosphere conducive to learning and growing, keeping in mind that influence is like water. Although it can be splashed upward for brief periods of time, both water and influence tend to flow from the top down.

We are almost always more effective and wiser if we can regularly consult and broaden our perspectives by brainstorming and confiding in trusted colleagues. Discussing the wisdom of crowds, James Surowiecki (2004) cited many studies that illustrate that the wisdom of many almost always trumps the ability of the individual, no matter how talented or bright that person might be. Especially when considering matters of ethics, drawing from the wisdom of others helps us to expand our perspectives and become more aware of the full spectrum of the situation and possible pitfalls, solutions, and unintended consequences.

Hopefully, we have made clear that although much benefit can be derived from identifying and helping our supervisees to more fully develop their strengths, this does not mean ignoring real weaknesses. However, identifying and using our strengths is often the most effective way to manage the weak areas that we all have. As with all things, balance is important (again, we can thank Aristotle), and we only ignore the weaknesses of ourselves or our supervisees at our peril. However, humans seem to be hardwired to focus on the negative, which means that most of us need to give more intentional focus to strengths and successes to achieve a healthy and helpful balanced perspective.

This is especially important since—although we are usually very well intentioned when we focus on mistakes and problems so that we can learn from them, like driving a car—we tend to drift toward where we focus our attention. So, just like driving a car, it is imperative to train our sight on where we want to go or want our supervisees to go versus overly focusing on what we want to avoid. Thoughtful evaluation procedures and providing effective feedback can serve to help guide both the supervisor and supervisee. Well-chosen and when possible, hopefully mutually agreed-upon goals help focus energy and attention and enhance learning.

It is reasonable to assume that most of us in the helping professions have a sincere intent and desire to appreciate diversity; we probably shouldn't be in the helping professions if this isn't where our hearts lie. However, it is probably also somewhat like raising children: We all know that they are truly a blessing and a joy; however, the hard work and frustration that can also be involved in the day-to-day process usually is not fully appreciated until one actually has children. This is not at all to diminish the great reward of having children; in fact, the hard work and investment probably enhances the satisfaction and reward. However, it is also important to recognize that sameness can sometimes feel more comfortable than differences. But this challenge, although uncomfortable at times, truly can be a blessing, especially if approached from the perspective of not just trying to get all parties on the same page, but to be able to write even richer pages because our perspectives have been broadened.

One of my pet peeves when reading clinical books is the short shrift that is typically given to the possibility that clients might deviate from the "script" neatly presented in the book. I think that only makes clinicians feel more inept when their real clients respond in ways different from the smooth process presented in the case examples. Books that imply that quick and easy "cures" are the norm can set the stage for unrealistic expectations for both clients and clinicians. At least minor difficulties and challenges in supervision are all but inevitable. Hopefully, some useful models and suggestions were presented to help manage and work through the stuckness that can easily occur in these situations.

We believe that, although as supervisors we all want our supervisees to master the basics and be able to function competently, ultimately our goal is for our supervisees to start on the path of becoming experts, which depends upon becoming lifelong learners. Ultimately, as supervisors, one of the greatest impacts we can make is to instill a love of learning and self-improvement. Hopefully, just as for our clients, our supervisees will internalize not merely just some of what we have said but also the processes of self-reflection, self-monitoring, and effective problem solving that we have modeled throughout supervision. As supervisors, especially as we accrue more years of experience, it is easy to become complacent and believe that we don't have anything else we need to learn. This can obviously be dangerous, especially in our role as supervisors as we are modeling learning. The story of the Buddhist teacher comes to mind, who welcomed his new student by pouring him a cup of tea. The teacher kept pouring and pouring, even after the cup had become full and was overflowing and spilling everywhere. At first incredulous, finally the student spoke up and said, "The cup is full, no more will go in!" The teacher then said that the same happens with the mind, asking how more knowledge can go in if it feels like your mind is already full.

Striving for excellence, both for ourselves and our supervisees, must be grounded in realism and an appreciation for the limitations and constraints of the human condition. Ben Franklin (e.g., Isaacson, 2003) provided a very useful example to help guide us in our efforts to learn and grow—weeding the garden. He compiled a list of 13 virtues he wanted to improve within himself. Knowing the inherent limitations of attention and discipline, he chose a single virtue each week to particularly focus on. As he did so, he tried to strengthen the good behaviors and practices within the chosen area and to weed out the bad habits. As he cycled through the different domains every 13 weeks, he noticed that some bad habits had reemerged after weeks of neglect, just like weeds. However, he also noticed that even though perfection was not to be had, with each cycle, similar to weeding a garden, there were less bad habits and that getting "back on track" was easier each time. Moreover, the "garden" as a whole seemed to be thriving much more fully. Although the goals or targets we strive for are typically at the higher end of the spectrum, we all have blind spots and can struggle with the "basics." Weeding also involves the courage to open our eyes and look for possible bad habits, even if they seem very basic. As a supervisor, could I possibly be perceived as having favorites? As an administrator, do the practical constraints of the agency allow room for effective and ethical service provision to be practiced?

This book has touched on many areas and tried to provide many suggestions for practice and questions for reflection. Probably the greatest danger using any book is to feel overwhelmed and not do anything. We'd encourage you to try to channel Benjamin Franklin, and while keeping your expectations simple and realistic, pick one specific thing you'd like to focus on this week. Pick a row and let's start weeding!

References

Beck, M. (2013, July). May we help you? *Oprah,* 38–41.

Hanson, R. (2009). *Buddha's brain: The practical neuroscience of happiness, love, and wisdom.* Oakland, CA: New Harbinger Publications.

Isaacson, W. (2003). *Benjamin Franklin: An American life.* New York: Simon and Schuster.

Maslow, A. (1971). *The farther reaches of human behavior.* New York: Viking Press.

Seligman, M. E. P. (2011). *Flourish: A visionary new understanding of happiness and well-being.* New York: Free Press.

Senay, I., Albarracin, D., & Noguchi, K. (2010). Motivating goal-directed behavior through introspective self-talk: The role of the interrogative form of simple future tense. *Psychological Science, 21,* 499–504.

Surowiecki, J. (2004). *The wisdom of crowds: Why the many are smarter than the few and how collective wisdom shapes business, economies, societies and nations.* New York: Random House.

Watson, J. B. (1930). *Behaviorism* (Rev. ed.). Chicago, IL: University of Chicago Press.

Index

Printed in the USA
CPSIA information can be obtained
at www.ICGtesting.com
CBHW041350061023
1264CB00012B/111

9 780826 1073